Peter Cox and **Peggy Brusse**... including the huge No. 1 s... *Cooking* and many other be... *Cholesterol Counter*, the inter... series, and the award-winni... *You Don't Need Meat* which ignited Britain's vegetarian revolution. They are married and live in London with their two children.

IMPORTANT NOTE

The details in this book are for informational purposes only and not to be taken as professional advice for health problems. If you have any medical condition or are on medication, always obtain medical advice before taking additional medicines – drugs can and do interact in complex ways, and your doctor has ready access to tables of drug interactions. Children, the elderly, people with impaired liver or kidney function and pregnant or breast-feeding women need particular protection from the effects or combined effects of certain drugs, and the advice of a doctor or qualified pharmacist should be sought before any treatment is commenced. Always read the label on medicines and carefully observe the dose and any special instructions.

This book may include words, brand names and other descriptions of products which are, or are asserted to be, proprietary names or trademarks. No judgement concerning the legal status of such words is made or implied thereby. Their inclusion does not imply that they have acquired, for legal purposes, a non-proprietary or general significance nor any other judgement concerning their legal status.

Free Update

If you would like to receive a free update to the information in this book, please send an A4 size stamped self-addressed envelope to: BM Box Superliving, London, WC1M 3XX

Secret
Ingredients

Peter Cox and Peggy Brusseau

BANTAM BOOKS
LONDON · NEW YORK · TORONTO · SYDNEY · AUCKLAND

SECRET INGREDIENTS
A BANTAM BOOK : 0 553 50554 8

First publication in Great Britain

PRINTING HISTORY
Bantam edition published 1997

Set in Times New Roman and Helvetica
by Phoenix Typsesetting, Ilkley, West Yorkshire.

Bantam Books are published by Transworld Publishers Ltd,
61–63 Uxbridge Road, London W5 5SA,
in Australia by Transworld Publishers (Australia) Pty Ltd,
15–25 Helles Avenue, Moorebank, NSW 2170,
and in New Zealand by Transworld Publishers (NZ) Ltd,
3 William Pickering Drive, Albany, Auckland.

Reproduced, printed and bound in Great Britain by
Cox & Wyman Ltd, Reading, Berks.

CONTENTS

INTRODUCTION:
Some Secrets Shouldn't Be Kept!

It's half past midnight, and we must stop writing . . . but we can't. D'you think the publisher will give us another day – or two? Surely we can squeeze just one more tiny little article in – I really want to write a piece about food irradiation (the ultimate secret ingredient) . . . No, wait – I *need* to add that item about fluoridation . . .

Stop! We have to draw the line somewhere, and this is it. Since we started this project, our lives have been turned upside down. We no longer watch television, go to the movies or read books like normal people do. We read product labels instead.

We admit it, we've become obsessed. Once you start looking under the bonnet – at what *really* goes into the products we choose to consume (and sometimes, those we have no option but to consume) then you're hooked. And what a fascinating world it is . . . Full of subtleties, ingenuities, paradoxes, high technological achievements, low human cunning . . . and a few heroes and villains, too. Every substance in this book has a story to tell. This book has a cast of hundreds . . . some are mere bit-part players, while others are full-blown stars. And while some will already be known to you, others will be strangers whom you really ought to get to know. Hopefully, *Secret*

Ingredients will not just introduce you, but give you a bit of a background check – just as any good introduction agency ought to.

That's why we wrote the book – because we wanted to provide ready access to the information it contains. It seemed extraordinary to us that there was no book available which would tell us the basic things we wanted to know about the ingredients in the products we buy. So – we decided to write one. In the 1980s, those ubiquitous 'E' numbers got a lot of publicity, most of it bad, and a great many people tried to avoid food with 'Es' in it. Which was just about as silly as trying to avoid telephone numbers with the number '9' in them. Because the 'E' numbers are simply a numbering system, and actually quite a good one. 'E' doesn't mean bad, dangerous or hazardous – E300 (try looking it up!) is actually one of the safest substances present in food that you'll ever find, whereas aflatoxin (with no 'E' number) is one of the most dangerous.

Our attitude while writing and researching *Secret Ingredients* has been one of cautious common sense. We are not conspiracy theorists, and we use the term 'secret' not because there is some vast conspiracy to put toxic substances into the products we consume, but simply because many of the ingredients in many of the everyday products we all buy are, to a large extent, extremely obscure to most consumers. For example: pick up a packet of chewing gum – the ingredients list tells you it contains sorbitol. You've probably seen sorbitol listed on many products – but never really known what you were buying. Well, now you will!

If a substance has been judged to be carcinogenic, or possibly carcinogenic, then we want to know about it. We also want to know about significant adverse effects associated with it, in any dose or form. Regulatory authorities often appear to take the view that there's nothing for us consumers to be concerned about, because they've done all the worrying for us. While we appreciate their work, we'd just as soon know a little bit more about the substances in the products we buy, and take our own decisions for ourselves. We think that's our right – and our prerogative – as consumers.

As you will see, *Secret Ingredients* is divided into two parts. *Part One – Living With Secret Ingredients* is a compendium of fascinating, practical information which we hope will answer many of the questions and concerns you may have about the issues surrounding the ingredients in the products we buy. *Part Two – Revealed!* is an alphabetical encyclopedia of over 500 common substances – including all those 'E' numbers – which are, or have been, used in consumer products. We have also included a series of quick reference charts and a glossary which explains what the technical words means, although jargon has been kept to a minimum.

Well, the second-hand is ticking away . . . the piece on fluoride made it, the one on food irradiation didn't. We really want to write *Secret Ingredients II* – there are so many more substances out there to explore, research and report on. Do send us any ideas or suggestions you might have (the address is on the reverse of the title page). We're very keen to hear from you – did you find *Secret Ingredients* useful? How would you improve the next edition? If you enclose a stamped addressed envelope, we'll be sure to reply (but do be patient – it can take a few weeks).

With best wishes –

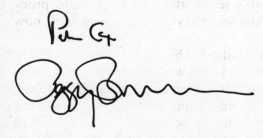

London

Part One

Living With Secret Ingredients

A Survival Manual

The Do-it-Yourself Food Allergy Detection Kit

The first time that most people really become interested in the ingredients in the products they consume is when they think they might be allergic to them. To put it simply, we live in a chemical soup. While researching *Secret Ingredients* we became aware of over 100,000 substances for which some kind of toxicity data exists.[1] When you consider the potential for possible combinations, and individual reactions to those combinations, then you can quickly see why no-one will ever be able to definitively list all the possible reactions to every substance. But the good news is . . . if you *are* sensitive to one or more substances in your micro-environment, with a little effort you can probably find out what that substance is – and eliminate it. This section tells you how to investigate your diet for possible allergic substances. The next section tells you how to start detoxifying your home.

Chemicals cause disease in one of two ways: by causing immediate cellular changes in organisms, either aggravating an existing disease or creating a new one; or by damaging DNA molecules, eventually creating birth defects or cancer. That is, chemicals can both poison us and cause mutations. Although it is quite easy to detect – and avoid – obviously toxic substances, it is far from easy to identify those subtle substances which may have effects at the other end of the scale – the ingredient to which you may personally be sensitive, but other people aren't.

Most conventionally trained allergists insist that only 2 to 5 per cent of children and fewer than one in 100 adults are truly allergic.[2] On the other hand, in a recent study, 43 per cent of the 3,300 adults surveyed said that they experience adverse reactions to foods.[3] Perhaps those specialists ought to listen a little more carefully to what their patients are telling them. One British doctor with considerable experience in the field comments: 'Of the patients I see, at least a third have been told by a doctor that their symptoms are psychosomatic. Yet they respond very well to dietary treatment, and they remain well afterwards, which is what matters.'[4]

The word allergy comes from the Greek words *allos* and *ergon*, literally meaning 'altered reaction'. For reasons which are not always clear, some people may suddenly become abnormally sensitive to otherwise harmless substances – such as pollen, dust, household chemicals, fur, feathers, cosmetics, textile dyes, smoke . . . the list is endless. When this happens, the immune system, which normally defends us against dangerous foreign substances such as invading bacteria and viruses, is tricked into mounting a full-scale attack. Antibodies are released, histamine is produced, and the immune system swings into action against a non-existent enemy – producing unfortunate side-effects. The most common symptoms of allergy often involve the upper respiratory system – the nose, inner ears, mouth and throat. Hay fever reactions such as sneezing, itchy, watery eyes and a sore throat are also very common. Other sufferers may experience breathing problems, with asthma, wheezing and shortness of breath, or flu-like symptoms, migraine, depression or fatigue. In more serious instances, these reactions are accompanied by vomiting, loss of appetite, diarrhoea and weight loss – sometimes, a life-threatening anaphylactic shock can rapidly occur, which unless promptly treated, can lead to asphyxiation and death.

Typically, the symptoms of food intolerance take far longer to appear than conventional allergies, and are much more varied. Charles Darwin, the father of the theory of evolution, suffered all his life from intermittent nausea, vomiting, headaches, fatigue, palpitations and eczema. These symptoms were never adequately explained in his lifetime, but today there is support for the view that Darwin may himself have suffered from a type of food intolerance.[5]

How To Test

Means of testing for food intolerance vary greatly. RAST tests (radioallergosorbent tests) and ELISA tests (enzyme-linked immunosorbent assays) are designed to detect the effect of possible allergic substances on blood samples. Their results may be difficult to interpret and the tests are quite costly to undertake. Some alternative practitioners use dowsing – where a pendulum is swayed over a patient's hair sample or photo-graph in the presence of certain foods. Another alternative technique is applied kinesiology (sometimes called muscle testing). Here, food is placed under the tongue and the arm is then tested for strength. Any apparent weakness supposedly indicates a particular sensitivity. Many of these tests have poor accuracy. When the Consumers' Association carried out an experiment on five allergy testing clinics in Britain, they found that all five failed to spot genuine allergies of real sufferers, while issuing lists of problem foods to those who had no known complaints.[6]

Although it may seem like a detective's nightmare – an endless list of suspects and no real evidence – it *is* possible to pinpoint the substance or ingredient that you may not tolerate. As Sherlock Holmes might have said, it is simply a matter of elimination. To identify the culprit, you need to undergo what is called an elimination diet; only by excluding certain substances will you discover if they are at fault. At this stage, all foods are potentially guilty, but proteins, dairy products, chocolate, fish, wheat, corn, tomatoes are often the prime suspects.

Week One

For the first week of the elimination diet, you will be eating very plain food which is unlikely to cause a reaction – some examples are given below. You should keep a 'food diary' in which to record details of your daily menus, and any symptoms which occur. This can then be used to discuss your reactions with your medical adviser.

VEGETABLES

Artichokes	Asparagus
Avocados	Broccoli
Brussels Sprouts	Cabbage
Carrots	Cauliflower
Celery	Cucumbers
Kale	Leeks
Lettuce	Okra
Parsley	Parsnips
Pumpkins and other squashes	Radishes
Rice	Spinach
Swede	Turnips
Water Chestnuts	Watercress

FRUIT

Apples	Apricots
Bananas	Cherries
Coconuts	Dates
Figs	Grapes
Kiwi Fruit	Mangos
Melons	Nectarines
Peaches	Pears
Pineapples	Plums
Prunes	

NUTS

Almonds	Brazil Nuts
Cashews	Chestnuts
Hazelnuts	Pumpkin Seeds
Sesame Seeds	Sunflower Seeds

SEASONINGS

Bay Leaves	Celery Seed
Cumin	Tahini
Vinegar	

BEVERAGES

Mineral or spring water	Juices from permitted fruits

A TYPICAL DAY'S MENU

For Breakfast:
Half a canteloupe melon
Mineral water or fruit juice

For Lunch:
Avocado salad, consisting of:

One medium avocado
a quarter of a crispy Iceberg lettuce head
half a cup of sliced radishes
half a cup chopped watercress
one ounce each of sesame seeds and sunflower seeds
one tablespoon of vinegar to dress

Mineral water or fruit juice

For Dinner:
Rice and vegetables, consisting of:

One cup of brown rice
Half a cup of boiled spinach
Half a cup of boiled, mashed pumpkin
Half a cup of steamed, chopped broccoli
Tablespoon of tahini to dress

Mineral water or fruit juice

As a snack anytime:
A mixture of 2 ounces dried almonds and 2 ounces roasted pumpkin seeds
Fruit

The above menu supplies 1,794 calories, and is high in protein and other essential nutrients.

Week Two

In the second week you can start to add other foods back into your diet again (for example, wheat and dairy products). Remember to keep a record of your reactions in your food diary. Foods should be added back into your diet in their simplest form. For example, when reinstating wheat, start with plain puffed wheat rather than bread, which contains other substances, such as yeast, that might contribute to your symptoms.

When you find a food which brings your symptoms on again, try eliminating it from your diet again completely for a few days. If your symptoms clear, the chances are you have found your enemy!

When you have identified the offending food or foods, you are then faced with the prospect of avoiding them. If you suffer from fits of violent sneezing every time you eat a papaya, this won't be too much of a problem. If, however, you discover you have an egg allergy, you will need to become an expert in reading food labels and questioning restaurants. This is not always as simple as it sounds; for example, 'albumin' listed as an ingredient on a product means it contains egg. Different recipes and replacement foods will also need to be on your new menu. In baking, half a teaspoon of baking powder can be used in place of each egg, while you can buy products such as eggless mayonnaise and corn noodles.

If you encounter difficulty in getting support from your own doctor, remember that there are a number of groups which offer support and all-important information. Action Against Allergy is one such charity, which encourages research and provides an information service giving details of relevant medical assistance in your area.[7]

The Hyperactive Child

Hyperactivity – sometimes called Attention-Deficit Hyper-activity Disorder (ADHD) – is an increasingly widespread problem among children. In America, disruptive classroom behaviour is now so common that well over a million school children are regularly prescribed amphetamine-type drugs ('pep pills') in an attempt to control their behaviour.[8] While it may seem paradoxical that stimulant drugs are administered to already highly active children, their use appears to have the effect of concentrating their attention, making them easier for teachers to handle, and generally more compliant.[9] It is ironic that, while the war against illegal drugs becomes ever more intense, doctors are busier than ever prescribing stimulants to young children and teenagers. Hyperactivity has several possible causative factors, e.g.:

- Genetic. An inherited tendency to hyperactivity. It is also speculated that excess alcohol consumption during pregnancy may predispose the child to subsequent hyperactive behaviour.
- Medical. Head injury; mental illness; sight and hearing problems; meningitis and hypoglycaemia can all result in hyperactive behaviour.
- Environmental. Social upheaval, family breakdown and disturbed homelife, and lead poisoning may all be factors.
- School-related. Hyperactivity which is brought on by academic failure, stress, lack of rapport with the teachers or antagonism within the class situation.

While diagnosis and treatment of hyperactivity needs to be carried out by a sympathetic child psychologist or medical specialist, there are several courses of action you may want to consider – especially in the area of food and diet. For example, children whose diets emphasize junk food products may be deficient in the trace elements which the body needs to assemble key enzymes and hormones, some of which are used in the brain's production of neurotransmitters, the chemical messengers that are necessary for proper brain function. At least eleven trace elements – copper, iron, zinc, cobalt, iodine, molybdenum, manganese, magnesium, selenium, chromium, and fluorine – have been recognized as essential for human development and overall health. Daily consumption of a variety of wholefoods, such as grains, vegetables, fruits, and sea vegetables (the highest single source of trace elements) can easily supply our trace element needs – but junk food can't. Mineral losses in refined wheat flour, for example, average 75 per cent, and similar losses occur in other refined grain products.

A landmark British study has suggested that food additives such as tartrazine (see page 435–5) might seriously affect children's behaviour.[10] Seventy-six children who had been clinically diagnosed as hyperactive were treated with a simple, bland diet which contained none of the usual substances associated with hyperactivity. After treatment, sixty-two of the children had noticeably improved, and in twenty-one of these the symptoms of hyperactivity had entirely disappeared. The researchers found that artificial food colourings and food preservatives were the ingredients most likely to provoke bouts of hyperactivity.

Another remarkable study carried out among young institutionalized offenders found that, on average, displays of antisocial behaviour could be cut by about 50 per cent simply by reducing their sugar consumption.[11] The researchers replaced soft drinks and junk food snacks with fruit juices and nutritional snacks, and eliminated high-sugar desserts and cereals. After 12 months, the number of assaults had fallen by 82 per cent, thefts had dropped by 77 per cent, general rule violations had gone down by 23 per cent, and fighting had declined by 13 per cent. Most significantly, after the experiment ended and the inmates were allowed to eat junk food again, incidents of antisocial behaviour once again climbed to their previous levels.

Another study from the Yale University School of Medicine gave equal amounts of sugar to children and adults.[12] They found that the children experienced a rise in blood levels of the 'flight or fight' hormone adrenaline, which was twice as great as the adults'. As the level of blood sugar dropped, the children also experienced more intense symptoms of hypoglycaemia (low blood sugar) than the adults. The scientists concluded that these changes 'may be important contributing factors to adverse behavioural and cognitive effects after sugar ingestion in healthy children'. In other words, children may be far more susceptible to dietary sugar than adults.

The One-Week Diet

If you suspect a food allergy is related to your child's hyperactivity, try the one-week diet. This is based on the idea that hyperactive behaviour will – if it is caused by an allergy to a foodstuff – disappear while your child is eating a plain diet, and return when the offending food is re-introduced. This diet requires attention to detail, diligence and accurate recording but it is definitely worth trying. So for the first week make sure your child doesn't eat any of the following seven foods, which are considered the most likely to produce an allergic reaction:

- Milk
- Wheat
- Egg
- Cocoa
- Sugar
- Corn
- Food colourings

After one week without any of these suspect seven foods, see if there's an improvement. If there is, you're on the way to discovering what causes your child to be hyperactive, and to curing the problem too. So during the second week, re-introduce them, one by one:

- Sunday – Milk (Dairy products, Cheese, Yoghurt)
- Monday – Wheat (Bread, Cake, Bakery products)
- Tuesday – Sugar
- Wednesday – Egg

- Thursday – Chocolate
- Friday – Food colouring (observe labelling)
- Saturday – Corn

Should you discover a food triggers your child's hyperactivity, then permanently alter his or her diet, to eliminate the offending foodstuff.

All About Those Additives

Detailed below is an at-a-glance guide to the E numbers which may have been associated with some sort of health concern – often the potential to produce allergic responses. Following this is a listing of those foods which, according to European Community regulations, are not permitted to have any additives. You will also find a complete schedule of all the food additives currently permitted to be added to food under EC regulations in Appendix A, together with comprehensive lists of foods which are only permitted certain additives or colours. More detailed information on each entry appears in Part Two – Revealed!

TABLE 1
E-NUMBERS WE'D RATHER AVOID

NUMBER	WHAT IT IS	WHAT IT DOES
E102	Tartrazine	colour
E110	Sunset Yellow FCF, Orange Yellow S	colour
E122	Azorubine, Carmoisine	colour
E123	Amaranth	colour
E124	Ponceau 4R, Cochineal Red A	colour
E127	Erythrosine	colour
E129	Allura Red AC	colour
E131	Patent Blue V	colour

E133	Brilliant Blue FCF	colour
E142	Green S	colour
E150c	Ammonia caramel (caramel colour class III)	colour
E151	Brilliant Black BN	colour
E153	Vegetable carbon (carbon black)	colour
E154	Brown FK	colour
E155	Brown HT (Chocolate Brown HT)	colour
E210	Benzoic acid	preservative
E211	Sodium benzoate	preservative
E212	Potassium benzoate	preservative
E213	Calcium benzoate	preservative
E214	Ethyl p-hydroxybenzoate	preservative
E215	Sodium ethyl p-hydroxybenzoate	preservative
E216	Propyl p-hydroxybenzoate	preservative
E217	Sodium propyl p-hydroxybenzoate	preservative
E218	Methyl p-hydroxybenzoate	preservative
E219	Sodium methyl p-hydroxybenzoate	preservative
E220	Sulphur dioxide	preservative
E221	Sodium sulphite	preservative
E222	Sodium hydrogen sulphite	preservative
E223	Sodium metabisulphite	preservative; bleaching agent
E224	Potassium metabisulphite	preservative; antibrowning agent
E226	Calcium sulphite	preservative
E227	Calcium hydrogen sulphite	combined preservative and firming agent
E228	Potassium hydrogen sulphite	preservative
E232	Sodium orthophenyl phenol	preservative

E249	Potassium nitrite	preservative; colour fixative
E250	Sodium nitrite	preservative; colour fixative
E251	Sodium nitrate	preservative; colour fixative
E252	Potassium nitrate (saltpetre)	preservative; colour fixative
E284	Boric acid	preservative
E285	Sodium tetraborate (borax)	preservative
E320	Butylated hydroxyanisole (BHA)	antioxidant
E321	Butylated hydroxytoluene (BHT)	antioxidant
E512	Stannous chloride	antioxidant; colour retention agent
E553b	Talc	anticaking agent; dusting powder; filter aid; carrier
E621	Monosodium glutamate	flavour enhancer
E942	Nitrous oxide	propellant
E954	Saccharin and its Na, Kand Ca salts	sweetener
E1440	Hydroxy propyl starch	emulsifier; thickening agent; binder; carrier

TABLE 2
FOODS WHICH ARE NOT PERMITTED TO HAVE ADDITIVES[13]

Unprocessed foodstuffs

Honey

Non-emulsified oils and fats of animal or vegetable origin

Butter

Pasteurized and sterilized (including uht sterilization) milk and cream (including skimmed, plain and semi-skimmed)

Unflavoured, live fermented milk products

Natural mineral water and spring water

Coffee (excluding flavoured instant coffee) and coffee extracts

Unflavoured leaf tea

Sugars

Dry pasta

Natural unflavoured buttermilk (excluding sterilized buttermilk)

Food Poisoning – How To Protect And Survive!

If you unexpectedly go down with cramp, nausea, shivering, diarrhoea, double vision, a severe headache or overwhelming fatigue – then you may have food poisoning, and you should get yourself to a doctor. But far better to take steps now to avoid this most unwelcome secret ingredient in too many people's diets. There are three distinct types of food-poisoning bacteria: listeria, salmonella and botulism. These food bugs are present in the soil, water and air around us. They can get into your food at any stage from production to sale – and from purchase to eating.

- Listeria hits the headlines every so often, when chilled foods and soft cheeses are found to be contaminated.
- Salmonella – the most common cause of food poisoning – usually infects poultry and red meat, unpasteurized milk and eggs.
- Botulism is the most dangerous bacterium of all – a single teaspoonful of the pure substance could kill hundreds of thousands of people. It is far less common in the United Kingdom than in France or the USA. Nevertheless, in 1989, 26 people in England were taken seriously ill when a batch of yoghurt was infected.

Prevention is obviously better than cure, so here's what you can do to protect yourself against the risk of food poisoning.

- Take chilled or frozen food home as quickly as possible, particularly in the summer. Bacteria thrive in the heat, so putting supermarket food into the boot of a car on a hot day is like putting it into a greenhouse. It's well worth investing in a cool-bag.

- Buy a thermometer for your fridge. It's been estimated that 80 per cent of UK fridges are set too high. The recommended temperature is no more than 5°C.

- Although it may seem to be the safest thing to keep eggs in the refrigerator, it isn't. Condensation can unplug tiny, porous holes in the shell, allowing dangerous bacteria to penetrate. And the lowered temperature of the yolk means it needs even longer cooking.

- Never eat raw eggs in any form (e.g. mayonnaise) – always make sure they're thoroughly cooked.

- Cook everything thoroughly. If you still eat meat, it's worth investing in a meat thermometer, too. Beef should be cooked to an internal temperature of 60°C or above for rare, 70°C for medium and 77°C for well done. Lamb and pork need to be cooked to an internal temperature of 77°C.

- Don't stuff poultry – cook the stuffing separately.

- Refrigerate cooked meat quickly – don't leave it at room temperature for more than 90 minutes.

- Be particularly careful if you use a microwave oven. The evidence suggests that you shouldn't rely on it to kill off bacteria in your food. Always follow the recommended standing times.

- Discard the packaging from chilled foods – whether you're heating them in a microwave or a conventional oven. You don't want to take a chance on poisonous chemicals melting and finding their way into your food. Styrene, which is used in polystyrene, is a suspected carcinogen.

- Store raw and cooked foods separately. Never leave left-over canned food in its tin. Try to buy salads and vegetables that are unprepared and unprocessed. One of the most devastating listeria epidemics, in 1981, was traced back to ready-made coleslaw.
- Wash food before you eat it – even if you've grown it yourself. Vegetables and fruit can harbour bacteria from the soil. It is possible to wash away salmonella which is living in meat and poultry.
- Never reheat food more than once. Make sure it's not underheated.
- Don't take chances. If your food smells off, throw it away.
- Make certain that frozen food is thoroughly defrosted before cooking.
- Keep all kitchen towels, sponges, surfaces, food equipment and cutting boards clean. When you're preparing a meal, it's also prudent to wash utensils and worktops between stages – don't use the same knife or chopping board for raw meat, cooked food and fresh vegetables without washing them between times. The ideal system is to keep one chopping board for meat and another for vegetables.
- Put all rubbish and scraps of food straight into the waste bin – and always keep the lid securely down, so that flies can't get in and germs can't get out.
- Cut down on the quantity of food you cook. This reduces the amount of left-overs in your diet, which are a major source of food poisoning.
- It's better to be careful than to be sick. By incorporating these precautions into your daily routine, you will minimize the risk of food poisoning.

In addition to the above, here are some basic suggestions which – if adopted – would mean we can eat without fear:

- An end to the intensive rearing of animals and birds.
- Stricter temperature controls should be introduced in

shops. All shop refrigerators should display thermometers, so we can be sure the food we're buying has been correctly stored.

- All food should be labelled with recommended storage temperatures.
- Compulsory training of food handlers – leading to a certificate of competence – should be introduced.
- All new domestic fridges should be fitted with thermometers.

The whole question of food safety is too important to remain simply a matter of personal responsibility. The fact is that food producers must change their habits. If you are concerned about food poisoning, write to your supermarket and member of parliament to ask when they intend to implement these simple measures.

Preserving The Nutrients In Your Food

The level of nutrition you receive from your diet depends not only on what food you choose to eat but also on how you store and cook it. This provides three opportunities for nutrient loss. If you lead a hectic, demanding life, you need these nutrients even more and therefore need to know how you can safeguard them:

CHOICE OF FOOD

- The more a foodstuff is processed, the greater the loss of natural nutrients. So buy only unprocessed wholefoods.
- If possible buy organic food, preferably from local producers. Organic foods are more likely to have their nutrients intact and, if they are from local producers, they will not have been in long storage during transit. Nutrients decay with time – so eat close to the soil!
- Do check the use-by date. Old produce will have suffered

severe nutritional decay. Shopkeepers always put older stock at the front of the display – so disarrange their display, and buy from the back.

- Canning and bottling reduces the levels of vitamin C, thiamin and folic acid. Vitamin C loss continues during storage. If you have to buy canned food, do not keep it overlong. Although it may be safe to eat, its nutrients may be severely depleted.

- Foods which contain sulphur dioxide as a preservative will have almost entirely lost their thiamin (vitamin B1) content.

- Freeze-dried foods are relatively good since there is no heating to deplete nutrients.

- Frozen foods suffer some thiamin and vitamin C loss. However, the loss is less than in fresh food which has been kept for a number of days (see *Storage*, below). If shopping for fresh food is a problem for you, frozen foods are probably the next best alternative, but be extra careful not to overcook them (see *Cooking*, below).

- Choose unrefined monounsaturated oils like olive oil for cooking. Pure, refined polyunsaturated oils turn rancid more easily.

- Don't buy tinned goods which are damaged – no matter how good a bargain they appear to be. Small cracks in the lining inside the cans affect the contents, which will in turn certainly affect the delicate vitamins and other nutrients and may even cause the food itself to turn bad.

STORAGE

- Store oils, fats and oily foods like cheeses and shelled nuts in the refrigerator. This will help to slow down the process of oxidation which turns them rancid.

- Vitamin C, thiamin, riboflavin and folic acid all decay quickly in air. Once vegetables are harvested, the damaged tissues release an enzyme which starts to destroy the vitamin C. Blanching inhibits the enzyme, which is why freezing fresh vegetables is much better than keeping them unfrozen and eating them many days later.

- Vegetables lose around 70 per cent of their folic acid content within three days if they are stored in the light. Store vegetables in the refrigerator until you are ready to use them, or freeze them straight away.
- Store grains and cereals whole and in a dry, cool place.
- Milk supplies the best source of riboflavin, but up to 50 per cent is destroyed within two hours in sunlight! That pinta left on the doorstep will still lose 20 per cent even if the weather's cloudy.

COOKING

- Cooking is generally harmful to the nutrients in food. However, it also changes starches, proteins and some vitamins into accessible forms for us, as well as releasing nutrients in some foods which are otherwise bound in, like the amino acid tryptophan in cornmeal. Cooking is necessary for other foods to destroy toxic substances such as those found in soya beans and kidney beans. Cooking also makes some foods, like meat, palatable to eat. However, there are ways in which you can reduce the nutrient loss in foods during the cooking process.
- Pressure cooking is perhaps the best way to reduce nutrient loss. Invest in a non-aluminium pressure cooker which, because of the reduced cooking times, will also reduce energy consumption and therefore the size of your fuel bills.
- After pressure-cooking, steaming and microwave cooking are the next healthiest options. Buying a steamer is obviously a lot cheaper than a microwave oven! Further down the list are:
- boiling
- grilling

- stir-frying (at high temperature where the fat seals in the nutrients)
- sautéing
- deep frying
- If you cook with fat don't let it become so hot that it starts to smoke. At this temperature the essential fatty acid, linoleic acid, is destroyed immediately.
- Fats which have been used for cooking once must be discarded since the linoleic acid and vitamins A and C will have been lost.
- If you boil food, do so for the minimum amount of time and then use the water for stock afterwards. The fragile water-soluble vitamins, as well as some minerals, leach into cooking water, which is why soups are so nutritious.
- Don't add bicarbonate of soda to cooking water, even if you see it recommended in cooking pulses. It destroys valuable B vitamins.
- Prepare food immediately before cooking – remember that vitamin C is destroyed once cells are damaged in vegetables – and for the same reason try not to chop them too finely. Scrubbing vegetables is better than peeling them.
- Once prepared, immerse the vegetables in ready boiling water straightaway.
- Use pans with close-fitting lids and avoid using copper pans which encourage oxidation and vitamin C loss.
- Once food is cooked, eat it straightaway. Keeping it warm will only result in further nutrient loss, which is why eating out too frequently may be less than healthy for you.

If you lead a hectic lifestyle, and consider that you don't have time for some of the advice given above, think again. The life you lead is totally dependent on a good nutritional support system – without which, you're just running on empty. And you can only do that for so long.

Avoiding Residue In Your Food

Pesticides are poisons. Their basic purpose is to kill pests. In an ideal world, pesticides are not supposed to leave any residue on food by the time it's ready for us to eat. However, a huge amount of evidence clearly shows that the food we eat *can* be tainted with pesticide residue, even if it's been washed many times.

INSECTICIDES

Used to kill bugs and beetles which threaten a farmer's crops, some insecticides are chemically very similar to nerve gases, and work by attacking the central nervous system of the animals they are intended to kill. Another type of insecticide – the organochlorines – includes DDT, which biologist Rachel Carson first warned the world about in 1962 in her book *Silent Spring*. Carson believed that the use of DDT (see p. 218–19) was causing a dramatic decrease in the numbers of many species of birds – hence the title of her book. We now know it isn't only birds who suffer from the effects of DDT and similar substances. This group of chemicals is classified as 'persistent' – in other words, it isn't easily destroyed or degraded, so it sticks around for years. The organochlorines are also attracted to fatty substances, so they can be found in greater concentrations in milk, cheese, meat, and human breast milk.

HERBICIDES

Farmers spend twice as much on herbicides as they do on insecticides and fungicides put together. They are used to kill off weeds by either preventing their growth, or sometimes by causing unnaturally rapid growth. Many of these herbicides are designed to be absorbed directly into the system of the plant itself, so that it is impossible to get rid of them simply by washing.

One such systemic herbicide is 2,4,5-T (short for

(2,4,5-trichlorophenoxy acetic acid) which was an ingredient in Agent Orange, the herbicide used by the US Army in Vietnam. The army used Agent Orange in 1963 to destroy the food supply of the Vietcong, and strip them of cover in dense mountainous regions. Certainly, at the time it was first used, there was no evidence that it brought immediate illness and death in its wake. But years later, the effects started to be noticed. Vietnamese exposed to it showed an unusually high level of clinical abnormalities such as miscarriages, birth defects and sterility. American soldiers also became ill with ailments ranging from cancer to deformations in their children. The probable cause of these devastating problems was another substance present in the herbicide called dioxin (see p. 222–4), which is formed during the 2,4,5-T manufacturing process.

Another connection between the use of herbicides and human illness was revealed when a scientist exposed a statistical connection between the use of herbicides and Parkinson's disease, which affects the central nervous system in humans.[14] It is suspected that a certain group of herbicides (chemically very similar to MPTP, a designer drug which is known to produce an irreversible Parkinsonian-like syndrome in humans) is capable of bringing about the slow destruction of a specific group of brain cells, thus causing Parkinson's disease. Again, this effect can take many years to occur, making it very difficult for scientists to prove that there's a health problem – until it's too late.

FUNGICIDES

These substances limit or kill fungal infections in food products. One class of fungicides, which contain ethylene bisdithiocarbamate (EBDC) has been estimated to be used on up to 70 per cent of potatoes, 40 per cent of apples and 10 per cent of wheat in the UK.[15] Studies show that, both on food and in the body, EBDC can gradually break down into a chemical called ethylenethiourea (ETU) which has caused tumours and birth defects in laboratory animals.[16]

THE ANSWER'S IN THE SOIL

Thankfully, many supermarket chains have now started to stock organic produce. So what is organic food? The Soil Association states that 'Organic food is produced responsibly, taking account of the needs of consumers, farm animals and the environment. Organic farmers produce food which:

- Is grown without artificial pesticides and fertilizers.
- Tastes good rather than just looks good.
- Is never irradiated.
- Contains no artificial hormones, genetically manipulated organisms or unnecessary medication.
- Is not over-processed to remove the goodness.
- Does not contain flavourings, dyes or other additives.
- Is nutritious, living food which promotes positive health and well-being.

At the moment then, the standards which organic farmers and producers work to are not government controlled. Instead it has been left to independent bodies, namely the Soil Association and the UK Register of Organic Food Standards, to work things out. Between them these two bodies have established working standards and have developed a symbol system so that organic produce can be easily identified by the consumer. This well-known symbol provides assurance that the produce has reached certain standards. The symbol system's standards reach further than addressing just the food and aims to make sure that the farming practices are environmentally friendly. Farmers, growers, food processors, distributors and industrial manufacturers (who make farm products) can all apply to use the Soil Association's symbol.

Of course, organic food needs to be safe for the environment as well as for us. In America, the National Academy of Sciences reported that agriculture was responsible for about 50 per cent of all American water pollution. In many areas of Britain, nitrate pollution of the water supply is a major health problem (see first chapter). It has been clearly established that modern biological-organic farming methods lead both to lower leaching of nitrates into the water supply, and to lower nitrate content in vegetables.[17] So going organic is good for the environment, too.

CHILDREN AT ESPECIAL RISK

A report from the American National Resources Defense Council indicates that children consume about four times more cancer-causing pesticides than adults – and one child out of 3,000 may develop cancer from eating chemical residues.[18] Clearly, if these figures are even remotely accurate, there is major cause for parental concern. In fact, a panel set up by the highly respected National Academy of Sciences has confirmed that children are more sensitive to pesticides.[19] The panel recommended that the US government improve the way it calculates pesticide risks to include the difference between children and adults, and also to collect more detailed data on the amount of food children actually eat. 'Children's systems can retain a greater portion of a given toxin because their gastrointestinal tract is more easily penetrated,' says Steven Markowitz, MD, assistant professor in the division of environmental and occupational medicine at Mount Sinai School of Medicine in New York City. 'And kids eat more per unit weight than adults do, so the tissues in their bodies may be more exposed to these substances.' On top of this, children are dramatically more susceptible to carcinogens than adults, because infancy and childhood are periods of rapid cell division. 'The cells of many different tissues in the body are proliferating, and that increases the chances that a genetic change leading to cancer will result,' says Steven Markowitz.[20] So if you can't afford to provide organic food for all the family, do try giving it to just the youngest – they are the most at risk from the long-term health effects of pesticides.

CONTROLLING THE COST

The organic symbol scheme goes a long way towards ensuring consistently high standards of food production, and should be supported. However, the cost of buying organic food can be prohibitive. Lowering the price of organic food – and thus making it available to many more people – must be the next goal for the producers. In reality, organic agriculture is not necessarily any more expensive for the farmer. In 1983, the first well-documented scientific study was published which showed that an organic farm can achieve crop yields comparable to conventional farms at less cost, and with half the pollution and soil erosion produced by orthodox farming methods. The study, undertaken by the independent Rodale Research Center of Emmaus, Pennsylvania, demonstrated that farming costs were slashed by between 10 and 30 per cent, because organic farming doesn't use expensive chemical fertilizers. At the same time, crop yields equalled or exceeded state averages. For example, corn yields averaged 108 bushels per acre, compared to 85.3 bushels produced by conventional chemical farming.[21]

Splashing Out On Pure Water

Reducing your chemical exposure by eating organic food is one important step, but there may also be more pollutants in your water than you think. Aluminium, lead, cadmium and nitrates may all be present – check their entries in Part Two for information on ways of eliminating them. Additionally, chlorine is routinely added to tap water in order to disinfect it. You may be surprised to learn that chlorination does *not* kill all disease-causing organisms. Chlorine is not effective against many viruses and protozoa – two classes of micro-organisms which can be just as lethal as bacteria. Organisms which are resistant to chlorination include enteric viruses such as polio; the viruses that cause hepatitis; rotavirus which causes infantile diarrhoea; giardia which causes chronic diarrhoea, weight loss and cramp. Perhaps the most resistant of all are those intestinal parasites called helminths, which are otherwise simply known as worms. All these disease-causing organisms can survive the process of water chlorination, and serve to remind us that chlorinated water is not necessarily pure water.

However, there is a further problem with the chlorination of water, which occurs when chlorine comes into contact with natural organic compounds which are formed from decaying vegetation. Surface water – such as rivers and streams – often contains considerable amounts of decaying vegetation. When chlorine reacts with these substances, it produces compounds known as trihalomethanes (THMs) which could threaten our health. One such THM is chloroform (see p.199) which is possibly carcinogenic. Although research is still underway at the moment, other THMs may ultimately prove to be equally questionable. It does at least seem prudent to try to reduce our exposure to these compounds:

• A combined activated-carbon / reverse-osmosis water treatment system can significantly reduce THM levels. Reverse osmosis can also reduce micro-organism levels significantly.

ORGANIC CONTAMINANTS

Organic chemicals are potentially dangerous to us because, just like the chemistry of life itself, they are based on carbon. As a result, they can easily enter into human tissues and seriously disrupt the body's complex chemical reactions, perhaps precipitating cancerous changes.

Organic chemicals can pollute your water if you live near a toxic-waste landfill, or in an agricultural area where herbicides and pesticides are heavily used. Some industries also discharge their organic waste directly into river water, which is used as a source for tap water.

There are millions of organic chemicals but some of the better-known ones include benzene, carbon tetrachloride and chloroform. Many of these water-polluting substances can be vaporized in a hot shower and researchers have found that you could actually absorb up to 100 times more pollutants simply by breathing the air around a shower than you could by drinking all the water that passes through the shower. Taking a long, hot shower is therefore much more of a health risk than taking a bath. Steps to reduce your intake of organic contaminants include:

- Take cold showers or warm baths
- Use a combined activated-carbon / reverse-osmosis water treatment system

Because of increasing public concern about the quality of drinking water, some private laboratories now offer a full water-testing service. You may find local ones listed in your local phone book. You can also contact your local water authority and ask them to do an analysis of your own house supply.

CHOOSING A WATER TREATMENT SYSTEM

There are four main types of domestic water treatment systems.

1. Filtration. Water filtration systems can be used to remove small particles such as dirt or sediment, and sometimes even bacteria, from your water supply. However, simply filtering your water will not remove any chemical contamination which may be present. If you happen to obtain your water supply from a stream or borehole, a good water filter makes an important first stage in the purification process. Otherwise – don't bother buying expensive filtration

equipment because all domestic tap water is pre-filtered by the time it reaches your home.

2. Activated-carbon filters. Activated-carbon filters have become very popular recently and can be seen in many homes in the form of a plastic jug with a centrally mounted carbon filter through which water is allowed to trickle. Carbon is 'activated' by steam-heating charcoal to a high temperature without oxygen. The resulting granules are honeycombed with a labyrinth of tiny channels which greatly increase the available surface area. As water flows through this network of tiny tunnels, molecules of contaminating chemicals are trapped in this honeycomb, and the water is purified. Since the contaminants build up inside the filter, the cartridge obviously needs to be changed quite frequently. Activated-carbon filters can remove many objectionable tastes and odours, including chlorine, and will also reduce many of the organic contaminants in water. They are not as effective in removing nitrates or dissolved metals such as iron, lead, or copper.

3. Reverse osmosis. Revere osmosis is a process by which impure water is forced through a very fine membrane. The extremely tiny pores in the membrane can filter out very small bacteria, and will also remove many kinds of chemical molecules, including lead and nitrates. Small molecules such as the trihalomethanes, the group that includes chloroform, are not removed very effectively. Reverse-osmosis filters are usually self-cleaning and therefore have a greater lifespan than activated-charcoal filters, although initially they are much more expensive.

4. Distillation. Contrary to popular belief, distilled water isn't totally pure water. Here's how it works. As the water boils in the still, it produces water vapour which is collected and condensed in another container, thus leaving behind many of the contaminants. However, those substances which have a boiling point very close to that of water, like some

of the trihalomethanes, cannot be removed. Like kettles, stills accumulate scale, a build-up of magnesium and calcium, and need to be cleaned periodically. Distilled water should not be stored for long periods since bacteria can breed very easily in it. Distillation is a slow process which doesn't produce water in large quantity.

WHICH TO CHOOSE

The best all-round water treatment system is not cheap. Because each method is good for some types of contaminants, but not for others, it is best to install a system which combines reverse osmosis and activated carbon. A number of companies now sell these combined units, from about £300 upwards. The system should be properly installed under the sink. The carbon filter will need to be changed quite frequently to preserve its effectiveness.

BOTTLED WATER

Don't buy bottled water thinking it's bacteriologically purer than tap water. In independent tests, some brands of still, bottled water were shown to have some 10,000 bacteria per millilitre, which exceeds the EC regulations for tap water.[22]

Bottled water's advertising plays heavily on its chic, healthy image, and sometimes talks about 'minerals'. In fact, the mineral content provided by bottled water is relatively insignificant, especially if you are already eating a varied diet. Some do specify a low sodium content, which may be of use if your doctor has prescribed this for you.

THE DO-IT-YOURSELF HOME DETOX KIT

Sick-building syndrome isn't just something that happens in offices and factories. It can also affect many homes, including yours; and many people, including you. A 'yes' answer to two or more of the following questions strongly suggests that your home may need detoxifying.

QUESTION	NO	YES
Do you suffer from the symptoms of ill health (a persistent runny nose, for example) which go away when you leave the house and return when you return?		
Does more than one member of the family suffer like this, especially those who spend the most time at home?		
Do the symptoms get worse when the heat is turned on?		
Did you start feeling bad when you moved into a new house, remodelled your house, bought new furnishings or curtains, sprayed with pesticides, or changed your activity level?		

Did symptoms develop after energy conservation work (such as lagging, cavity foam, etc.) was done on your house?		
Do the symptoms become most severe when the house is tightly sealed in cold weather?		

There are hundreds of potential indoor air pollutants, ranging from dust, smoke and airborne bacteria to the paints, cleaners, solvents, dyes, glues and household sprays you use every day to clean and improve your home. They all pollute your inner space. Here are just a few possible sources to consider:

- Your new curtains and carpets may emit unpleasant substances.
- Your home insulation may discharge man-made fibres, or even asbestos, into the air you breathe.
- Your pressed-wood and fibreboard furniture and fittings can emit chemicals.
- In your home office, your computer generates heat and radiation.
- The copier produces ozone.
- Electromagnetic radiation from household appliances like the TV, fridge and even your electric blanket, can also adversely affect your health.
- Even taking a refreshing hot shower to wash all the pollution away can be risky – you actually absorb more pollutants by taking a shower (from breathing the fine water spray) than you would from simply drinking the water.[23]

Step 1: Health Through Chemical Vigilance

On a basic level, you can cure a sick house by becoming chemically vigilant. Remove as many chemical products from your environment as you can, especially air fresheners, moth crystals, carpet shampoos, aerosols and stored chemicals (including paints and solvents). Store those chemicals you just can't do without in a locked outdoor shed or container. Your catchphrase should be: eliminate or minimize. Use the following chart to find effective alternatives to many unnecessary sources of chemical exposure:

CLEANING UP YOUR ACT:
EASY SOLUTIONS TO HOME POLLUTION

PRODUCT	PROBLEM	ALTERNATIVE
Aerosol air fresheners	Tiny particles, with impurities attached, could irritate lung tissue if inhaled	• Certain house plants are very effective air cleaners (see p. 38) • Pot-pourri • A bowl of bicarbonate of soda will effectively absorb odours
Carpets	'Out-gassing' or emissions from carpets may cause allergy or flu-like symptoms in some people. Dust mites in carpets can trigger asthma attacks. Carpet cleaning may put children at risk from Kawasaki syndrome[24]	• Ask suppliers to air out a synthetic carpet for at least a week before installation • Use adhesives that are low in VOCs (volatile organic compounds) or are water-based • Keep room very well ventilated for at least 72 hours after a carpet is laid • Swap carpets for cotton or cotton/wool rugs without backing • Replace synthetic carpeting with nonporous ceramic tile or hardwood floors sealed with a nontoxic finish that doesn't need waxing • Try natural linoleum
Dry cleaning	Solvents used in the dry-cleaning process may cause toxic reactions resulting in headaches	• Leave dry cleaning outside for a few hours until the chemical smell has disappeared • Never sleep with freshly dry-cleaned clothes in the bedroom wardrobe

PRODUCT	PROBLEM	ALTERNATIVE
Flea collars and Products	May contain substances that are toxic to humans as well as pets	• Use herbal-based collars that prevent infestation • Use a flea comb to remove fleas, then • Apply pyrethrum (see pp. 371–2) to areas of the home where fleas may hide, such as cracks and skirting • Vacuum frequently • Wash pets' bedding frequently
Gas cookers	A poorly ventilated kitchen can be contaminated with carbon monoxide and nitrogen dioxide. Young children in homes using gas cookers may suffer from more respiratory ailments than children in homes where electricity is used	• Keep a window open when cooking • If you have an exhaust fan, use it as well
Hair colouring products	May sensitize and cause skin irritation or allergy. Some studies suggest use of permanent or semi-permanent hair dyes for 16 or more years increases risk of cancer[25]	• Choose natural products such as henna or chamomile for colour and conditioning • If you must colour, try the 'frosted' or 'streaked' style which reduces chemical exposure • Don't leave the dye on your head any longer than necessary • Rinse your scalp thoroughly with water after use • Wear gloves when applying hair dye • Never mix different hair dye products, because you can induce potentially harmful reactions

PRODUCT	PROBLEM	ALTERNATIVE
Hair colouring products (cont.)		• Be sure to do a patch test for allergic reactions before applying the dye to your hair • Never dye your eyebrows or eyelashes
Limescale removers	May contain sodium hypochlorite or phosphoric acid, both of which can irritate lungs if inhaled	• Sponge white vinegar onto mineral deposits on shower curtain • Mix 4oz bicarbonate of soda with enough water to make a paste; scrub onto tiles and sinks with hard bristle brush
Moth repellents	Unnecessary exposure to chemicals	• Cedar marbles or sachets of cedar chips repel moths • Store clean clothes in zipped, plastic covers • Place sachets of lavender in amongst clothing • Place pot-pourris of clove, caraway, lavender and rose in cupboards
Oven cleaners	If containing sodium hydroxide, may burn skin, eyes or internal tissues	• Spread a soft paste of bicarbonate of soda and water over the bottom of the oven and leave 8–12 hours. Wipe clean and rinse with soapy cloth
Pesticides	Some have been associated with cancer and birth defects	• Use natural alternatives (see Step 4, p. 49)
Radon	Radioactive gas which damages lung tissue, causes 2,500 deaths each year in UK from lung cancer.[26]	• Ask your local council's environmental health department for help in determining if you have a radon problem, and if so, for financial assistance in curing it • Radon can be prevented from

PRODUCT	PROBLEM	ALTERNATIVE
Radon *(cont.)*	Seeps up into houses through gaps in floors and walls. Radon hot-spots exist in Devon, Northampton-shire, Cornwall, Avon, Cumbria, Staffordshire, the West Midlands and Wales	seeping into your home by building a suspended concrete floor. • Underfloor fans beneath the building can suck the gas away • Contact the Radon Survey (National Radiological Protection Board) tel. 01235-831 600 for further guidance
Skin cream	Some people develop skin irritation from those which contain fragrance or lanolin	• Use a lotion of rose water and glycerine instead • Fresh lemon juice will soften and fragrance the skin
Timber treatment	Chemicals used in timber treatment may cause serious illnesses	• Check the history of any house you move into for evidence of timber treatment • Ask any timber-treatment company you think about employing for full, written safety data about the chemicals they use, and a written guarantee saying they'll be responsible for any adverse health effects

Step 2: Health Through Air Cleaners

Don't take the air quality in your house for granted. Because of poor building design, new construction techniques, and the increased need to conserve energy, today's home now resembles a sealed box. That expensive double glazing you installed certainly keeps in the heat, but it also stops fresh air from circulating. According to studies by the US Environmental Protection Agency, the air inside energy-efficient houses is often two to five times more polluted than the air outside![27] Indoor pollution will be one of the major environmental issues of the twenty-first century. One of the natural ways you can reduce the toxic burden in the air is by filling your home with living plants. In the same way as the Amazon rain forest is said to be the 'lungs of the planet', so certain plants have been found capable of 'scrubbing' the air inside your own micro-environment. Remarkable research by NASA scientists shows that certain species can remove health-threatening pollutants such as formaldehyde, benzene and trichloroethylene from the air we breathe. While researching life-support systems for future space stations, NASA found that three common house plants – golden pothos (*scindapsus aureus*), nephthytis (*syngonium podophyllum*) and the spider plant (*chlorophytum elatum vittatum*) can all remove substantial amounts of chemical contamination. Further research suggests that philodendrons may be even more effective.[28]

How many plants should you use? B.C. Wolverton, a NASA environmental research scientist, says: 'If you have an office or a home that isn't making you sick but is a wee bit stuffy, then put a dozen or more plants in there. But if you're having symptoms of sick building syndrome, or if someone in there smokes, go ahead and put plants in, but supplement them with a high-efficiency filter.'[29] Wolverton has himself designed just such a filter, which takes the revolutionary approach of using several plants' root systems as the means by which to 'scrub' the air. Using a fan, fifty cubic feet of air can be cleaned every minute, by drawing it through their roots. Unlike other carbon-filter systems, it doesn't need to be changed because the roots and the bacteria which live there seem to consume the pollutants as their food source.[30]

Also Consider . . . Ionizers

There are basically two types of air pollutants: particulate matter and molecular pollutants. Particulates include dust, pollen, and tobacco smoke (smoke is actually composed of millions of microscopic particles that can be isolated and trapped by some filter systems). Molecular pollutants, on the other hand, are substances such as carbon monoxide and nitrogen oxide, and are very difficult for domestic ionizers, air filters or purifiers to eliminate.

Ionizers work on the principle that negative ions not only have a 'tonic effect' on the nervous system, but also clear the air of dust particles, smoke, pollen and smells. Negative ions exist in plentiful numbers in nature. They are produced by the continual, electrical re-charging of particles by the action of the sun, wind, rain and lightning. They are particularly in evidence on mountain tops, near seas, rivers and waterfalls, after thunderstorms and in your own shower! It has been claimed that the presence of negative ions can regulate the body's production of serotonin, a chemical present in the brain which helps control moods.

Ionizers work by giving a negative charge to airborne particles which then drift to grounded surfaces such as walls and ceilings, where they stick. Unless the ionizer is combined with a fan and a filter of some type, the particles tend to be attracted to walls and other nearby surfaces, causing unpleasant staining. When used in conjunction with air filters which sift the air for tiny pollutants (some models combine both features in one unit) ionizers may provide a partial answer to your indoor air pollution.

Also Consider . . . Air Purifiers

There are three basic types of air purifier: conventional air cleaners, purifiers with an air-freshener stage, and purifiers which also incorporate ionizers. Air purifiers use a small fan to draw the contaminated air through a woven fabric filter, usually followed by an activated-charcoal filter. Some systems follow this with an air-freshener step, where the air passes through a wire mesh coated with tiny crystals of lemon-lime air freshener or some other fragrance. Finally, some versions also incorporate a negative ion generating stage before the air is recycled into the room. Here's what they can and can't do:

- If you suffer from allergies, a combined ionizer/air purifier may work for you. The problem is that larger particles of dust and other material which you may be allergic to will quickly settle on the floor, beyond the reach of the purifier.
- If you live or work among machines which give out positively charged ions (such a television sets, monitors, VDU screens) and suffer from persistent headaches, try using an ionizer for a time. There are many personal reports of dramatic improvements under such conditions.
- Most air purifiers can do a good job of removing tobacco smoke from the air, thereby reducing eye, nose, and throat irritation. However, they may not remove the actual smell of smoke as effectively – the molecules are too small to be filtered out.
- Most domestic air purifiers won't be able to tackle the threat posed by dangerous gases such as carbon monoxide, oxides of sulphur and nitrogen, and ozone.

A good air filter may cost several hundred pounds, and need its filters changed every month or two. If you value your family's health, you'll find the expenditure worthwhile. Consider using a humidifier for air which seems too dry or dusty (a side-effect of central heating).

YOU MUST BE CHOKING!
A GUIDE TO AIR QUALITY STANDARDS

Today, the air quality in many British, European and North American cities is a public disgrace. Friends of the Earth estimate that over 10 million people in the UK are at risk from contaminated air. Groups particularly at risk include young children, the elderly, and pregnant women, as well as people with respiratory illnesses such as asthma, hay fever, bronchitis, angina and emphysema. Very often, you can experience the pollution at first hand – smelling it, and tasting it – and yet the official line is that the air quality is 'good'. Be suspicious! Find out the actual measurements, and check to see whether they exceed the World Health Organization (WHO) guidelines, below. These guidelines do *not* include a 'wide safety margin', as officials may sometimes have you believe. According to the WHO: 'When populations are exposed to air pollutant levels above the Air Quality Guideline, adverse health effects may occur. In any population, a number of people will be especially sensitive to a given pollutant. Young children and the aged are likely to be more sensitive, as are people with pre-existing lung disease and/or cardiovascular disease. People who exercise or work outdoors will increase the inhaled dose and, hence, be at increased potential risk . . . Since the Air Quality Guideline value incorporates little or no margin of protection, widespread acute effects of the respiratory tract may be caused. The frequent and repetitive nature of ozone exposure might contribute to the irreversible decline of lung function as well as to structural lung damage.'[31]

Sulphur Dioxide	350 µg per cubic metre for 1 hour exposure
	125 µg per cubic metre for 24 hour exposure
	50 µg per cubic metre for 1 year's exposure
Carbon Monoxide	30 mg per cubic metre for 1 hour expoure
	10 mg per cubic metre for 8 hour exposure
Ozone	150–200 µg per cubic metre for 1 hour exposure (76–100 parts per billion)
	100–120 µg per cubic metre for 8 hour exposure (50–60 parts per billion)
Nitrogen Dioxide	400 µg per cubic metre for 1 hour exposure
	150 µg per cubic metre for 24 hour exposure

Note: the abbreviation 'µg' means 'microgram'. You will sometimes see it also abbreviated to 'mcg'. A microgram is one millionth of a gram. It is a thousand times smaller than a milligram (mg).

You can contact the National Society for Clean Air (tel. 01273 326 313) or the Women's Environmental Network (tel. 0171 247 3327) for the latest information and guidance.

Step 3: Light Up Your Life

One of the most important – and yet secret – ingredients in a healthy home is the quality of its lighting. Most people seem to ignore its impact on their health – but *you* shouldn't. Far from being a substitute for sunlight, some research suggests that artificial lighting may actually damage your health, being associated with illnesses as wide-ranging as impotence, depression, blindness, headaches and eyestrain.

FLUORESCENT LIGHTING

Fluorescent tubes were supposed to be the miracle, energy-efficient alternative to ordinary lightbulbs. And they are certainly much cheaper to run – unlike ordinary incandescent bulbs, they generate very little unwanted heat, and so waste little energy. They give off a bright light and the tubes last much longer than old-fashioned bulbs. However, fluorescent tubes have some drawbacks, as well – typical health complaints which seem to be associated with this type of lighting include nausea, eyestrain, headaches, depression and even panic attacks.

Scientists have been unable to establish exactly why fluorescents should appear to cause these problems. What they do know is that fluorescent lights flicker on and off at a very rapid rate – 60 times per second – and they can also generate radio waves and sometimes an audible hum. All these phenomena may affect certain sensitive people.

A 1982 paper in the medical journal *The Lancet* reported how an Australian scientific study suggested that there could be a connection between exposure to fluorescent lighting and melanoma – skin cancer.[32] The report was largely ignored at the time it was published, and some subsequent research has not confirmed the same relationship. However, other research has suggested that exposure to fluorescent lighting, as used in certain work environments, may act as a tumour promoter – it might aid in the development of cancers which were originally caused by other factors.[33]

When fluorescent lights are used in nurseries for premature babies, they can literally cause blindness. The People's Medical Society estimates that up to 2,500 premature infants may be blinded by excessive light in American intensive care nurseries each year.[34] This entirely preventable cause of blindness has been the subject of a 'Turn Off The Lights' campaign, which aims to bring this scandal to the public's attention. The problem could be solved by:

- Replacing fluorescent lights in the intensive care nursery with incandescent bulbs.
- Fitting babies with isolettes and protective side shields.
- Turning off the lights at night so that babies experience a natural light and dark cycle.

Even more disturbingly, it has been suggested that there might be a link between childhood leukaemia and fluorescent lighting.[35] We interviewed Dr Shmuel Ben-Sasson, of the respected Hubert H. Humphrey Centre for Experimental Medicine and Cancer Research in Jerusalem, who explained it like this: 'It started out of pure intellectual curiosity,' he told us. 'To me, childhood leukaemia was a real puzzle.' What bothered him so much was the strange pattern seen in childhood leukaemia – which peaks in children at about the age of four. Most other types of cancers don't behave like this – they become more prevalent with age. So why does it peak like this, at such a young age? 'When you see a peak,' he told us, 'it is an indicator for a single causative event. For example, after the atomic bomb was dropped, there was a peak of leukaemia a few years later.' So working backwards, Dr Ben-Sasson calculated that some kind of leukaemia-causing event must be occurring at about the time of birth. What made him suspect fluorescent lighting as the cause was the striking fact that white children are more susceptible to leukaemia than black children. 'And that suggests that the pigmentation in black children is serving as a protective screen against harmful light,' he believes.

But how could this happen? His colleague, Dr Devra Lee Davis of the American National Academy of Sciences spoke to us from her base in Washington. 'Immediately after birth', she explained, 'the liver of the new-born is putting out new blood cells which circulate throughout the body. Fluorescent light of a certain wavelength can penetrate the skin and damage these cells, which may increase the chance of developing cancer of the blood, which is what leukaemia is.'

Dr Ben-Sasson's theory has received very little publicity (he found it nearly impossible to get it published in a scientific journal – many of them believed it might cause mass panic). Fluorescent lighting is clearly not the sole cause of leukaemia in children – but it could be a completely preventable cause.

HOW CHILDHOOD ACUTE LYMPHOCYTIC LEUKAEMIA MAY HAPPEN . . .

1.   Fluorescent tubes emit blue light (400 nm wavelength)
2.   Light penetrates the skin, produces free radicals
3.   Free radicals damage child's DNA
4.   Damaged DNA causes leukaemia to develop

. . . AND WHAT COULD BE DONE TO PREVENT IT

1.   Cheap plastic filters could be fitted to fluorescent lights in maternity wards
2.   The type and intensity of lighting in maternity wards could be changed

Full-Spectrum Lighting

Full-spectrum lighting is the very latest technological development in lighting. It's a kind of fluorescent light which is designed to mimic both the visible and ultraviolet light radiated by the sun – artificially generated sunlight. As we know, the same ultraviolet light that helps you manufacture Vitamin D can also give you skin cancer if you get too much of it. The question is whether working eight hours a day under full spectrum lighting, which includes ultraviolet light, is too great a risk.

Opinions vary as to the answer. The makers of full-spectrum lighting argue that the risk of over-exposure is almost non-existent because their lights are designed to minimize the emission of ultraviolet radiation. But until we've seen more evidence of the safety of full-spectrum lighting, we wouldn't want it in our home.

Incandescent Lighting

Normal incandescent lights have several advantages over fluorescent lights: they don't flicker, they don't hum and they don't produce any radio waves. They also emit very low levels of UV. 'Incandescent' literally means glowing with heat – normal light bulbs come under this category. Incandescent light is generated by an electric current being passed through a carbon or tungsten filament. The disadvantage is that it gives off considerable amounts of heat as well as light, and so is not energy efficient – in fact, they probably use up more energy in heat than light. On the other hand, the bulbs are very cheap to buy and replace. However, because of energy inefficiency and the short life of incandescent bulbs, the cost to the environment is not so low. Furthermore, the *quality* of light is not ideal – especially when compared to sunlight.

Quartz halogen

The Quartz Halogen light is becoming increasingly popular. Basically, it's an incandescent bulb, filled with a highly reactive halogen gas (usually iodine). The bulb is made from quartz, because the gas generates enough heat to melt glass – which could constitute a fire hazard.

Chromalux

Probably the best indoor light currently available is Chromalux. It radiates 28 per cent less heat than normal incandescent bulbs, it emits light similar to the visible spectrum of sunlight, and it gives off a safe level of ultraviolet light. And the cost is low – cheap when you consider that it usually lasts over five times as long as a conventional incandescent bulb. It's been manufactured by the Lumiram Corporation in Finland since 1960.

And Of Course . . . Natural Sunlight

Don't forget the oldest, most natural form of all lighting, the sun. When moving house, or when having structural work carried out, give a moment's thought to the possibility of bringing more sunlight into your home. This could mean opening up another window or rooflight, or even using large mirrors, cleverly positioned, to reflect the glow of the morning or evening sun. Apart from saving on energy costs, you'll also be getting more healthy sunlight, which is good for your body. These days, mainly because of the diminishing ozone layer, we tend to think of the sun as a rather dangerous source of cancer-causing radiation. But the fact is that, if you deprive yourself of natural sunlight, you put your health on the line. Your body uses sunlight in a variety of ways:

• To help you fight off colds, tiredness and depression.
• To help your body to produce and absorb certain vitamins

and minerals. We all know that calcium builds strong, healthy teeth and bones, but in order to absorb calcium your body needs vitamin D, which is produced by your skin during exposure to sunlight. About ten minutes of sun exposure a day will be sufficient to manufacture vitamin D. More than that will not increase the amount of vitamin D you make, and will raise your risk of skin cancer.

• A lack of natural sunlight has been linked with obesity, hyperactivity and even cancer.

Sunlight can also stop your body producing the hormones which have been linked to Seasonal Affective Disorder (SAD). There may be more than half a million SAD sufferers in Britain alone, and most are thought to be women. There is nothing new about getting winter blues – over two thousand years ago Hippocrates noted that 'Some are well or ill adapted to Winter' and advised doctors to study meteorology before getting to grips with medicine!

SAD usually starts in autumn and continues during winter through to spring. You might feel low, have less energy, put on a few pounds, and experience difficulty in getting up in the morning. Clinical SAD is so overpowering that it can affect jobs and relationships for the larger part of each year. Shift workers are particularly prone to it, because they intentionally change normal patterns of behaviour so that their natural body rhythms are disrupted on a regular basis. They tend to be unhappy, unproductive in their jobs, and suffer a higher incidence of illness. Research suggests that shift workers must eliminate noise and interruption from their lives as much as possible in order to cope with the syndrome.

Scientists do not know yet why women are four times more likely to suffer from SAD than men. The link between depression and premenstrual tension and the existence of postpartum depression suggest that hormonal changes may influence women's moods. Originally, it was thought that SAD sufferers had an imbalance of the light-sensitive hormone melatonin, which is secreted into the bloodstream at night by a gland at the base of the brain, but the hormone's role in SAD, if any, is as yet unclear.

Very often, a sufferer from SAD will also have a craving for carbohydrate-rich foodstuffs. It is thought that carbohydrate consumption sets off a complex biochemical chain of events, eventually leading to higher levels of serotonin in the brain. Serotonin is a neurotransmitter, one of the chemicals in the brain that is involved in sleep, pain perception and motor activity and helps to control moods. And it is possible that a seasonal serotonin deficiency may be brought on by low levels of sunlight during the winter months.

If you feel that you are a SAD sufferer, seek advice from a psychiatrist, psychologist or a social worker, and ask to complete a Seasonal Pattern Assessment Questionnaire or SPAQ. This assesses whether your sleep, social life, mood, weight, appetite and energy vary according to the seasons. If you have a low score, your depression is probably caused by something else.

Light therapy can cure SAD completely and has few known side-effects. The treatment is simple. Sufferers regularly expose themselves to bright levels of light, often in the comfort of their own homes. The light must be at least 2,500 lux – normal indoor lights are about 400 lux and have no effect on SAD.[36] You should not look directly at the light but you are free to read, write or eat meals. Users should stick to a regular schedule because skipping a few days of treatment will bring back the blues. Light therapy usually starts in the autumn or winter and continues through to the end of April. By then, natural light is usually sufficient to create a happy mood and plenty of energy!

For further advice and information on SAD you can contact the SAD Association, PO Box 989, London W7 2PZ.

Step 4: Terminate The Toxins

The most lethal substances present in many of our homes are chemicals that are specifically designed to kill – pesticides. Pests are creatures with whom we co-exist (and sometimes co-habit!) with a great deal of reluctance and antipathy. In home or garden, pests are those creatures which we consider un-hygienic, dangerous or damaging to property. They include a huge number of insects and some mammals: flies, wasps and bees, aphids, mice, rats, slugs and even birds. In recent decades a huge industry has sprung up to deal with our aversion to so-called pests – an industry based largely on killing the offending creatures. It seems that for every pest or combination of pests we encounter, there is a pesticide, insec-ticide, dusting powder or spray of some sort that will eliminate the problem.

Elimination usually means death, but what kills one species invariably has a profound effect on other, close to hand species – including humans. There are several hundred house-hold and garden pest products on the market, most of which contain powerful chemical ingredients which will upset the natural order of wild life, and many of which will pose a threat to you and your children's health. Pest control products may, for instance:

- Cause irritation or allergic reaction, including headache, cold symptoms, rashes, sore eyes and throat.
- Be very poisonous. In fact, some are fatal to humans and/or their pets. Most of these products contain warnings on the label but not everyone reads labels thoroughly. There are also, for instance, numerous cases of a spray used in one garden drifting to neighbouring gardens and poisoning unsuspecting people, plants and wildlife.
- Cause cancer, genetic mutation or birth defects in humans and animals. Studies to prove such effects take years and years to conduct and are surrounded by much secrecy and

controversy. Meanwhile, many suspect products are still on the market.

- Kill wildlife that is not considered a pest. Harmless insects, birds, plantlife and pets may be killed in the wake of a pest control product being used against one particular creature. This slaughter greatly upsets the natural balance of wildlife in the garden and can lead to greater pest problems than before.

There are steps you can take now to greatly curtail or eliminate the use of dangerous pest control products in your home and garden.

PHYSICAL BARRIERS

- Ensure doors and windows are well fitting. Mice often just walk into your house through an open door or window in spring or winter, so keeping the doors and windows closed is a simple answer to a potential problem.
- Fit insect screens on windows and adopt the American use of screen doors in front of solid doors. These let the light and air through, but nothing else. You might hang bead or plastic strip curtains in open doorways instead. These will reduce flying visitors, though not necessarily walking ones.
- In the garden, chicken wire fencing may help to reduce visitations by moles and rabbits. Dig a trench 12–18 inches deep around your garden and embed the chicken wire in it, leaving the remaining width of fencing to stretch between posts above ground. Fill the trench and tightly pack the earth around the buried fencing. This will prevent the creatures gaining access by digging or walking.

HYGIENE

- Vacuum upholstery, bedding and carpets regularly, working right up to the skirting boards. This simple precaution helps reduce the number of insect eggs tucked away in folds, creases and crevices.

- Clean clothes or bedding to be stored, then wrap them in plastic or paper along with strongly scented spice or herbal sachets.
- Be prompt and efficient clearing away your rubbish. Keep dustbins well covered and securely tie any refuse sacks. This is standard practice to reduce the incidence of flies, mice and rats.
- Store loose food in plastic or glass containers in a cool, dry place to prevent infestation by insects such as flies, beetles, silverfish and moths.
- Don't treat your compost bin as a rubbish tip. Follow the rules of good composting and don't add bacon rind or other fatty or fleshy foods which will attract rats and flies. Paper and very woody twigs and branches will also slow the decaying process and should be kept out of your compost bin.

CATCH, DON'T KILL!

There are many ways of catching pests and setting them free again outside.

- Place a glass over insects and then gently slide a postcard underneath. You can then carry them outside without having killed them (or touched them!).
- Buy a spider catcher, a long-handled, specially designed dustpan to help you catch creepy-crawlies even when they're high up.
- Buy a mousetrap which doesn't kill – available from most pet shops. The mouse can then be set free outside.

DETER AND REPEL

The kindest and most gentle way to deal with pests is to deter and repel them. Quite simply, to make them want to go elsewhere instead! These methods are also the safest for you and yours and they quickly and easily become part of your routine of cleaning, gardening and general housekeeping.

. . . FOR THE HOME

- Ants can be deterred by keeping sweet substances well cleaned and covered – no gooey drips of jam on the cupboard shelves, for instance. If you have a nest of ants or a seasonal caravan of them through your sitting room, place ammonia-soaked cotton wool or bunches of the herb wormwood at their point of entry to your house.
- Add sachets of lavender, rose petals, cedar wood chips or a blend of cloves, cinnamon and allspice to drawers, cupboards and stored clothing to deter moths, flies and other insects.
- Hang bunches of lavender in doorways or windows to deter flies and grow rue, basil, tansy and mints, especially penny-royal, in window boxes or in tubs by doors.
- Use netting and protective clothing as a first resort when dealing with mosquitoes. Citronella and pennyroyal herbal products, such as the citronella soap available from Oxfam, can act as repellents.
- The smell of peppermint, turpentine or cats usually deters mice and rats. Peppermint is easy to grow in your garden or windowsill. Turpentine should be kept well out of reach of children or pets, and is usually poured onto cotton wool and placed in the mouth of a mouse hole or rat run. While cats usually deter mice and rats, they also kill them so be prepared to face a few carcasses. Sonic pest repellers are said to deter mice, rats and moles.
- Bats are a protected species and it is illegal to try to evict them from their roost, even if it happens to be your attic. In fact, bats should never be considered pests in the first place: they do no damage to people or property, their droppings do not cause damage or offence and they help to

control insect pests in your garden. You may encourage and safeguard bats in your vicinity by avoiding the use of chemical pesticides and timber treatment and by hanging bat boxes in trees and on the outside of sheds.

. . . AND IN THE GARDEN

• Adopt companion-planting techniques. This ancient form of pest control relies on the idea of mutual benefit when planning your planting scheme in orchard, flower, herb or vegetable patch. For example: the roots of African, French or Mexican marigolds excrete the same chemical compound as pyrethrum. Eelworms, wireworms, millipedes and other root-eating pests are brought under control when you plant a ring of marigolds around your vegetables, or plant them in amongst your vegetables.

• Garlic planted near roses helps to prevent black spot and aphids. Onions should be planted in rows alternate to rows of carrots, to prevent carrot root flies on the carrots and onion root flies on the onions!

• Nasturtiums have a strong essence which aphids and white fly find obnoxious. Their root excretions deter root lice and strengthen neighbouring plants' resistance too. Grow them in amongst your tomatoes and round the base of your fruit trees.

• Every pest has its natural predator and you may find that pest control is best achieved by encouraging these predators to thrive in your garden. Your garden will become an attraction for these natural predators when you stop using chemicals that kill them or the insects they feed upon.

• Birds eat slugs, caterpillars and a variety of insects. Allow plenty of leaf cover for nesting and ensure feeding opportunities such as leaving seedheads intact for birds to eat.

• Hedgehogs eat slugs, beetles and other insect pests. Leave a rough and tumble corner of your garden for them to nest in, or build a hibernation box.

- Toads and frogs eat insects. Patches of long grass, piles of rotting wood and ponds are attractive to them.
- Ants may be a nuisance in the home, but they should be welcome in the garden. They feed on aphids and tree dwelling insects. They nest in old wood or under rocks.
- Ladybirds are voracious consumers of aphids and no healthy garden should be without them. They live in orchards, shrubbery and meadow-like grasses. Stop spraying pesticides to encourage these mini pest controllers, or collect some from a friend's garden.
- Regularly change the varieties of annual flowers and vegetables you grow and practise crop rotation to create a 'pest resistant' garden.
- Adopt organic gardening methods; these aim to work with Nature, not against her. You may have to wait a year or two to achieve a natural balance of pests and predators, but your garden will become a productive haven for a huge variety of wildlife.

THE SECRET INGREDIENTS HOT LIST – THIRTY THINGS YOUR HOME CAN DO WITHOUT

Most of the substances on the Hot List have been rated for carcinogenicity by the International Agency for Research on Cancer. For those which are not suspected of being carcinogens, brief details as to why they've been included will be found under the 'Other Concerns' column. For fuller information, check their entry in Part Two.

Cancer is the word used to describe malignant forms of a larger class of diseases known as neoplasms (literally, 'new formation'). It is initiated by exposure to a carcinogen (cancer-causing substance) which can be a chemical, a virus or something physical, such as radiation. Certain cancers can also arise as a result of hereditary factors.

A general characteristic of the development of cancer is the time lag between the first exposure to a carcinogen, and the subsequent development of cancer (scientists call this period the tumour-induction time). Whether cancer eventually develops, and how quickly, is partly the result of the degree of exposure to a second class of substances called promoting agents. Although tumour promoters do not themselves *initiate* cancer, they can have a great bearing on its outcome. This two-stage process of initiation followed by promotion is a central characteristic of the cancerous process. It also introduces a wildly uncertain element into the equation. It explains, for example, why not everyone who is exposed to a carcinogen will contract cancer.

Cancer begins as a single abnormal cell which starts to multiply uncontrollably. This is the essential feature of cancer – an uncontrolled growth of cells. Malignant groups of such cells form tumours and invade healthy tissue, often spreading to other parts of the body, in a process called metastasis. Because of this fundamental ability to invade and destroy other parts of the body, the Greek doctor Hippocrates called this disorder *karkinos*, literally meaning 'crab' – from which the modern word cancer is derived.

Neoplasms are divided into two fundamental types – benign or malignant. A benign neoplasm does not metastasize – in other words, it only grows at its point of origin – and is usually named by tagging the suffix 'oma' on to the word for the tissue concerned. For example, the Greek for 'fat' is *lipos*, so a benign tumour of fat cells would be called a 'lipoma' (there are, however, several exceptions to this general rule).

Malignant neoplasms (cancers) grow more rapidly than benign forms and invade adjacent, normal tissue. They are described by adding either 'carcinoma' or 'sarcoma' to the the word for the site of the cancer (a malignancy of the fat cells would be therefore be termed a 'liposarcoma'). These two general classes of malignant neoplasms are defined like this:

- *Carcinomas* affect the skin and tissue that covers both the external and internal body, for example, breast cancer, prostate cancer, or cancer of the uterus.
- *Sarcomas* affect the body's supportive and connective tissue, such as muscles, blood vessels, bone and fat.

It may take years for a noticeable tumour to develop, and it is undoubtedly true that speed of diagnosis can be a life-saving factor. The American Cancer Society suggests seven warning signs which, even if only one is present, should provoke a prompt investigation. They are:

- A change in bowel or bladder function
- A sore that does not heal
- Unusual bleeding or discharge
- A thickening or lump in the breast or elsewhere
- Indigestion or difficulty in swallowing
- An obvious change in a wart or a mole
- A nagging cough or hoarseness.

The prospects for survival depend, amongst other things, on the site in the body affected, the speed of diagnosis, the treatment given, and, to a considerable extent, on the attitude of the patient towards the disease.

Chemical Carcinogens

Chemicals can initiate cancerous changes in the body by combining with DNA and RNA (the substances that guide the reproduction of cells and organisms) and creating a DNA molecule whose code for reproducing a new protein or cell has been significantly altered. At this stage, cells or proteins may have been altered, but they have not yet become cancerous. They may remain this way for ever; never causing any health problem, or they may go into the second stage, called promotion.

The promoting chemical is thought to increase enzyme activity inside the affected cell. The cell now has two major sources of imbalance: altered DNA, plus a change in its enzyme-protein relationships. Although the exact mechanisms are not yet understood, the cell is now cancerous: it can reproduce, but has no guidelines for specializing and becoming a contributing member of the whole organism. Thus, a tumour can grow from a single cell. Even a very small dose of a chemical can help create a parent cell that produces a whole colony of cells – a tumour. This makes it extremely difficult to estimate safe levels of exposure, or the general hazard of any new chemical substance. We suggest a prudent course of action is, therefore, as follows:

1. Any substance that is shown to cause cancer in animals should be considered a potential cancer hazard for humans.
2. No level of exposure to carcinogenic chemicals is to be considered 'insignificant' or 'safe'.
3. No chemical substance should be assumed safe without careful studies.
4. Any study showing a chemical to be carcinogenic pre-empts any other study showing it not to be carcinogenic.
5. Any chemical that produces tumours, even if those tumours are considered benign, must be considered carcinogenic.
6. Permissible exposure levels of zero should be maintained unless such maintenance can be proven impossible.

These guidelines indicate that chemicals must be treated with respect, and they provide us with a set of criteria for taking prudent action to protect ourselves and our families from potential carcinogens.

THE SECRET INGREDIENTS HOT LIST

SUBSTANCE	FUNCTION	CARCINOGENIC	PROBABLY CARCINOGENIC	POSSIBLY CARCINOGENIC	OTHER CONCERNS
Acrylonitrile	Food Contaminant		x		
Aflatoxins	Food Contaminant	x			
Amaranth	Food colour				Cancer concerns
Arsenic and arsenic compounds	Food Contaminant	x			
Asbestos	Contaminant	x			
Benzo[a]pyrene	Contaminant		x		
Boric acid					Toxicity
Butylated hydroxyanisole (BHA)	Food Additive: antioxidant			x	
Cadmium and cadmium compounds	Food Contaminant		x		
Carbon black extracts	Food Additive: food colour			x	
Chloroform	Medicinal Substance; Flavouring			x	
Creosote derived from coal tars	Preservative		x		
DDT	Pesticide			x	
Dioxins – TCDD	Contaminant			x	
Erythrosine	Food colour				Thyroid gland/cancer concerns

59

SUBSTANCE	FUNCTION	CARCINOGENIC	PROBABLY CARCINOGENIC	POSSIBLY CARCINOGENIC	OTHER CONCERNS
Formaldehyde	Preservative		X		Toxicity concerns
Hexachlorophane	Antimicrobial				
Lanolin	Emollient				Allergy; possibility of pesticide carry-through
Lead	Contaminant				Toxicity; devastating effect on children
Monosodium glutamate	Flavour enhancer				Excitotoxicity concerns
Nickel compounds, evaluated as a group	Contaminant	X			
Ochratoxin A	Contaminant			X	
Patulin	Contaminant				Toxicity
Potassium nitrite	Preservative				Toxicity concerns; pre-carcinogen
Saccharin	Sweetener			X	
Sodium metabisulphite	Preservative				Allergy
Solanine	Contaminant				Toxicity
Styrene	Contaminant			X	
Sulphur dioxide	Preservative				Allergy
Talc containing asbestos fibres	Dusting agent	X			

PILL POPPING – WHAT YOU NEED TO KNOW

One significant source of chemical exposure in our lives comes from the prescription medication we all occasionally use. In order to get the right medication – and consequently reduce the risk of being exposed to inappropriate substances – we have to know how to communicate clearly with our health advisers. If you can't decipher the words your doctor uses when he or she talks to you, then your health could be in real jeopardy. Frequently, doctors use language that seems calculated to be obscure, deceptive or fraudulently erudite. For example, why should a headache be labelled 'cephalagia', or itching 'pruritis'?

As you might have suspected, physicians actually have their own ancient and mysterious jargon which is only intended to be understood by insiders. More than two thousand years ago, the Greek physician Hippocrates warned doctors: *'Those things which are sacred are to be imparted only to sacred persons; and it is not lawful to impart them to the profane until they have been initiated in the mysteries of the science.'* Today, many doctors still seem to be following his advice. Before a medical student can become a doctor, he or she must be initiated into the secrets of a language which, it has been estimated, contains 10,000 new words[37] – words which, to the rest of us, seem just as extinct as the Greek or Latin from which they originated. Nevertheless, and contrary to the impression that it is designed to create, 'Medspeak' is *not* difficult in itself to learn or understand. Here are three steps that will help you to crack the code when jargon rears its head:

- First, ask your doctor to explain precisely what s/he's trying to tell you in clearer language. This should give you a broad idea of the meaning of the terms being used, although don't expect a comprehensive or even strictly accurate explanation of your condition and its treatment. Write down any words you're unsure about.
- Later, check a medical dictionary (available in any reference library) to expand and define the terms used.
- Finally, and working with the dictionary if necessary, use a current, general-purpose medical textbook (again, available in libraries) to give you a deeper understanding of your disorder, its causes and options for treatment.

Once you understand the jargon your doctor is using, you will be in a much stronger position to evaluate, control and, if necessary, query your diagnosis and treatment. Watch out for the words 'idiopathic', 'agnogenic', 'essential' or 'cryptogenic' – they're all obscure ways of saying 'we don't actually know what's causing your problem, but don't wish to say so in plain language'.

How To Talk To Your Doctor

Although they are supposed to learn the subtle art of being a good listener in medical school, many physicians either never acquire it, or lose it under the pressures of work. It is dangerous to assume that everything – or even the majority – of what you say in the surgery gets through. A busy doctor may jump to a wrong diagnosis too soon, perhaps ignoring vital information that only becomes apparent after a few minutes' conversation. The answer is to plan your interview before your visit. Follow this 1-2-3 model:

1. Briefly describe the **Chief Complaint**. 'I have a sore throat/pain in my lower back/chest pain', etc. Be simple and direct – confine yourself to an accurate description of your symptoms, don't try to present your doctor with a ready-made diagnosis.

2. Describe the **Present Illness**. When did the problem start? Are you taking any medication? Could you be pregnant? Have you been exposed to sources of infection (e.g. foreign travel)? Also report changes in your temperature, pulse, weight or other bodily functions which you may have noticed, even if they don't seem to be directly relevant.

3. Finally, describe those areas of your **Medical History** which could be important, such as allergies, similar illness in the family, childhood diseases, exposure to chemicals at work, or social and emotional problems. It really pays to give a lot of thought to all these areas before your interview – your doctor will be impressed with your thoroughness, and the time available to you both will be used to its maximum effectiveness.

BE YOUR OWN SECOND OPINION

Years ago, it used to be common practice to ask for a 'second opinion' whenever a doctor's judgement was in doubt. This was, and still is, prudent advice. Doctors can and do make mistakes in diagnosis, and, what's more, they don't always agree among themselves upon the best course of treatment. It has been estimated that unnecessary and incompetent medical treatment kills millions of people every year in Western countries (more than 200,000 in America alone[38]) and malpractice lawsuits are one of the biggest growth areas of all for lawyers. By the age of 40, it is possible that your doctor will no longer know about many of the advances in medical science that have taken place since he or she qualified.[39] Therefore, the diagnosis and treatment you are offered today could be some years out of date.

All this means that you must become your own 'second opinion' by acquainting yourself with the basics of medicine as it applies to your own complaint. In order to do this, you need access to information, which is not difficult to find in most reference libraries. The more serious your complaint, the greater your need to be sure that the proposed treatment will be effective. As a patient, you will almost invariably be offered one diagnosis for your complaint and one proposed course of treatment. A wise patient will validate both. Some key points:

- Diagnosis. Ask your doctor just how certain s/he can be that the diagnosis you are offered is accurate. It is a medical maxim that 70 per cent of every diagnosis comes from what the patient tells the doctor; 20 per cent from the physical examination; and only 10 per cent from medical tests.[40] The more tests your doctor orders, the less certain s/he is likely to be about your problem. Check with professional medical textbooks to confirm for yourself whether your symptoms really match the complaint. Effective treatment depends on an exact assessment of your condition, and in many cases, doctors are simply wrong. The fact that misdiagnosis is not uncommon was dramatically confirmed in a study conducted by two British pathologists. They carried out 400 careful examinations on patients who had died in hospital, and found that over half the patients had been wrongly diagnosed! Additionally, they found that potentially treatable disease had been missed in 13 per cent of cases, 65 out of 135 cases of pneumonia went undiagnosed and untreated, and of 51 patients who had suffered heart attacks, 18 of them had been completely missed by their doctors. The pathologists concluded their study by writing: *'The findings closely parallel those from other units both in Britain and overseas, and suggest that there is currently a high diagnostic error rate, which varies remarkably little from one institution to another.'*[41]

- Tests. If you have a laboratory test, ask your doctor about the per cent error rate, and what s/he proposes to do to confirm the test results. Medical testing can be both dangerous and inaccurate. Although many doctors seem to regard lab tests as invariably trustworthy, the American Center for Disease Control points out that an average of one out of every seven test results reported back to doctors from laboratories may either be in error or unreliable.[42] For example: the stress electrocardiogram, in which your ECG is taken while you are exercising, has been rated at best as only 21 per cent accurate, and may 'reveal' heart disease in 50 per cent of patients who are ultimately shown to have no heart disease at all.[43] The accuracy of most blood tests can be affected by your physical activity, diet, stress, medication and even your body's position while giving blood. Or the lab can let your blood sample sit around for hours before testing, use chemicals that are out of date, operate the testing machine incorrectly or mislabel your specimen. Dr Edward Pinckney, a fellow of the American College of Physicians and a former editor of *The Journal of the American Medical Association* has pointed out that one of the most common blood tests used to diagnose a heart attack, called creatine phosphokinase, can show a false positive result in a healthy person simply because he did nothing more than exercise moderately a few days earlier.[44]

- Side-effects. Insist on being told (and check for yourself) of any possible side-effects associated with any test that your doctor proposes. Another hazard of medical testing is the damage the test may directly inflict – it has been estimated that 800 people die every year in America alone as a consequence of reactions to the dyes used in gall bladder X-rays.[45] Other side-effects of this test may include kidney failure, mental aberration and chromosome damage. Invasive tests, such as biopsies, catheterizations and bronchoscopies, all carry a degree of risk. Even certain non-invasive procedures, such as X-rays, may carry some element of risk which needs to be weighed against any information they may yield.

- Treatment. Find out for yourself about the possible side-effects of any drugs you are prescribed. Your doctor uses a small paperback called the *British National Formulary* for impartial information about drugs, and you can use it too as an authoritative guide to prescription medicines and their drawbacks.[46]

- Repeat prescriptions. Although some people with long-term disorders (such as diabetics) need regular supplies of medication, many prescriptions issued by doctors may be written without the doctor seeing the patient. This leads to continuing dependence on medication, which may well have its own adverse consequences on your health. Most prescription drugs are potent, and therefore potentially dangerous. You should aim to reduce, and eliminate if feasible, your need for medication as soon as you and your doctor agree that it is possible. Obviously, this will never happen if your doctor automatically issues repeat prescriptions without meeting you and reviewing your case.

- Alternatives. If surgery is suggested to you, ask about alternative therapies and ask for the surgeon's success (and survival) rates. Being operated on is a traumatic experience for the body. About one out of every hundred patients will die as a result of it.[47] It is well worth considering an alternative to the knife – for example, peptic ulcers can be treated with drug therapy with greater success than surgery. Remember that specialists in surgery will automatically tend to recommend their own procedures above other therapies, and in fact may not be knowledgeable in other treatments. When the Rand Corporation (an independent American think-tank) examined coronary bypass operations, they found that of 400 operations studied, only 56 per cent met approved medical standards to balance benefits against risks, and 44 per cent were done for inappropriate reasons.[48] And despite a huge programme of coronary bypass operations in many Western countries, the hard evidence to show its overwhelming usefulness (compared to other forms of treatment) is often absent. Britain's *Drug and Therapeutic Bulletin* has reported that 20,000 appendix operations are performed unnecessarily every year. The Chief Medical Officer at the Department of Health has stated that many of the 90,000 tonsillectomies (removal of tonsils) are of 'questionable' benefit.[49]

Medical procedures often follow trends. Quite recently, it became fashionable to prescribe cyclotron treatment for certain cancers (it kills cancer cells by bombarding them with neutrons). Millions of pounds were raised by charities to buy cyclotrons, and even the British Prime Minister supported the appeal. Then the side-effects started to be reported – holes appeared in flesh and bone, and patients suffered persistent ulcers and lockjaw, rendering them unable to eat or drink. Eventually, the Medical Research Council and a number of cancer specialists called for the treatment to be abandoned.[50] So before agreeing to an invasive procedure, it would be wise to consider these questions:

- What is the overall success rate for the procedure? (and how is 'success' defined?)
- What is the likely outcome in my own situation?
- What other therapies are available, and how do they compare?

- What is the individual success rate of the specialist/surgeon involved?
- How does this compare to other specialists in the same field?
- What is the quality of my life going to be after the procedure?

A good doctor will take the time to answer these questions with you.

WHAT'S UP, DOC?
A BEGINNER'S GUIDE TO MEDSPEAK

JARGON	MEANING
Ambulatory	You can walk
Pruritis	You itch
Ecchymosis	You've got a bruise
Pyrosis	You've got heartburn
Acute rhinitis	You've got a bad cold
Rhinorrhea	Your nose is running
Sternutation	You sneeze
Cephalagia	Your head aches
Xanthochromic	You look yellow
Adverse patient outcome	You've just died

If you would like to receive current information on a range of health-related subjects, write to What Doctors Don't Tell You, 4 Wallace Road, London N1 2PG enclosing a stamped addressed envelope.

SECRET ALTERNATIVES – HOMOEOPATHY IN THE HOME

Homoeopathy is a system of healing founded on the very ancient idea that 'like cures like'. A substance which would, in a healthy person, cause a specific problem acts, instead, to cure the problem when taken in a minute dose by a person already suffering from that disorder. Thus, a homoeopathic remedy triggers the body's ability to heal itself, and so builds up the patient's health by stimulating their body to function optimally. This is greatly different from the approach of orthodox (allopathic) medicine which tends to treat symptoms only and then generally prescribes to suppress those symptoms. As an alternative to many of the over-the-counter remedies described in this book, it is very appealing – not least because it *never* has any side-effects.

The method of diagnosis used by homoeopaths also differs from that of their orthodox colleagues. Where conventional medical doctors allow approximately ten minutes per consultation and base their advice on the symptoms presented, a homoeopathic practitioner will usually allow one hour for the first consultation (slightly less time for subsequent visits) and will base their advice on what they observe of the whole person. Diagnosis may not be presented in terms of an illness with a specific name, but rather in terms of how you and your body have responded to various pressures and onslaughts upon your health. Accordingly, treatment is often given in 'layers' so that, not only is your immediate health problem dealt with, your total, long-term health is also treated.

Remedies prescribed in homoeopathy are usually presented in pill, tablet, tincture or cream form and are based on such minute doses of the 'active ingredient' that they are considered completely safe and impossible to overdose on. In addition, they can be taken with other medication (though your homoeopathic practitioner may recommend certain amendments to your medication routine).

Modern homoeopathy was born with Samuel Hahnemann (1755–1843). He became known as the Father of Homoeopathy when he became dissatisfied with the crude and often violent medicine of his day which commonly involved purging, cupping, leeching and bleeding, for instance. While translating the *Materia Medica* of the English physician William Cullen into German, Hahnemann decided to experiment with the Peruvian bark (*Cinchona succirubra*, from which quinine is derived), which he'd just read about. Taking it himself, he was surprised to find that it produced all the symptoms of malaria, which it was actually intended to cure. Over several years, Hahnemann conducted more experiments with other drugs, and found that the effect was uniform: in a healthy person, a drug would produce the symptoms of the disease which in a sick person it was supposed to cure. This paradoxical effect became the cornerstone of his curative theory which he eventually named homoeopathy after the Greek word *homoeos*, meaning 'same'.

Hahnemann then proposed that the 'potency' of a drug could actually be increased by diluting it. The more a drug is diluted, the more it is 'dematerialized' (becomes unrestrained by its physical and chemical nature) and its ultimate healing power is thus liberated. The first stage in the production of a homoeopathic medicine is the production of a 'mother tincture'. Then follows a whole series of dilutions, producing ever-increasing potencies. The first dilution involves taking one part of the mother tincture and combining it with nine parts of water. This is then rhythmically succussed (shaken) for an exact time in order to fully potentize the liquid. The resulting dilution is known as 1X. Repeating the process (one part of 1X to nine parts of water) produces 2X, and so on. Reading the labels of homoeopathic medicine you will often see 3X, 6X, 30X. Potencies referred to simply by a number (6, 30, etc.), or with a C suffix (1C, 30C) are centesimal potencies – prepared in exactly the same way as above, but diluted with 99 parts water.

Homoeopathic remedies were traditionally made from naturally occurring substances, and they still form the basis of most treatments. However, the homoeopathic principle is also being carried forward to deal with problems related to our contemporary lifestyles. For example, small doses of additives, colourants or preservatives are now administered homoeo-pathically as a remedy for allergic reactions.

In fact, most health problems will respond to homoeopathic treatment, especially if the patient's vitality is high and their visit to the practitioner is made as soon as they notice any problem, however small. Even if the patient has already under-gone orthodox treatment such as surgery, homoeopathic remedies will help to strengthen them and speed the healing process. Chronic disorders may take a little longer to treat than disorders that seem to occur suddenly, so a little patience and perseverence is required. Having said that, chronic disorders – both physical (such as arthritis) and mental (such as depression or anxiety) – are among the more common problems which bring people to a homoeopath, and an experienced practitioner will readily advise as to the likely duration of treatment before the problem is resolved.

To find a good homoeopath, contact the following organ-izations who supply a register of practitioners, as well as further information leaflets about homoeopathy and self-treatment. Please enclose a large SAE when contacting them by post:

British Homoeopathic Association
27a Devonshire Street
London W1N 1KJ
tel: 0171-935-2163

The Homoeopathic Society
(including the Homoeopathic Trust for Research and Education)
2 Powis Place
London WC1N 3HT
tel: 0171-837-9469
Note: this register is for medical doctors who are also homoeopaths

The Society of Homoeopaths
2 Artizan Road
Northampton NN1 4HU
tel: Northampton (01604) 21400

Not all homoeopaths wish to enrol on a register, however, and sometimes it is as well to rely on word of mouth as a recommendation.

To obtain homoeopathic supplies, contact the following specialist pharmacies:

Ainsworths Homoeopathic Pharmacy
36 New Cavendish Street
London W1M 7LH
tel: 0171-935-5330

Freeman's
7 Eaglesham Road
Clarkston
Glasgow G76 7BU
tel: 0141-644-1165

Helios Homoeopathic Pharmacy
97 Camden Road
Tunbridge Wells
Kent TN1 2QR
tel: 01892-536393

Nelson Homoeopathic Medicines
73 Duke Street
London W1M 6BY
orders tel: 0171-495-2404
shop tel: 0171-629-3118

Weleda (UK) Ltd.
Heanor Road
Ilkeston
Derbyshire DE7 8DR
tel: 01602-303151

Both Ainsworths and Nelson's pharmacies are open for passing trade as well as mail or telephone orders, and all these provide a list of recommended reading for those who wish to learn more about self-treatment in a variety of circumstances. In addition, many orthodox chemist shops and health food shops offer a range of homoeopathic remedies for sale, usually in potencies of 6 or 30.

What to Expect

Your first visit to a homoeopath will last about one hour. This is your time and you should anticipate talking as much as possible about yourself, your feelings and your health and family history. The practitioner will ask questions, observe you and probably take notes as well. Do not expect that they will 'examine' you in the same way an ordinary doctor might – homoeopathy is considered a non-intrusive form of treatment. Neither will you need to disrobe or provide 'samples'. If you have had a diagnosis of some sort from your doctor, the homoeopath may wish to hear it. Generally, however, the diagnosis made by the homoeopath is not symptom specific. In fact, it is not really a diagnosis in the classic sense but more of a profile of you: your character, preferences, circumstances *and* your symptoms.

At the end of the consultation, the homoeopath will recommend (and often supply) a remedy or course of remedies. These are usually in the form of tablets but may include mother tinctures or creams. The homoeopath may, additionally, recommend certain changes in your diet or aspects of your lifestyle such as exercise or relaxation. The practitioner will also describe the likely pattern of healing which you may expect and will suggest a follow-up appointment.

When taking homoeopathic remedies it is important to have a 'clean' tongue. This generally means that you must have taken nothing into your mouth for at least 20 minutes prior to taking the remedy. The remedy, if in tablet form, should be allowed to dissolve gradually under the tongue, then nothing further taken into the mouth for a further 20 minutes, at least.

Certain substances are usually considered to nullify or 'antidote' the effects of homoeopathic remedies. These include coffee, camphor, menthol (mint), peppermint and eucalyptus but may include other strong-smelling substances. If in doubt, avoid! You may, for instance, need to use a non-minty toothpaste while taking remedies. Some homoeopaths consider that X-rays (such as those used in security checks) will also antidote remedies and they recommend that you have your remedies checked manually and not processed through X-ray machines.

Your homoeopath will suggest a remedy for your malady which will have a certain potency or, if appropriate, a remedy repeated over several days but with increasing or decreasing potency at each dose. Additionally, they may specify the approximate times of day at which you should take the remedies. The potency and timing, or frequency, of dosage they advise should be adhered to as these stimulate a reaction which enables healing to occur.

Most homoeopaths will advise that a 'healing crisis' is likely to occur at the point when your body has responded fully to the remedy. What this means is that you are likely to feel worse for a time, but then will feel greatly better once the crisis has passed – usually a matter of minutes or hours. It is useful to have the homoeopath's phone number to hand during your first treatment, so that you may ring them and describe what you are experiencing at this time. This is very reassuring and will ensure that you do not rush out and buy all sorts of over-the-counter products which will mask your symptoms and prevent real improvement. In fact, most practitioners advise you to stop taking the remedies they have prescribed as soon as any change in your state is noticed. So whether you experience a 'healing crisis' or whether you simply start to feel better, that is the time to stop the remedies and let your body take over. As mentioned earlier, a disorder that is chronic may take longer to resolve than one which appears suddenly, often called an 'acute'. However, there may be acute reactions within the resolution of a chronic problem. Keep in close contact with your homoeopath while taking remedies so that changes such as these may be dealt with as they happen.

Self-treatment is possible with homoeopathic remedies, though the more well-read you are on the subject and the remedies, the more likely the treatment will be effective. We feel that it is best to use a practitioner for most problems but to self-treat when travelling, in an emergency or on those occasions when the practitioner is not available. Ours, for instance, is available for telephone consultation but takes most weekends and holiday periods off. Although she provides alternative practitioners, we are not always able to use them and so self-treatment is our preference at these times. We have a collection of remedies at home and continue to read the books and leaflets which are published on this fascinating method of treatement.

What follows is a basic chart offering guidance for self-treatment.

Remedies for Early Symptoms

These remedies are listed for general use and are known to be effective. Certainly, a cache of homoeopathic remedies kept at home will help you to treat disorders that occur both on a chronic basis and in the 'off' hours of the night and weekends, when your homoeopath may be unavailable. A consultation with a homoeopath will usually result in a more complete 'picture' of your needs than can be accomplished in a listing of this sort, and a more accurate remedy being made available for your particular problem as a result. If you do not already use a homoeopath, please contact the associations listed above to find one local to you.

A PILL FOR EVERY ILL:
HOMOEOPATHIC ALTERNATIVES TO
OVER-THE-COUNTER DRUGS

MAIN SYMPTOM	DETAILS	REMEDY
Catarrh	Thick green or yellow discharge; worse in evening, better in cool air	Pulsatilla
	Stringy or thick yellow discharge; with sore throat or cough and ache at base of nose; worse between 4 a.m. and 5 a.m.	Kali. Bich.
	Streaming discharge and watery eyes	Euphrasia
	Feels settled on chest; cannot cough it up	Bryonia
	Clear discharge with sensation of burning; chilliness and exhaustion	Arsen. alb.

MAIN SYMPTOM	DETAILS	REMEDY
Colds	Come on suddenly, especially after being in a cold wind; worse at night	Aconite
	With influenza-like shivering, aching and possibly sore throat; better in warmth	Gelsemium
	With painful sneezing; thirsty and chilly; worse after eating or in the cold; may feel like hay fever	Arsen. alb.
	Much sneezing with cold settling in chest; great thirst and dryness; improves with stillness and lying down	Bryonia
	Much sneezing with watery discharge which develops into thick yellow discharge; worse in a draught, very irritable	Hepar Sulph
Constipation	With urge to push but no stool produced	Nux. vom.
	Large stools that are painful to pass	Sulphur
	Stool begins to pass, then moves back into rectum	Silicea
Coughs	Sudden onset, often at night, of dry, harsh cough; often with anxiety	Aconite
	With a constant rattling of phlegm; better from sitting up	Ant. tart.
	With soreness in chest, headache; thirsty and often irritable	Bryonia
	With hoarseness; tickle in throat, starts coughing from deep in chest; spasms may cause vomiting; yellow sputum; worse when reclining	Drosera
	Violent, dry, racking cough with yellow discharge; sore throat; great thirst and anxiety	Phosphorus

MAIN SYMPTOM	DETAILS	REMEDY
Diarrhoea	From food poisoning; maybe with vomiting; great restlessness	Arsen. alb.
	Worry, excitement or anxiety induced; concern for the future	Argent nit.
	When urgent, especially first thing in the morning	Sulphur
Earache	From teething	Chamomilla
	Ear is red, hot and feels throbbing	Belladonna
Fatigue	From mental effort	Kali. Phos.
	After sickness or diarrhoea	Arsen. alb.
Haemorrhoids	Which bleed dark blood	Hamamelis
	Which itch, protrude and sometimes bleed	Calc. Fluor.
	Which protrude and are painful, stinging	Ignatia
Hay fever	Eyes are light sensitive, tears are 'burning'; asthmatic feeling; exhaustion and worry	Arsen. alb.
	Eyes are swollen and heavy; sneezing with sore or constricted throat; no energy; giddiness	Gelsemium
	Eyes are light sensitive; headache or migraine with itching of inner ear; difficulty breathing	Nux vom.
	Eyes, throat, nose all swollen and with thick discharge, often yellow; usually a cough	Kali. bich.
Headache	Sudden onset; better when reclining; often feelings of anxiety or restlessness	Aconite
	Violent and throbbing; over-sensitive to movement, light, noise; face red and hot	Belladonna

MAIN SYMPTOM	DETAILS	REMEDY
Headache *(continued)*	As in migraine: great thirst and nausea with aversion to movement	Bryonia
	Better when the head is resting backwards	Hypericum
	With humming in the ears	Kali. phos.
	From over-indulgence; sensitive scalp and possibly giddiness; better with rest	Nux. vom.
Indigestion	Stomach pain which feels like burning; often vomiting and diarrhoea; feels cold and benefits from warmth and warm drinks; thirsty and restless	Arsen. alb.
	Food sits heavily 'like a stone' in the stomach; huge thirst; cannot bear motion or company; may feel faint on rising	Bryonia
	Usually after over-eating or from nervous tension; discomfort 1–2 hours after eating ranging from nausea to desire to vomit; irritable; hot drink may help to feel better	Nux. vom.
Influenza	At the first signs of 'flu, especially if the onset seems sudden through fever or chill	Aconite
	Great exhaustion; sneezing and runny nose; chills and anxiety; possible vomiting and diarrhoea	Arsen. alb.
	Fever with generalized aching and weakness; head and eyes ache; spine feels chilled and crawling	Gelsemium
	With constipation, nausea and general irritability; in fever, much sweating	Nux. vom.

MAIN SYMPTOM	DETAILS	REMEDY
Rheumatic pains	A feeling of being bruised inside; a great fear of being touched; extreme tenderness	Arnica
	Causing irritability; worse from any movement, better from rest and cool air, drinks or food	Bryonia
	After too much exercise, a strain or sprain, any form of joint pain, sciatica, etc.; movement causes pain but this eases after a few moments and condition improves	Rhus. tox.
Skin disorders	For eczema that is cracked and weeping; especially eczema on fingertips; may suffer dandruff	Graphites
	Injuries of any sort tend to form pus; lower lip often cracked in the middle	Hepar sulph
	Skin is very itchy and sometimes feels on fire; needs to sleep with feet outside bedcovers; lips may be very red	Sulphur
	With dandruff and possibly warts; condition usually chronic	Thuja
Sore throat	After being out in the wind	Aconite
	When the throat is very dry and burns or stings; thirsty but needs tiny sips as swallowing may be painful	Arsen. alb.
	With runny nose; probably painful to swallow	Gelsemium
Varicose veins	Often accompanied by piles; feelings of bruising and great fatigue in affected areas	Hamamelis

ALTERNATIVES TO PILLS – NATURAL WAYS TO REDUCE STRESS AND PAIN

The term 'stress' was originally used in physics, engineering and the physical sciences to describe strains and pressures involved in the normal or expected status of a material or construction. Perhaps due to our over-use of a mechanistic view of ourselves, this term has made an easy transition into everyday language. Whatever we decide to call it, stress has been present throughout human history and appears with equal force in the corridors of office blocks as in the 'idyllic' settings of tribal cultures. This is because stress is a physical or psychological reaction to a perceived threat and, as such, can result from virtually any situation or stimulus.

The now-famous 'fight or flight' summary of our response to a perceived threat is as clear and concise a description of the stress reaction as we require. For at once we recognize in it the mixture of aggression and fear that combine so power-fully in a moment of stress. Our response is instantaneous: profound biochemical changes occur which promote effective, streamlined action as well as our total attention. We move from shock or alarm, into active response and then out of that into exhaustion. At least, that's what we should do. However, this extraordinary survival response can be caught in a sort of loop where the effective action never quite happens, so the alarm phase never quite ceases, and then the relief or exhaustion never actually happens. This loop is what is now, in common parlance, considered to be a state of stress.

The stress our body was designed to deal with doesn't seem to be the same as the stress we *are* dealing with. For one thing, it is clearly chronic, unrelenting; for another it is devillishly destructive. Where resolved stress is relatively brief in duration, reasonably effective and concludes with a period of collapse or even euphoria, unresolved, persistent stress destroys health and finds a variety of ways in which to do so. We think of stress as expressing itself in the form of symptoms, some relatively minor and some relatively distressing.

For example, acute stress may be accompanied by trembling, giddiness or faintness, dry mouth and throat, hot flushes or an urge to empty the bowels or to urinate. The most serious problem with chronic, unresolved stress is that it can impair proper functioning of your immune system and thus lower your resistance to *any* disease. Suddenly, what was considered a psychological problem (how well we 'cope'; how good our 'nerves' are, etc.) becomes a physiological problem also: the mental and emotional aspects of ourselves creating an expressive bridge to our physical self.

It is at this precise juncture that we may be most able to undermine the negative effects of stress. For once we recognize that we are suffering stress, we are in a better position to trace its cause and then eradicate or minimize its adverse effects. We have listed a few of the more common symptoms of stress; yet you probably already know, deep down, whether you suffer stress and even precisely how it is affecting the quality of your life.

Apart from obvious exceptions such as running from an escaped lion or being taken hostage by a gang of cut-throat terrorists, most modern-day stress is of a subtle nature. In our physical world, stress can result from our environment, the substances we consume as well as our physical experience. Our environment, for instance, is a canvas of noise, lighting, colours, smells and quality of air – all of which we can manipulate once we realize how they are affecting us. Our consumption of food, drink, stimulants, pollutants, drugs and water can create a cocktail of residues, allergens and other potentially harmful substances which can cause physical stress expressed as illness, discomfort or general loss of well-being. Finally, our physical experiences – from rushing through crowds to changes in our living accommodation – can create stress that has the power to erode our health. The good news is that all of these elements of our physical world can be manipulated to minimize the symptoms of stress we experience.

In our inner lives, too, we have the ability to recognize the causes of stress and to minimize and manipulate their effects. Any mental and emotional experience has the power to cause stress – anxiety, frustration, depression, changing relationships, an alteration in work or financial status – these and countless other experiences are felt by the inner self and may, over time, create physical responses which can include illness and disorder.

What is to be done? Certainly, stress is an essential in our repertoire of responses: it is nothing less than a life-saver when experienced in its 'original' form. Then emergency and alarm are dealt with in a speedy manner with a usually appropriate mixture of aggression and defensiveness that helps us survive. Brilliant! It is the chronic, day after day, unresolved, health-eroding, sometimes extreme form of stress that we need to deal with. How can we manage this sort of stress so that it does not harm us? There seem to be two basic steps to effective stress management.

The first step is to achieve awareness of the fact that you are suffering stress and, if possible, awareness of its source. Your awareness should include both physical and psychological expressions, symptoms, of stress. In other words, you should take note of any symptoms – whether physical, mental or emotional – that you know or suspect are stress-related. Make a list of them and beside each symptom write a number between one and ten: one represents a 'weak' symptom, ten a 'strong' symptom. You may wish to ask your spouse, partner or a special friend to comment, or add any signs of stress they have observed in you to the list. This can provide an invaluable insight into the strength and duration of your stress symptoms. We often continue on a course of action even when it is harmful to us and the observations of a person who cares for us can sometimes be the thing that pulls us back from disaster.

The second step towards effective stress management is to gain control of how stress resolves. It's there, inside you, and it's going to come out one way or another. Up until this moment, it has chosen its own route. Now *you* are taking over. The list which follows gives a selection of practices and therapies which can help you to build awareness of stress and/or help you gain control of the way in which you express it.

Pain

Open the pages of a medical dictionary and look under pain. Ours defines it clearly enough but it also lists nearly *forty* different types of pain. A tiny friend of ours has given birth to two large babies yet swears she would rather do that several times over than to pluck one single hair from her eyebrows. Another friend, of more advanced years, daily walks one mile with chronically painful arthritic knees but a paper cut on his finger brings tears to his eyes. How are we to consider pain relief – of any sort – when there is such a range of experience?

Pain and stress experiences go hand in hand: chronic pain

usually causes chronic stress and for many people stress expresses itself through symptoms of pain such as sciatica, migraine, aching neck and shoulders and so on. In fact, the relationship goes even deeper, for the brain deals with stress and pain in a similar way. Like stress, pain is a useful – no, essential! – survival mechanism which warns the body to act in a certain way. For instance, the 'fight or flight' response described above is also used to explain why pain is sometimes greatly diminished in an emergency, for it warns the body of danger or injury then 'switches off' temporarily while you fight or flee.

Chronic pain and stress both diminish quality of life, both demand a great deal of your attention, and fortunately, both can be controlled or resolved using similar techniques. The list which follows includes some, but by no means all, of the therapies and practices which are currently used to control pain and stress. Each one has helped many people, but it is up to you to find the one or two which will be most effective and appropriate for your situation and personality.

Help in Your Hands: Therapies and practices which you can use to control pain and stress

AFFIRMATIONS

Very simple, positive and emotionally powerful statements which you repeat to yourself, audibly or inaudibly, in order to enhance or preserve well-being.

In stress: For both awareness and control.

In pain: For the pain of recovery from injury or illness.

Suggested Reading: *You Can Heal Your Body*, Louise Hay, Eden Grove, also *Living in the Light*, Shakti Gawain, Eden Grove.

Contact Point: Zen Practice Centre Trust, 2 The Colonnades, 4 West Street, West Malling, Kent ME19 6QZ.

AROMATHERAPY

The use of essential plant oils for medicinal and mood-enhancing purposes.

In stress: For both awareness and control. The more knowledge you have of your symptoms, the more effectively you can select and use appropriate oils.

In pain: For most types of pain. Again, the more precisely you can define your pain, the more appropriate and effective will be your selection of oils.

Suggested Reading: *The Fragrant Pharmacy* and *The Fragrant Mind*, Valerie Ann Worwood, Bantam Books, London, 1991 and 1995 respectively.

Contact Point: International Federation of Aromatherapists, Stamford House, 2–4 Chiswick High Road, London W4 1TH, tel: 0181-742-2605

AUTOGENICS

A form of self-hypnosis combined with profound relaxation techniques which is taught in order to be self-administered: you get in charge and stay in charge.

In stress: Very effective for both awareness and control.

In pain: Very effective for some people.

Suggested Reading: *Autogenic Training: the effective way to conquer stress*, K. Kermani, Thorsons, HarperCollins Publishers, London, 1992; *You and Autogenic Training*, C. Rosa, Dutton, New York, 1976.

Contact Point: British Association for Autogenic Training and Therapy, Heath Cottage, Pitch Hill, Ewhurst, Nr. Cranleigh, Surrey GU6 7NP.

Please enclose an SAE.

BACH FLOWER REMEDIES

The use of dilute essential tinctures from 38 different plants to deal with the seven basic categories of what Dr Bach calls 'state of mind'. Based on the homoeopathic principle, entirely harm-less, versatile and self-administered.

In stress: For both awareness and control. Proceed for several weeks for fullness of benefit.

In pain: Fairly immediate results for infants and children, longer for adults.

Suggested Reading: *Illustrated Handbook of Bach Flower Remedies,* Philip M. Chancellor, C.W. Daniel Co. Ltd., Saffron Walden, Essex, 1971.

Contact Point: The Edward Bach Centre, Mount Vernon, Sotwell, Wallingford, Oxon OX10 0PD.

BIOFEEDBACK

A high-tech method of learning, by means of visual or audio signals – hence bio (life) feedback – what your body does during stress or pain and how to control it. Specifically, machines which indicate your heart-rate, skin temperature, muscular activity, brain-wave pattern and so on are wired to you (one or several) and you learn what the tones, lights or meters they produce mean in terms of your health. Then you manipulate these feedback messages by relaxing specific muscles, instructing your body to reduce blood pressure, pain sensation and so forth. The precise machinery, mode of feed-back and advised method of relaxation varies from one clinic to another. The outcome is highly successful, however, and only needs to be practised in the wired-up state for a few weeks or months. Most people then perform equally well without the apparatus. Clinics are available in many hospitals.

In stress: Very successful for gaining awareness and control.

In pain: Very successful for many forms of pain relief.

Suggested Reading: *The Awakened Mind: biofeedback and the development of higher states of awareness,* C.M. Cade and N. Coxhead, Element Books, Shaftesbury, Dorset, 1987; *New Mind, New Body: biofeedback, new direction for the mind,* B. Brown, Irvington, New York, 1984.

Contact Point: The Awakened Mind Ltd., 9 Chatsworth Road, London NW2 4BJ, tel: 0181-451-0083.

BREATHING EXERCISES

As commonly taught in meditation, yoga or relaxation classes. Breathing with a deep, thorough movement of the diaphragm so that inhalation is slow and sustained and exhalation is controlled and complete. Affirmations are sometimes used simultaneously.

In stress: Most effective for control of stress symptoms, after awareness has been gained.

In pain: For pain that is anticipated, such as an injection, or for pain that is sudden, from an injury for instance.

Suggested Reading: *Bodymind Energetics: towards a dynamic model of health*, M. Seem and J. Kaplan, Healing Arts Press, Rochester, Vermont, U.S.A., 1989.

Contact Point: The Relaxation Society, 84 Herbert Gardens, Willesden, London NW10 3BU, tel: 0181-969-6704

COLONIC IRRIGATION

The use of water, sometimes with herbal decoctions added, to cleanse high up into the colon. More comfortable and thorough than an enema, impacted faeces which may have been in the colon for years are sometimes freed and expelled. You either love it or hate it.

In stress: May help free certain people of stress-induced disorders, such as skin problems, chronic headaches or digestive disturbances.

In pain: Not usually considered a form of pain therapy, though may ease chronic bowel disorders such as constipation.

Suggested Reading: *Probiotics: the revolutionary 'friendly bacteria' way to vital health and wellbeing*, Leon Chaitow and Natasha Trenev, Thorsons, 1990.

Contact Points: Colonics International Association, 26 Sea Road, Boscombe, Bournemouth, Dorset.

International Colonic Hydrotherapy Foundation, 62 Alexandra Road, Hemel Hempstead, Herts.

COUNSELLING

Talking, whether to a trained listener or to your best friend, is often the best way of releasing the build-up of stress in your life. Try your friend first, then use your local library or health food shop notice board to discover the trained counsellors available in your area. If you don't like the first one, try another. Counselling works when the relationship is right.

In stress: Useful for both awareness and control. Especially helpful when trying to discover the real cause of stress.

In pain: There are self-help groups in which people suffering a specific type of pain (that of endometriosis, for instance) meet to support one another and talk through issues.

Suggested Reading: *Mind as Healer, Mind as Slayer: a holistic approach to preventing stress disorders*, K. Pelletier, Delacorte, New York, 1977.

Contact Point: United Kingdom Council for Psychotherapy, 167–169 Great Portland Street, London W1N 5EB, tel: 0171-436-3002

EXERCISE

Dance, sport or regular movement that makes your brain and body work hard together helps to keep you healthy and happy. It has been said in many ways for hundreds of years and it's true. Find a form that you find pleasant and appropriate to your lifestyle and practise 3–5 times per week.

In stress: Very useful for both awareness and control.

In pain: Some forms of exercise, such as swimming, stretching or yoga, are used to ease chronic pain such as that from arthritis.

Suggested Reading: *Aquarobics*, Glenda Baum, Arrow, 1991. *Soft Exercise*, Arthur Balaskas, Unwin Health, 1985.

Contact Point: The National Register of Personal Fitness

Trainers, Thornton House, Thornton Road, London SW19 4NG, tel: 0181-944-6688.

HERBALISM

The use of plants as medicines. Generally the plant is used in a 'whole' form: the active ingredient is not separated out as it might be in orthodox pharmicology. Self-treatment through widely available teas and herbal tablets is common.

In stress: Teas such as chamomile and linden (lime flower) are useful for chronic stress. Tablets of herbal substances are available for sleep disorders and acute stress.

In pain: Use a qualified herbalist.

Suggested Reading: *A Modern Herbal*, M. Grieve, Jonathan Cape, London, 1982.

Contact Point: British Herbal Medicine Association, 1 Wickham Road, Boscombe, Bournemouth, Dorset, BH7 6JX.

MASSAGE

Manipulation of muscle tissue to improve circulation of blood and lymph. This generally requires someone to massage you, though you can massage feet and leg muscles yourself. Ask a close friend or find a qualified practitioner.

In stress: Excellent way to develop awareness and keep stress under control.

In pain: Use a qualified practitioner who will listen to your description of the pain and advise if massage can help.

Suggested Reading: *Massage for Total Relaxation*, N. Lacroix, Dorling Kindersley, London, 1991.

Contact Point: British Massage Therapy Council, Greenbank House, 65a Adelphi Street, Preston PR1 7BH.

MEDITATION

See Autogenics and Breathing, above.

Suggested Reading: *Getting Well Again*, O.C. Simonton,

S. Mathews-Simonton and J. Creighton, Tarcher Books, Los Angeles, 1978.

Contact Point: International Stress Management Association, Southbank University, LPSS, 103 Borough Road, London SE1 0AA.

OCCUPATIONAL THERAPIES

A fancy word, perhaps, for hobbies or pursuing subjects for pleasure and interest alone. Everyone should have one!

In stress: Helps build awareness and control.

In pain: May help 'take your mind off it'.

Suggested Reading: *Art as Medicine: creating a therapy of the imagination*, S. McNiff, Shambalah, Boston, 1994; *The Singing Cure: an introduction to voice movement therapy*, P. Newham, Shambalah, Boston, 1995.

Contact Point: For workshops on playing: Ann-Marie Woodall on tel: 01372 451979 or David Sumeray on tel: 0171 485 2922.

REFLEXOLOGY

The use of gentle massage and point pressure on specific points (reflexes) on the feet and/or hands. These points represent areas of the body and stimulating them by massage or pressure serves to treat the body area to which they correspond. Sounds wacky but it works and you can self-treat or give your loved ones a treat!

In stress: Very effective at control and gradually builds awareness, too.

In pain: Very effective at easing pain. Find tender reflexes and apply point pressure for 5–7 seconds only. Repeat half-hourly and see for yourself. Don't overdo it though: less is more for this therapy.

Suggested Reading: *Reflexology*, C. Stormer, Hodder & Stoughton, London, 1992; *Reflexology – Foot Massage for Total Health*, I. Dougans and S. Ellis, Element Books, 1991.

Contact Point: Association of Reflexologists, 27 Old Gloucester Street, London WC1N 3XX; International Federation of Reflexologists, 76–78 Edridge Road, Croydon, Surrey CR0 1EF.

RELAXATION TECHNIQUES

See Autogenics and Breathing, above.

Suggested Reading: *Love, Medicine and Miracles*, Bernie Siegel, Rider Books, London, 1989.

Contact Point: Relaxation for Living, 168–170 Oatlands Drive, Weybridge, Surrey KT13 9ET.

VISUALIZATION

A practice of creating, holding and manipulating images in your mind to build overall awareness and well-being. This practice is as old as humankind and may be used in almost any setting and for any purpose. It takes a month or two to become skilled, but then it is yours for life. A very powerful tool.

In stress: Excellent for gaining awareness and control.

In pain: Excellent here, too, for gaining control and minimizing discomfort.

Suggested Reading: *Peace, Love and Healing: bodymind communication and the path to self-healing*, Bernie Siegel, Rider Books, London 1990; *Visualization for Change*, Patrick Fanning, New Harbinger Publications, Oakland, California, 1988.

Contact Point: International Stress Management Association, Southbank University, LPSS, 103 Borough Road, London SE1 0AA.

YOGA

A holistic practice of movement, breathing and visualization techniques which has a long and successful history, especially for men, of rebuilding physical, mental and emotional health. There are several types of yoga so search out what is available to you locally and try each class until you find the type and the teacher which most impresses you.

In stress: Excellent to build awareness and exercise control.

In pain: Very useful to diminish pain from, say, arthritis or chronic headaches. Physical health is gained alongside a shift in your state of mind, so anything can happen.

Suggested Reading: *The Complete Yoga Book*, J. Hewitt, Rider Books, London 1993; *Yoga for Common Ailments*, R. Nagarathna, H.R. Nagendra and R. Monro, Gala Books, Stroud, 1991.

Contact Point: Yoga for Health Foundation, Ickwell Bury, Ickwell Green, Northill, Biggleswade, Bedfordshire; British Wheel of Yoga, 1 Hamilton Place, Boston Road, Sleaford, Lincs NG34 7ES.

Part Two

Revealed!

The Secret Ingredients in the Products You Buy

HOW TO USE PART TWO

Here is an alphabetical encyclopedia of over 500 common substances – including all those 'E' numbers – which are or have been used in consumer products. Information is laid out as follows for each entry:

SUBSTANCE NAME – The most common name (together with E number, if relevant) given to the substance. Most chemicals have a number of synonyms, but only the most commonly used ones are included (there's little point, for example, in including the fact that caffeine is also called 1,3,7-trimethyl-2,6-dioxopurine). If it is followed by the 'caution' symbol ⚠ then that indicates there is some health concern associated with the substance, outlined under 'What You Need To Know'.

FUNCTION – Underneath the substance name you'll find a brief description of its function. Sometimes, there may be several: calcium carbonate, for example, has a number of functions both as a food additive (colour, carrier, anticaking agent, stabilizer) and as a medicinal substance (antacid). If any of these terms are unfamiliar to you, and some of them can be rather obscure, you'll find them defined in the glossary.

REGULATIONS – This gives you a summary of the European Community (EC) regulations which govern the use of this substance – where it may be used, in what sort of dose, and any restrictions. At the moment, EC regulations do not extend to cover substances used in over-the-counter medications, although harmonization will undoubtedly occur at some point in the future. This is a pity, because EC food additive regulations are masterpieces of clarity and simplicity (the relevant EC directive is also cited – for example, 'Directive 94/36/EC') which inform both consumers and manufacturers.

ACCEPTABLE DAILY INTAKE – Here you'll find a number, a range of numbers, or some other comment from the Joint Food and Agriculture Organization of the United Nations / World Health Organization Expert Committee on Food Additives (abbreviated to JECFA). While it does not have the force of law, it represents the conclusion of what is probably the world's most authoritative body on food additives. The number(s) are an estimate of the amount of a substance in a food or drinking water that can be ingested daily over a lifetime without appreciable risk. Unless otherwise stated, the number(s) are expressed on a body-weight basis: milligrams per kilogram body weight per day.

Let's give an example: If you check the entry for that much-maligned food additive tartrazine, you'll find the acceptable daily intake to be 0 – 7.5. The 'standard human' weighs 60 kilograms, so you multiply the range given by 60, to arrive at an acceptable daily intake range of 0 to 450 milligrams of tartrazine per day, for a 60-kilogram human.

Sometimes the acceptable daily intake will be stated as 'not specified'. This *doesn't* mean that the JECFA haven't considered the substance – it actually means that they *have* thought about it, and have decided that it is 'a substance of very low toxicity which, on the basis of the available data, the total dietary intake of the substance arising from its use at the levels necessary to achieve the desired effect and from its acceptable background in food does not, in the opinion of JECFA, represent a hazard to health . . . An additive meeting this criterion must be used within the bounds of good manufacturing practice, i.e. it should be technologically efficacious and should be used at the lowest level to achieve this effect, it should not conceal inferior food quality or adulteration , and it should not create a nutritional imbalance.'[51]

How is the acceptable daily intake determined? Almost invariably by animal experiments. Like most people, we deplore vivisection. Because we explain the process here doesn't mean that we approve of it. Animal testing usually involves small groups of animals, perhaps 20 to 50. They will be given the substance being tested in a variety of concentrations for 6 – 12 months and then will be killed and examined. In long-term feeding experiments, they may be allowed to die from old age (or the toxicity of the compound being tested – whichever comes first). The aim is not to prove that the substance is safe – it is to find out how much of the substance can be consumed on a daily basis without the development of toxic effects. This maximum level is termed the 'no observable effect level', or NOEL, and it is expressed as a daily intake of so many milligrams of the substance for every kilogram body weight of the animal. This number is then usually divided by 100 to obtain the acceptable daily intake for humans. Why 100? It is supposed to represent two 'safety factors' of 10 each – one to allow for unknown differences between the laboratory animal species and humans, and the other to allow for individual differences in sensitivity between one human and another. As you can appreciate, although the acceptable daily intake may appear to be a very accurately expressed number (down to a decimal point), it is not, in fact, precise.

WHAT IT IS – A short description of what the substance is, how it is obtained, whether it is of animal origin, and any other background information which we think you would like to know.

WHAT YOU NEED TO KNOW – Here we note and reference (for any further reading you may care to do) any interesting information or research we have discovered about the substance as an entity, but not necessarily pertaining to any specific use or dosage. Not every substance has an entry here (lack of an entry does not imply that the substance is absolutely safe under all conditions – it simply means that we haven't uncovered anything particularly interesting). Sometimes, the entries here may be rather contradictory – as in the case of fluoride, for example (see p. 394–7), where opinions violently differ.

One of today's most important health issues is the carcinogenicity of the substances to which we may be exposed (often in great dilution, but often over an extended period of time). Rather than become hopelessly bogged down by quoting individual carcinogenicity experiments, we have instead decided to give you a broader, more comprehensive overview by summarizing the findings of the highly authoritative International Agency for Research on Cancer (IARC). Because a substance has been found to be 'possibly', 'probably' or definitely carcinogenic, it does not follow that you or your family will contract cancer from being exposed to it. We are, of course, surrounded by carcinogens all the time. Partly because of this, however, you may wish – as we do – to choose to limit your exposure to substances which IARC has judged to be carcinogenic.

Finally, scattered throughout Part Two you will find little featurettes which we've termed 'Fact Files'. These mini-articles will provide you some quick insight into those things that you've often heard about, but never really understood. Just what are emulsifiers, anyway? You've heard about them, you've eaten them, you've seen them on the side of food packets . . . Well, now you can read about them!

Abietis oil

MEDICINAL SUBSTANCE: COUNTER-IRRITANT; INHALANT; FLAVOURING

What It Is: Made from the conifer tree *Abies Siberica*, this oil is also known as Siberian Fir Oil and has a pleasant aroma and medicinal-type taste – which is probably why it may be included as a flavouring in cough, cold and throat sweets.

Acacia gum (gum arabic) (E414)

FOOD ADDITIVE: CARRIER; THICKENING AGENT; STABILIZER; EMULSIFIER

Regulations: EC permitted for all foodstuffs following the *quantum satis* principle (except those specified in Table 2 on pp. 15–16 and in Appendix B on pp. 469ff). Directive 95/2/EC

Acceptable Daily Intake: Not specified

What It Is: The use of acacia gum dates back at least 4000 years to the ancient Egyptians, who used it as a base for making paint colours. It is produced by the Acacia tree – native to Sudan, Senegal, Nigeria and other arid or semi-arid regions – as the tree's response to a bacterial or fungal infection, and is only exuded by unhealthy trees – drought or other environmental stresses will increase the yield. Wounds are often intentionally made in the bark by farmers to stimulate production.

What You Need To Know: Virtually non-toxic in food.[52] Has been used in printing as an anti-offset agent – workers exposed to gum arabic mist have suffered from allergic reactions, often known as 'printer's asthma'.[53] Scientific studies do not raise carcinogenic or reproductive concerns.[54]

SECRET INGREDIENTS FACT FILE
EMULSIFIERS

'*Emulsifier*' – we've all seen that odd little word on the ingredients list, but how many of us actually know what it is – or how important emulsifiers are to today's food industry?

Read on, and you'll learn all you need to know in the next sixty seconds . . .

An emulsion is a seemingly impossible substance: everyone knows that oil and water don't mix, and yet when animal fat is successfully mixed into a watery medium, we call the result milk. Milk is just one emulsion, others include mayonnaise, ice-cream, most popular soft drinks that contain essential oils from fruit, and most dressings and sauces. Any substance – such as lecithin (see pp. 279f) – that possesses the near-magical property of being able to keep oil droplets suspended in water (or water droplets suspended in oil, in the case of margarine or butter) is much sought after by food manufacturers.

The manufacture of food products based on emulsions is only about 130 years old. It started with the production of margarine in 1870 followed by a major breakthrough early in the 20th century when hydrogenation of fats and oils was commercialized. Today, the food industry depends heavily on emulsions and emulsifiers – as you can see from the sheer number (over 40) of chemicals which are designated emulsifiers in this book. The increasing use of emulsifying agents in food products really parallels the rise of the mass-market food industry: in the days when food was less of a commodity, and almost always made at home from locally produced ingredients, synthetic emulsifiers were simply not needed (a few natural emulsifiers are still used: they include lecithin found in eggs and soya beans, milk, mustard and lanolin). Today's food, however, is very different: it may have travelled halfway round the world before it lands in your local supermarket, and it might have been manufactured weeks ago. Also, today's consumer (whoever that is) appears to value consistency in food almost above any other quality – this presents a tough challenge to manufacturers, who have to make allowances for the natural variability present in their raw materials. All these factors mean that emulsifying agents are absolutely indispensable ingredients in more and more food products. They make the process of manufacture easier and more controllable; they often add a certain quality (e.g. 'mouthfeel') to the product; they stabilize the product and help it resist the rigors of transport; and they extend its shelf-life.

Most synthetic food emulsifiers are produced by combining an edible fatty acid with an organic acid such as acetic, citric, lactic tartaric or succinic – or with sugar alcohols (polyols) such as glycerol, propylene glycol or sorbitol. Of all the emulsifiers, the category known as monodiglycerides probably accounts for three-quarters of all the world's production, and therefore they are the most important. They are made by combining fatty acids or oils (usually hydrogenated soya bean oil) with glycerol (see pp. 245ff).

Technically, emulsifiers work by reducing the surface tension between two immiscible (un-mixable) substances (oil and water). To achieve this, the emulsifier must display two different properties. It will contain a hydrocarbon chain which has an affinity for fats and oils, but it will also contain a polar group which is attracted to water. A successful emulsifier thus reconciles two opposite forces, rather like a good marriage guidance counsellor.

Apart from the obvious uses, such as making mayonnaise and ice-cream, emulsifiers have several important but usually hidden uses in food processing, namely:

- They react with the starch in bakery products (complexing) to prevent it from crystallizing, thus retarding the firming of the crumb which is associated with staling;
- They control crystallization in sugar and fat systems, e.g. in chocolate, where the use of emulsifiers prevents the solidification of fat on the chocolate's surface, thus creating a bright surface gloss;
- They enable surface wetting to take place more easily, for example, the addition of an emulsifier to a coffee whitener

allows it to dissolve easily in the coffee without clumping on the surface;
- They function as lubricants, for example, in caramels, by reducing their tendency to stick to cutting knives, wrappers – and teeth!

Emulsifiers clearly bring many benefits to the food processing industry. We should remember, however, that many synthetic emulsifers have only recently been invented, which means that we do not necessarily know precisely how they will affect humans in the long term. Where the emulsifer breaks down in the human gastrointestinal tract to normal dietary components, then there is unlikely to be any concern. When they do not, however, then we are being exposed to 'novel chemical forms with the potential to elicit toxic effects', as the British government's Food Advisory Committee put it.[55]

Acesulfame K (E950)

FOOD ADDITIVE: SWEETENER

Regulations: EC permitted for the following foods up to the total maximum usable dose specified:
- Water-based flavoured drinks, energy-reduced or with no added sugar, maximum usable dose: 350 mg/l
- Milk- and milk-derivative-based or fruit-juice-based drinks, energy-reduced or with no added sugar, maximum usable dose: 350 mg/l
- Water-based flavoured desserts, energy-reduced or with no added sugar, maximum usable dose: 350 mg/kg
- Milk- and milk-derivative-based preparations, energy-reduced or with no added sugar, maximum usable dose: 350 mg/kg
- Fruit- and vegetable-based desserts, energy-reduced or with no added sugar, maximum usable dose: 350 mg/kg
- Egg-based desserts, energy-reduced or with no added sugar, maximum usable dose: 350 mg/kg
- Cereal-based desserts, energy-reduced or with no added sugar, maximum usable dose: 350 mg/kg

- Fat-based desserts, energy-reduced or with no added sugar, maximum usable dose: 350 mg/kg
- Snacks: certain flavours of ready to eat, prepacked, dry, savoury starch products and coated nuts, maximum usable dose: 350 mg/kg
- Confectionery with no added sugar, maximum usable dose: 500 mg/kg; Cocoa- or dried-fruit-based confectionery, energy-reduced or with no added sugar, maximum usable dose: 500 mg/kg; Starch-based confectionery, energy-reduced or with no added sugar, maximum usable dose: 1 000 mg/kg; Cocoa-, milk-, dried-fruit- or fat-based sandwich spreads, energy-reduced or with no added sugar, maximum usable dose: 1 000 mg/kg; Chewing gum with no added sugar, maximum usable dose: 2 000 mg/kg
- Cider and perry, maximum usable dose: 350 mg/l
- Alcohol-free beer or with an alcohol content not exceeding 1,2% vol, maximum usable dose: 350 mg/l
- 'Biere de table/Tafelbier/Table beer' (original wort content less than 6 %) except for 'Obergariges Einfachbier', maximum usable dose: 350 mg/l
- Beers with a minimum acidity of 30 milli-equivalents expressed as NaOH, maximum usable dose: 350 mg/l
- Brown beers of the 'oud bruin' type, maximum usable dose: 350 mg/l
- Edible ices, energy-reduced or with no added sugar, maximum usable dose: 800 mg/kg
- Canned or bottled fruit, energy-reduced or with no added sugar, maximum usable dose: 350 mg/kg
- Energy-reduced jams, jellies and marmalades, maximum usable dose: 1 000 mg/kg
- Energy-reduced fruit and vegetable preparations, maximum usable dose: 350 mg/kg
- Sweet-sour preserves of fruit and vegetables, maximum usable dose: 200 mg/kg
- Sweet-sour preserves and semi-preserves of fish and marinades of fish, crustaceans and molluscs, maximum usable dose: 200 mg/kg
- Sauces, maximum usable dose: 350 mg/kg
- Mustard, maximum usable dose: 350 mg/kg
- Fine bakery products for special nutritional uses, maximum usable dose: 1 000 mg/kg
- Complete formulae for weight control intended to replace total

daily food intake or an individual meal, maximum usable dose: 450 mg/kg
- Complete formulae and nutritional supplements for use under medical supervision, maximum usable dose: 450 mg/kg
- Liquid food supplements/dietary integrators, maximum usable dose: 350 mg/l
- Solid food supplements/dietary integrators, maximum usable dose: 500 mg/kg
- Vitamins and dietary preparations, maximum usable dose 2 000 mg/kg
- EC permitted for chewing gum with added sugars, maximum level: 800 mg/kg
- Directive 94/35/EC

Acceptable Daily Intake: 0 – 15

What It Is: Synthesized by scientists in Germany in 1967, it has a sweetness that is, gram for gram, 200 times stronger than table sugar. Its taste resembles that of cyclamate – it has no metallic aftertaste, like saccharin.

What You Need To Know: It is not metabolized (thus contributing no calories) and is excreted unchanged, having no pharmacological effects.[56]

Acetic acid (E260)

FOOD ADDITIVE: FLAVOURING AGENT; ACIDIFIER; PRESERVATIVE

Regulations: EC permitted for all foodstuffs following the *quantum satis* principle (except those specified in Table 2 on pp. 15–16 and in Appendix B on pp. 469ff). Directive 95/2/EC

Acceptable Daily Intake: Not specified.

What It Is: The preservation of food with acetic acid in the form of vinegar dates back to antiquity and, indeed, vinegar (4 per cent acetic acid) is still made in the old-fashioned way: after alcoholic fermentation, the bacteria *Acetobacter* is deliberately introduced into the ferment, which provide the enzymes to convert the alcohol first to acetaldehyde and then acetic acid (industrial acetic acid is produced differently: either by oxidizing acetaldehyde or butane, or by combining methanol and carbon monoxide).[57] Dilute acetic acid can be found in some cough medicines, where it may be included to act as an expectorant (although it is questionable whether it can really help in the production of phlegm) but its most common use is probably to act as a sharp flavouring agent. Glacial acetic acid is a very strong form (over 99 per cent by weight) of the acid, which is corrosive (and painful) to the surface of the skin. It has been included in products sold to destroy corns and warts.

What You Need To Know: Acetic acid occurs naturally in plant and animal tissues and is involved in fatty acid and carbo-hydrate metabolism; it is a safe and natural food ingredient unless, of course, contacted in a strong solution, in which case it has extremely corrosive effects. A splash of vinegar in the eye can injure the corneal epithelium, and as little as 1 ml of pure (glacial) acetic acid can perforate the oesophagus.[58]

Acetic acid esters of mono- and diglycerides of fatty acids (E472a)

FOOD ADDITIVE: EMULSIFIER; CARRIER

Regulations: EC permitted for all foodstuffs following the *quantum satis* principle (except those specified in Table 2 on pp. 15–16 and in Appendix B on pp. 469ff). EC permitted as carrier. Restricted use: Colours and fat-soluble antioxidants. Directive 95/2/EC.

Acceptable Daily Intake: Not specified.

What It Is: Manufactured by combining mixed esters of acetic acid with edible fats and glycerol. Used as a lubricant in bread manufacture, to improve the aeration properties of high-fat recipes. Capable of forming very flexible films which stretch up to eight times their length before breaking; therefore used as a protective coating on meat products, nuts and fruits, to extend their shelf-life and improve their appearance. In whipped products, it agglomerates the fat globules to produce a stable foam.

Acetomenaphthone

MEDICINAL SUBSTANCE: VITAMIN ANALOGUE

What It Is: Acetomenaphthone is a substance with similar properties to vitamin K (promotes clotting of the blood). It has been used in preparations sold for the relief of chilblains, although there seems to be little evidence that it can alleviate the symptoms of chilblains.[59]

Acetone

MEDICINAL SUBSTANCE: SOLVENT

What It Is: Acetone is used to dissolve fats and other greasy matter, and is therefore found in some skin cleaning preparations, and also in nail polish removers. Acetone can be absorbed through the lungs and skin, and may be abused by 'glue sniffers'. Poisoning will result if the quantity absorbed is large enough – symptoms may include headache, sleepiness, vomiting blood, unconsciousness. It can be found in small quantities in normal human urine, and in larger amounts in that of diabetics.

Acetylated distarch adipate (E1422)

FOOD ADDITIVE: STABILIZER; THICKENING AGENT; BINDER; CARRIER

Regulations: EC permitted for all foodstuffs following the *quantum satis* principle (except those specified in Table 2 on pp. 15–16 and in Appendix B on pp. 469ff). Directive 95/2/EC.
Acceptable Daily Intake: Not specified.
What It Is: A chemically modified starch widely used as a stabilizer and thickener for frozen foods, bakery fillings, instant puddings and many other convenience foods. Manufactured by reacting starch (from potatoes, maize, etc) with adipic-acetic anhydrides.
What You Need To Know: Scientific studies do not raise carcinogenic concerns.

Acetylated distarch phosphate (E1414)

FOOD ADDITIVE: EMULSIFIER; THICKENING AGENT; BINDER;
CARRIER

Regulations: EC permitted for all foodstuffs following the *quantum satis* principle (except those specified in Table 2 on pp. 15–16 and in Appendix B on pp. 469ff). Directive 95/2/EC.

Acceptable Daily Intake: Not specified.

What It Is: Another chemically modified starch, obtained by reacting starch with phosphorous oxychloride and acetic anhydride or vinylacetate.

What You Need To Know: Scientific studies do not raise carcinogenic concerns.

Acetylated starch (E1420)

FOOD ADDITIVE: STABILIZER; THICKENING AGENT; BINDER;
CARRIER

Regulations: EC permitted for all foodstuffs following the *quantum satis* principle (except those specified in Table 2 on pp. 15–16 and in Appendix B on pp. 469ff). Directive 95/2/EC.

Acceptable Daily Intake: Not specified.

What It Is: Another chemically modified starch, made by reacting starch granules suspended in water with acetic anhydride or vinylacetate.

Acrylonitrile

FOOD ADDITIVE: CONTAMINANT

Acceptable Daily Intake: Provisional maximum tolerable daily intake: lowest level technologically attainable.

What It Is: First made in 1893 by the French chemist Charles Moureu, acrylonitrile is today a raw material for a wide range of chemical and polymer products. Human exposure to acrylonitrile occurs primarily among industry workers. However, there is a potential for the general public to be exposed to acrylonitrile in the air from its dispersal from production areas, car exhaust and cigarette smoke, as well as via ingestion from food which is in contact with plastic containers where acrylonitrile monomer has leached out.[60][61]

What You Need To Know: The International Agency for Research on Cancer has concluded that this substance is probably carcinogenic to humans. There was limited evidence of carcinogenicity in humans, but sufficient evidence of carcinogenicity in animals.[62]

Classified as a probable human carcinogen by the US Environmental Protection Agency. The observation of a statistically significant increase in the incidence of lung cancer in exposed workers and observation of tumours, generally astrocytomas in the brain, in studies in two rat strains exposed by various routes (drinking water, gavage, and inhalation) forms the basis for this classification.[63]

The US National Institute of Occupational Safety and Health recommends that acrylonitrile be regulated as a potential human carcinogen.[64]

Adipic acid (E355)

FOOD ADDITIVE: NEUTRALIZING AGENT; BUFFER

Regulations: EC permitted for the following foods (limits expressed as adipic acid):

- Fillings and toppings for fine bakery wares, maximum limit: 2 g/kg
- Dry powdered dessert mixes, maximum limit: 1 g/kg
- Gel-like desserts, maximum limit: 6 g/kg
- Fruit-flavoured desserts, maximum limit: 1 g/kg
- Powders for home preparation of drinks, maximum limit: 10 g/l
  Directive 95/2/EC

Acceptable Daily Intake: 0 – 5

What It Is: Two billion tons of adipic acid are manufactured every year – the majority of which is used in the manufacture of nylon and other important synthetic fibres. Adipic acid also has a few uses in the food industry. As a flavouring, it imparts a smooth, tart taste to foods and will improve the set of gelatin-based products. Can be used as an alternative to tartaric acid in baking powders, since it is an excellent slow-acting leavening agent that aids in the even release of carbon dioxide, thus increasing lightness and volume of the finished product. It also improves the melting characterisitics of processed cheese.

What You Need To Know: The ability of humans and other animals to metabolize adipic acid appears to be limited to a relatively small amount. A 1957 long-term feeding study on rats found no carcinogenic effect, although it did depress growth at 3 per cent and 5 per cent of the diet. The FAO/WHO has established the level causing no toxicological effect in rats' diet to be 500 mg/kg body weight, hence the human acceptable daily intake of 5 mg/kg, 100 times lower.[65]

Aflatoxins

FOOD ADDITIVE: CONTAMINANT

Acceptable Daily Intake: Lowest level practically obtainable.

What It Is: Aflatoxins are poisonous alkaloids produced by a fungus, *aspergillus flavus*. They are capable of causing acute liver damage, liver cirrhosis and indeed liver cancer. The primary route of human exposure is by eating contaminated food – grains and peanuts are among the foods on which aflatoxin-producing fungi commonly grow, although meat, eggs, milk, and other edible products from animals that consume aflatoxin-contaminated feed are additional sources of human exposure. One survey showed that approximately 26 per cent of the consignments of nuts and figs sampled at British ports exceeded the maximum statutory limit of 10μg/kg.[66]

What You Need To Know: The International Agency for Research on Cancer has concluded that this substance is carcinogenic to humans. There was sufficient evidence of carcinogenicity in humans, and sufficient evidence of carcino-genicity in animals.[67]

Agar (E406)

FOOD ADDITIVE: THICKENING AGENT; GELLING AGENT;
STABILIZER; CARRIER

Regulations: EC permitted for all foodstuffs following the *quantum satis* principle (except those specified in Table 2 on pp. 15–16 and in Appendix B on pp. 469ff). Directive 95/2/EC.

Acceptable Daily Intake: Not specified.

What It Is: Agar was the first seaweed known to be extracted, purified and dried when the process was accidentally discovered by a Japanese innkeeper in 1658, who threw out some agar jellies prepared from seaweed, only to find that they had dried in the sun to translucent flakes which could be reconstituted to agar jelly simply by the addition of hot water. Introduced into Europe and the US from China in the 19th century, agar was initially used as a gelatin substitute in the making of desserts, and was chosen by the bacteriologist Robert Koch (discoverer of the tuberculosis bacterium) as a suitable laboratory culture medium. It is used as a gelling agent in baking, confectionery and in meat, fish and dairy products.

What You Need To Know: Virtually non-toxic.[68]

Alcohol

MEDICINAL SUBSTANCE: SOLVENT, ANTIMICROBIAL, ASTRINGENT

What It Is: Also called ethyl alcohol or ethanol, alcohol is used as a solvent for many substances. When used externally on the skin, it will tend to toughen and harden it, and when used at a concentration of between 60 per cent and 90 per cent it will kill most bacteria (but not their spores). It is, of course, one of the most popular (and abused) recreational drugs, and when taken internally may interact with a range of other drugs. Cheers.

Alginic acid and its sodium, potassium, calcium and ammonium salts (E400 – 404)

FOOD ADDITIVE: THICKENING AGENT; STABILIZER; CARRIER

Regulations: EC permitted for all foodstuffs following the *quantum satis* principle (except those specified in Table 2 on pp. 15–16 and in Appendix B on pp. 469ff). Directive 95/2/EC.

Acceptable Daily Intake: Not specified.

What It Is: First extracted from brown seaweed by the British chemist E.C.C. Stanford in 1881, alginic acid is today mainly obtained from the Pacific giant kelp (up to 70 metres long) and from seaweeds growing off the west coast of Scotland. The weed is first left to soak in a sodium carbonate solution for 24 hours, which reduces it to a gelatinous mass; then it is treated with an acid to precipitate the alginic acid, which may be further converted to the most commonly used algin, sodium alginate (ammonium, potassium and propylene glycol forms are less commonly used). Used in the food industry as a stabilizer in ice-cream, water ices and cheese; as a thickening agent in beverages, as an emulsifier in dressings, and as a coating for meat, fish and other products.

What You Need To Know: Practically non-toxic, the greatest danger from ingestion of large quantities is intestinal obstruction.[69]

Scientific studies do not raise carcinogenic, genotoxic or reproductive concerns.[70]

Allantoin

MEDICINAL SUBSTANCE: ON THE SKIN

What It Is: To the surprise of many medical people in the trenches in the First World War, it was found that those soldiers whose wounds had become fly-blown (infested with maggots) sometimes healed more quickly than might have been expected. It was then discovered that the maggots excreted a substance – allantoin – that seemed to help cells to rebuild themselves. Nowadays, the maggots have been replaced by the test-tube, and allantoin is manufactured from uric acid (found in urine). It may have a soothing effect and be beneficial in some skin disorders.

Allura Red AC (E129)
FOOD ADDITIVE: FOOD COLOUR
Regulations: EC permitted to be used singly or in combination with other colours in the following foods up to the total maximum level specified.
- Non-alcoholic flavoured drinks, maximum level: 100 mg/l
- Candied fruits and vegetables, Mostarda di frutta, maximum level: 200 mg/kg
- Preserves of red fruits, maximum level: 200 mg/kg
- Confectionery, maximum level: 300 mg/kg
- Decorations and coatings, maximum level: 500 mg/kg
- Fine bakery wares (e.g. viennoiserie, biscuits, cakes and wafers), maximum level: 200 mg/kg
- Edible ices, maximum level: 150 mg/kg
- Flavoured processed cheese, maximum level: 100 mg/kg
- Desserts including flavoured milk products, maximum level: 150 mg/kg
- Sauces, seasonings (for example, curry powder, tandoori), pickles, relishes, chutney and piccalilli, maximum level: 500 mg/kg
- Mustard, maximum level: 300 mg/kg
- Fish paste and crustacean paste, maximum level: 100 mg/kg; Pre-cooked crustaceans, maximum level: 250 mg/kg; Salmon substitutes, maximum level: 500 mg/kg; Surimi, maximum level: 500 mg/kg; Fish roe, maximum level: 300 mg/kg; Smoked fish, maximum level: 100 mg/kg
- Snacks: dry, savoury potato, cereal or starch-based snack products: Extruded or expanded savoury snack products, maximum level: 200 mg/kg; other savoury snack products and savoury coated nuts, maximum level: 100 mg/kg
- Edible cheese rind and edible casings, maximum level: *quantum satis*
- Complete formulae for weight control intended to replace

total daily food intake or an individual meal, maximum level: 50 mg/kg
- Complete formulae and nutritional supplements for use under medical supervision, maximum level: 50 mg/kg
- Liquid food supplements/dietary integrators, maximum level: 100 mg/l
- Solid food supplements/dietary integrators, maximum level: 300 mg/kg
- Soups, maximum level: 50 mg/kg
- Meat and fish analogues based on vegetable proteins, maximum level: 100 mg/kg
- Spirituous beverages (including products less than 15 % alcohol by volume), except those mentioned in Annex II or III, maximum level: 200 mg/l
- Aromatized wines, aromatized wine-based drinks and aromatized wine-product cocktails as mentioned in Regulation (EEC) No 1601/91, except those mentioned in Annex II or III, maximum level: 200 mg/l
- Fruit wines (still or sparkling) cider (except cidre bouche) and perry, aromatized fruit wines, cider and perry, maximum level: 200 mg/l. Directive 94/36/EC

Acceptable Daily Intake: 0 – 7.

What It Is: A synthetic red monoazo dye.

What You Need To Know: Not approved for use in Canada in 1986 when the regulatory authorites concluded that the toxicological data submitted by the manufacturers was incomplete. The submission of further studies subsequently reversed this decision.[71]

People who suffer from asthma, rhinitis or urticaria may find their symptoms become worse following consumption of foods or beverages containing azo dyes. Such people may be mistakenly thought to be suffering from specific food allergies.[72]

Aloes

MEDICINAL SUBSTANCE: LAXATIVE

What It Is: Aloe juice is extracted from the leaves of the succulent aloe plant, which can be dried and used as an irritant laxative. Aloes should probably be avoided as a laxative since they have a drastic purgative action.[73] They may also produce severe spasmodic bowel pain. The use of aloes is recorded in the Bible (although this may refer to a different substance – *Aquilaria agallocha*) and the plant was grown on the Greek island of Socotra as early as the 4th century BC, and imported into Britain from the 10th century onwards.

SECRET INGREDIENTS FACT FILE
LAXATIVES AND DIARRHOEA REMEDIES

LAXATIVES

About 40 per cent of the population believe that they are constipated, and between 15 per cent and 22 per cent take laxatives.[74] There is strong evidence to show that constipation is associated with lack of fibre in the diet. One interesting study compared the diets eaten by different population groups in the United Kingdom, and correlated their fibre intake with the 'transit time' of food through their bodies. The study found that vegetarians (who naturally eat a lot of fibre) took on average 42.4 hours to process their food. At the other extreme, naval ratings and their wives (eating a refined, over-processed diet) took 83.4 hours to completely process their food.[75] A high intake of dietary fibre is also associated with a lower incidence of appendicitis, diverticular disease, and cancer of the large bowel (the second most common cancer). Vegetarians suffer less from all these diseases, and it is thought that their greater intake of fibre is partly responsible.

Despite their enduring popularity, laxatives (sometimes called cathartics, or evacuants, or purgatives) are rarely needed by healthy people. A change of diet to include more fresh fruit and vegetables may be all that is necessary to correct mild constipation. If you find you are taking laxatives regularly, or if your bowel habits change, you should speak to your doctor. The continuing use/abuse of laxatives can make you dependent on them, causing further health problems. Laxatives should never be taken to relieve abdominal pains or nausea. Some types of constipation are not diet-related (such as drug-induced constipation) and should be treated by a doctor, who should also advise the elderly, those who are pregnant or nursing, and people already under medical treatment. There are a number of different types of laxatives, which can be broadly categorized as follows:

BULK LAXATIVES
These substances increase the size of stools and stimulate bowel motion. They include ingredients such as bran and methylcellulose. They are generally safe, if somewhat slow to take effect, although internal obstruction may be caused if insufficient water is taken or if excessive amounts of the substances are consumed.

IRRITANT LAXATIVES
This group includes such substances as danthron, senna, aloes, rhubarb, and cascara (known as anthraquinone laxatives) and phenolphthalein and castor oil. They are thought to work by stimulating the intestinal smooth muscle, creating contractions and movement which leads to the passing of a motion, but they also may increase the amount of fluid in the intestines. As with all laxatives, over-frequent use can impair natural bowel functions.

SALINE OR OSMOTIC LAXATIVES
These substances which include magnesium sulphate, potassium sodium tartrate, sodium sulphate, lactulose and magnesium hydroxide, work by attracting water to the bowel and so increase the bulk of its contents, leading to a watery evacuation. Sodium salts should be avoided by those on low sodium diets, and people with impaired kidney function should avoid magnesium preparations, which could otherwise be absorbed into the system.

LUBRICANT LAXATIVES

Lubricant laxatives soften and lubricate the stools, making them easier to pass. Liquid paraffin and sodium dioctyl sulphosuccinate are two examples of lubricant laxatives and faecal softeners.

DIARRHOEA REMEDIES

Diarrhoea may be a symptom of an infection (such as food poisoning) which may require medical treatment. Although most cases of acute diarrhoea clear up by themselves, it is very important to replace lost fluids to avoid dehydration and depletion of the body's electrolytes (substances that are required to maintain the body's fluid, chemical and physiological balances), which can be a particularly serious threat to babies, children and the elderly. Medical advice should be sought if the diarrhoea does not clear up quickly, if it is associated with vomiting, bloody stools or fever, or if the sufferer is debilitated or otherwise at risk (e.g. infants, the elderly, etc). Milk should be avoided. For self-treatment, absorbent substances (such as kaolin) are usually preferable to more complex products.

Aloin

MEDICINAL SUBSTANCE: LAXATIVE

What It Is: A laxative made from aloes (see pp. 115–6) although more likely than aloes to cause kidney irritation. It works by irritating the large intestine into action. Regular use should be discouraged since it may cause kidney problems. Adverse effects may sometimes produce severe spasmodic bowel pain.

Aloxiprin

MEDICINAL SUBSTANCE: ANALGESIC

What It Is: Aloxiprin is a chemical combination of aluminium oxide and aspirin, and is used in a similar way to aspirin. The intention in combining the two ingredients is to reduce the gastric irritation that aspirin may cause (see pp. 142–3), as noted below.

SECRET INGREDIENTS FACT FILE
PAIN KILLERS

The word 'analgesia' comes from the Greek for 'painless-ness'. An 'analgesic' is therefore any substance (usually a drug) that tends to remove the sensation of pain. By contrast, an anaesthetic will remove all sensation – not just pain. All of us have benefited from commonly used over-the-counter analgesics at some time, but, because analgesics are so widely sold and promoted, we often tend to take them for granted, and forget that taking any drug involves a degree of risk. Aspirin, for example, is associated with gastrointestinal bleeding. Slight blood loss may occur in about 70 per cent of people who take aspirin.[76] This is not usually of clinical signifi-cance but it could cause iron-deficiency anaemia during long-term use. The point here is not necessarily to avoid taking aspirin: it is simply to treat all drugs respectfully, and use them only when appropriate. The first question we should therefore ask is: 'Is this pill really necessary?' Headache induced by tension, for example, might be better treated by relaxing (see the feature on stress reduction on page 81ff). Hangovers are best prevented by not over-indulging next time. And so on.

The second thing to realize is that pain generally serves some purpose in the body. It can be a way of telling us that something is wrong and requires treatment. For example, headaches which appear on waking up, and disappear during the day's activity may indicate a blood pressure problem. Any severe or persistent pain should always be diagnosed and treated by a doctor. And you should always consult your doctor before buying analgesics if you're already taking prescription medicines, or if you have stomach ulcers, high blood pressure, diabetes, heart, liver or kidney disease, or if you may be pregnant. Pain isn't just a nuisance – it might be trying to send you an important message.

VALUE FOR MONEY
Another point to bear in mind when choosing between OTC products is to read the label, and think about the drugs you are actually purchasing. This means ignoring the strong brand identity and pretty packaging that the manufacturer has carefully created, and getting down to the basic active ingredients. Often, you will find that you can buy standard preparations (e.g. Aspirin BP) at a fraction of the cost of branded products. In any case, it is worth asking the pharmacist if there is a 'BP' (this stands for British Pharmacopoeia) version available. Although manufacturers will often combine several different substances into one product identity, the evidence that such combinations are worth paying extra for is by no means conclusive.

SOME POINTS TO CONSIDER
- Both aspirin and paracetamol are analgesic (pain relieving) and antipyretic (fever reducing) in their actions, but aspirin also has anti-inflammatory properties and may be more useful where pain is due to tissue inflammation. Ibuprofen also has some anti-inflammatory action, and is analgesic and antipyretic.
- Since aspirin can cause stomach irritation, many doctors would advise you not to use aspirin preparations if you have indigestion.[77]
- Sometimes, substances other than straightforward analgesics can be found in analgesic products. Caffeine is one such example. The justification for its inclusion is that it acts as an 'adjuvant', that is, it contributes to the effectiveness of one of the active ingredients. Caffeine can certainly stimulate the nervous system, sometimes leading to nervousness, irritability, and – paradoxically – headache. (see pp. 171–4). Headache can also result from caffeine withdrawal symptoms, and, like aspirin, it

may also irritate the stomach. Caffeine is such a widely available drug that, if it does have an adjuvant effect, you could simply drink a cup of coffee with your pill.

- Analgesics combined with more unusual substances, such as laxatives, diarrhoea treatments, vitamins or anti-histamines tend to be found in older products. If the individual ingredients are required, they should be prescribed separately.[78]
- Migraines (sick headaches) are often uniquely personal in cause and symptoms. Diet, stress, and allergies may be implicated; symptoms may incude vomiting, visual disturbances, and incapacitating headache. Severe cases may be treated with prescription medicines, and in any case, it would be wise to consult your doctor if you start to have migraine attacks.
- You should remember that some preparations for children come in attractive flavours and colours (e.g. banana-flavoured elixir). The wisdom of making such potentially dangerous drugs as paracetamol attractive to children in this manner is questionable, and you should keep such tempting items well out of a child's enquiring reach.

Alpha-tocopherol (E307)
FOOD ADDITIVE: ANTIOXIDANT

Regulations: EC permitted for all foodstuffs following the *quantum satis* principle (except those specified in Table 2 on pp. 15–16 and in Appendix B on pp. 469ff). Directive 95/2/EC.

Acceptable Daily Intake: 307a d-alpha-tocopherol concentrate 0.15 – 2 307c dl-alpha-tocopherol 0.5 – 2.

What It Is: More commonly known as vitamin E, alpha-tocopherol belongs to the tocopherol family of substances, a group of chemically related compounds that occur naturally in plant tissues, especially in nuts, seeds, fruits and vegetables. Alpha-tocopherol has the most vitamin E activity (100 per cent), beta-tocopherol (15–40 per cent), gamma-tocopherol (1–20 per cent) then delta-tocopherol (1%). Tocopherols can be used commercially as antioxidants to reduce rancidity in oils and fatty foodstuffs, thus extending shelf life. They are, however, generally less effective than synthetic antioxidants (e.g. BHA, BHT) and therefore find relatively limited use. Commercially, tocopherols can be manufactured by extraction from the sludge that remains when vegetable oils and fats are deodorized; or in the case of alpha-tocopherol, may be produced by chemical synthesis.

What You Need To Know: Vitamin E is usually non-toxic, and intakes below 720 mg per day in humans generally do not cause any adverse effects.[79]

Scientific studies do not raise carcinogenic or mutagenic concerns – in fact, rather the opposite: alpha-tocopherol, when ingested simultaneously with food, may reduce human exposure to carcinogenic nitrosamines.[80]

Very high doses of vitamin E taken over prolonged periods have been associated with increased bleeding tendencies in vitamin-K deficient people, altered metabolism of hormones, altered immunity, impaired sexual function, and may increase the risk of thrombo-embolism in susceptible people.[81]

Aluminium (E173)

FOOD ADDITIVE: FOOD COLOUR

MEDICINAL SUBSTANCE: ANTACID

Regulations: EC permitted for external coating of sugar confectionery for the decoration of cakes and pastries. Maximum level: *quantum satis.* Directive 94/36/EC.

Acceptable Daily Intake: No acceptable daily intake allocated as colour. As a contaminant, provisional tolerable weekly intake 7.

What It Is: Aluminium is one of the commonest elements in the earth's crust. Despite that, our bodies have absolutely no dietary requirement for it. Today, there are strong suggestions that aluminium intake is linked to Alzheimer's disease – an increasingly common form of senile dementia. Aluminium gets into our water in two ways. In some areas, it is deliberately added to the water supply in order to make discoloured tap-water appear clear. In addition, there is growing evidence that acid rain, caused by emissions from power stations and motor vehicles, can slowly leech environmental aluminium deposits into the water table.

What You Need To Know: People with normal kidney functions can usually eliminate most of the aluminium they absorb, but those who suffer from kidney disease (or the elderly) may not be able to do so.[82] High levels of aluminium have been found in the brains of people suffering from Alzheimer's disease (senile dementia). Molecular biological techniques and sensitive elemental analysis have shed some new light on the way that aluminium may harm brain function. Aluminium in Alzheimer's disease may act by electrostatically crosslinking proteins and DNA. The consequence of such crosslinking is reduced transcription of at least one neuron-specific gene. A number of epidemiological studies support the hypothesis that environmental aluminium is a significant risk factor.[83]

Alzheimer's isn't the only disease associated with chronic aluminium consumption. Other studies suggest that heavy use of aluminium-containing antacids may produce bone abnormalities by interfering with calcium and phosphorous metabolism. One study of this problem concluded that 'several commonly used drugs induce significant calcium loss, particularly aluminium-containing antacids, and, if used for prolonged periods of time, can contribute to the development of osteoporosis.'[84] This is surprising, because aluminium-containing antacids have generally been regarded as very safe, and it was traditionally believed that only a negligible amount of aluminium was absorbed into the bloodstream through their use. One study examined 10 healthy volunteers, who were given a conventional aluminium-magnesium antacid tablet after the three main meals and at bedtime for four weeks.[85] The researchers found that urinary excretion of magnesium, calcium, and aluminium was increased by the tablets, and the concentration of aluminium in the bloodstream also increased. Most of the changes were normalized three to four days after cessation of antacid medication. The researchers concluded: 'The fact that even this low dose of antacid can provoke measurable changes in mineral metabolism, including aluminium absorption, is noteworthy, although we did not see any clinical symptoms from the biochemical changes.'

Using aluminium saucepans, aluminium-lined cooking utensils and containers can considerably increase the content of aluminium in food. This is particularly true when acidic foodstuffs are stored in aluminium utensils. When rhubarb was cooked in a stainless steel saucepan, it was found to contain up to 0.1 mg aluminium per portion. Cooked in an aluminium saucepan, it contained 25 mg per portion.[86] Aluminium exposure may also result from drinking from old (i.e. past sell-by date) cans. In one experiment, the concentration of aluminium in a soft drink 12 months past its 'best by' date significantly exceeded the EC limits for aluminium in tap water.[87]

SECRET INGREDIENTS FACT FILE
HOW TO REDUCE YOUR ALUMINIUM INTAKE

- Throw out any aluminium cooking utensils.
- Avoid using aluminium-containing medicines such as antacids.
- Check food labels for the addition of aluminium salts used as emulsifying, anti-caking, bleaching and raising agents. If they're present, throw them out.
- Cut down on tea consumption (tea contains significant amounts of aluminium).
- Use fresh food rather than those sold in aluminium tins. Don't buy fruit juices which are sold in cartons lined with aluminium foil, because the citric acid contained in the

juice can dissolve aluminium and increase the amount absorbed by the body.

- Increase your consumption of calcium-containing food, because aluminium may cause the body to lose calcium.
- Install a reverse-osmosis water treatment system for your drinking water – it will remove much more aluminium than an activated-carbon (jug type) filter.

Aluminium ammonium sulphate (E523)

FOOD ADDITIVE: STABILIZER; FIRMING AGENT

Regulations: EC permitted to be used similarly to aluminium sulphate (E520), see below. Directive 95/2/EC.

Acceptable Daily Intake: 0 – 0.6.

What It Is: Manufactured by crystallization from a mixture of ammonium sulphate and aluminium sulphate.[88]

Aluminium chlorhydroxyallantoinate

MEDICINAL SUBSTANCE: ASTRINGENT

What It Is: Also known as alcloxa, this substance contains allantoin (see pp. 113–4) and is used as an astringent (a drying agent) in skin products. It may also have keratolytic (skin softening and peeling) properties.

Aluminium glycinate

MEDICINAL SUBSTANCE: ANTACID

What It Is: This aluminium salt is an antacid used in a similar way to aluminium hydroxide. It is relatively insoluble in stomach fluids and therefore tends to have a longer-acting effect than more soluble antacids.

Aluminium hydroxide

MEDICINAL SUBSTANCE: ANTACID

What It Is: Aluminium hydroxide is an effective ingredient in many antacids. It is relatively insoluble in stomach fluids and therefore tends to have a longer-acting effect than more soluble antacids. It tends to produce constipation (very large doses may produce an intestinal blockage) and it may interfere with the absorption of other drugs.

Aluminium oxide

MEDICINAL SUBSTANCE: ABRASIVE

What It Is: Aluminium oxide is used as an abrasive substance in acne treatments, with the intention of scrubbing the face to physically remove debris from blocked pores. Such treatments will tend to cause drying and redness of the skin. The effectiveness of abrasive treatments is uncertain.[89]

Aluminium potassium sulphate (E522)

FOOD ADDITIVE: ACIDITY REGULATOR; STABILIZER

Regulations: EC permitted to be used similarly to aluminium sulphate (E520). Directive 95/2/EC.

Acceptable Daily Intake: No acceptable daily intake allocated.

What It Is: Alum is prepared from the mineral bauxite and sulphuric acid, with the addition of potassium sulphate.

Aluminium silicate (Kaolin) (E559)

FOOD ADDITIVE: ANTICAKING AGENT; CARRIER

Regulations: EC permitted to be used similarly to silicon dioxide (E551). EC permitted as carrier. Restricted use: colours, max. 5 per cent. Directive 95/2/EC.

Acceptable Daily Intake: Not specified.

What It Is: Prepared for pharmaceutical and medicinal purposes by levigating with water to remove sand.

What You Need To Know: Kaolin can be considered toxicologically inert after oral administration; it is rated as practically non-toxic.

Aluminium sodium silicate
MEDICINAL SUBSTANCE: ANTACID
What It Is: Another relatively insoluble, silica-based antacid, similar in action to aluminium hydroxide (see pp. 125–6).

Aluminium sodium sulphate (E521)
FOOD ADDITIVE: BUFFERING AGENT; NEUTRALIZING AGENT; FIRMING AGENT
Regulations: EC permitted to be used similarly to aluminium sulphate (E520). Directive 95/2/EC.
Acceptable Daily Intake: No acceptable daily intake allocated.
What It Is: Made by heating a solution of aluminium sulphate and adding sodium chloride.

Aluminium sulphate (E520)
FOOD ADDITIVE: FIRMING AGENT
Regulations: EC permitted for the following foods, individually or in combination with E521, E522 or E523, expressed as aluminium.
- Egg white, maximum level: 30 mg/kg
- Candied, crystallized and glacé fruit and vegetables, maximum level: 200 mg/kg.
 Directive 95/2/EC.
Acceptable Daily Intake: No acceptable daily intake allocated.
What It Is: Made by reacting freshly precipitated aluminium hydroxide with sulphuric acid.

Amaranth (E123)

FOOD ADDITIVE: FOOD COLOUR
Regulations: EC permitted for aperitif wines, spirit drinks including products with less than 15 per cent alcohol by volume, maximum level: 30 mg/l; permitted for fish roe, maximum level: 30 mg/kg. Directive 94/36/EC.
Acceptable Daily Intake: 0 – 0.5.
What It Is: A synthetic, bluish-red monoazo dye.

What You Need To Know: Approved for food use in the United States in 1906, but banned for use in foods, drugs and cosmetics in February 1976 after experiments by the US Food and Drug Administration indicated that amaranth appeared to cause a statistically significant increase in a variety of cancers in female rats exposed to it.[90][91]

The International Agency for Research on Cancer has concluded that this substance is unclassifiable as to carcinogenicity in humans. No data are available in humans. Inadequate evidence of carcinogenicity in animals.[92]

People who suffer from asthma, rhinitis or urticaria may find their symptoms become worse following consumption of foods or beverages containing azo dyes. Such people may be mistakenly thought to be suffering from specific food allergies.[93]

Ambucetamide
MEDICINAL SUBSTANCE: SMOOTH MUSCLE RELAXANT
What It Is: Smooth muscle is present in many internal organs, including the gut and the uterus. Contractions of this type of muscle may contribute to period pains, and in theory a substance such as ambucetamide, which relaxes smooth muscles, could be of help to people suffering from period pains.

Amethocaine
MEDICINAL SUBSTANCE: LOCAL ANAESTHETIC
What It Is: Amethocaine is a local anaesthetic used to provide temporary pain relief.

Aminacrine
MEDICINAL SUBSTANCE: ANTIMICROBIAL
What It Is: An antiseptic which is effective against many types of bacteria, although not as effective against fungal infections. It can be used on infected surfaces, and for the disinfection of wounds and burns, although prolonged application of antimicrobials may actually delay the healing process.[94]

Ammonia caramel (caramel colour class III) (E150C)

FOOD ADDITIVE: FOOD COLOUR

Regulations: EC permitted at *quantum satis* in all foods except those to which the EC only permits certain colours to be added (Appendix C, pp. 476ff) and those to which the EC forbids the adding of colours (Appendix D, pp. 482ff). Directive 94/36/EC.

Acceptable Daily Intake: 0 – 200.

What It Is: Prepared by the controlled heat treatment of carbohydrates with ammonium compounds.

What You Need To Know: Manufacturers have to ensure that this substance is not contaminated during production with 4-methylimidazole, a chemical which has been identified as the cause of convulsions in cattle and sheep fed ammonia-treated molasses. Concern has also been expressed about the principal toxic effect of ammoniated caramels, which can depress circulating lymphocytes and total leucocytes. Scientific studies do not raise carcinogenic concerns.[95] [96]

Ammonium acetate

MEDICINAL SUBSTANCE: EXPECTORANT

What It Is: Ammonium acetate is found in some cough medicines where it is supposed to act as an expectorant (to help you to expel sputum). In very large amounts it may irritate the stomach and produce nausea and vomiting.

Ammonium carbonates (i) Ammonium carbonate (ii) Ammonium hydrogen carbonate (ammonium bicarbonate) (E503)

FOOD ADDITIVE: ACIDITY REGULATOR; RAISING AGENT

Regulations: EC permitted for all foodstuffs following the *quantum satis* principle (except those specified in Table 2 on pp. 15–16 and in Appendix B on pp. 469ff). Directive 95/2/EC.

Acceptable Daily Intake: Not specified.
What It Is: Obtained by heating ammonium salts with calcium carbonate. Used in baking powders, for washing and defatting wool, tanning and dyeing.
What You Need To Know: These compounds are normal metabolites in man, and therefore presumed to be safe in the relatively small amounts found in food additives. Consumption of larger amounts (6 – 8 g ammonium chloride) will produce a change in the acid base balance and increased urinary excretion of magnesium, calcium and phosphate.[97]

Ammonium chloride
MEDICINAL SUBSTANCE: EXPECTORANT; DIURETIC
What It Is: Used in both diuretics (substances which increase urine production) and expectorants (substances which are supposed to help you to cough up mucus), ammonium chloride is very easily absorbed into the system. It has been used to treat urinary tract infections, since it increases the acidity of the urine which tends to discourage the growth of some organisms. It can also be used to flush some drugs out of the system (such as amphetamines) in cases of overdose. It is questionable whether its irritant effect contributes to any expectorant action.[98] Large doses may cause headache, sickness and vomiting, eventually leading to sleepiness and a raised acid level in the blood.

Ammonium hydroxide (E527)
FOOD ADDITIVE: ACIDITY REGULATOR
Regulations: EC permitted for all foodstuffs following the *quantum satis* principle (except those specified in Table 2 on pp. 15–16 and in Appendix B on pp. 469ff). Directive 95/2/EC.
Acceptable Daily Intake: Not specified.
What It Is: Made by reacting hydrogen and nitrogen, followed by addition of the resulting ammonia to water.

What You Need To Know: Ammonia is toxic by all routes (i.e. inhalation, ingestion, and skin contact) but hazardous exposure to this intensely pungent-smelling liquid is only likely to occur to those exposed occupationally, i.e. from its use in fertilizers, dyes, explosives, plastics, cleansing agents, fibres and resins. The amount used as an additive in food is too small to be toxic.

Ammonium phosphatides (E442)

FOOD ADDITIVE: EMULSIFIER; CARRIER

Regulations: EC permitted for cocoa and chocolate products as defined in Directive 73/241/EEC, maximum level: 10 g/kg; Cocoa-based confectionery, maximum level: 10 g/kg.
EC permitted as carrier. Restricted use: antioxidants. Directive 95/2/EC.

Acceptable Daily Intake: 0 – 30.

What It Is: An emulsifier similar in use and composition to lecithin (see pp. 279f) manufactured from a mixture of glycerol and partially hardened rape seed oil.

Ammonium sulphate (E517)

FOOD ADDITIVE: CARRIER; FLOUR TREATMENT AGENT;
STABILIZER

Regulations: EC permitted as carrier. Restricted use: none. Directive 95/2/EC.

Acceptable Daily Intake: Not specified.

What It Is: Made by reacting ammonia and sulphuric acid. The vast majority of ammonium sulphate produced is spread on the land, as a nitrogen source in fertilizer mixtures.

What You Need To Know: Low toxicity.[99]

Anise

MEDICINAL SUBSTANCE: FLAVOURING

What It Is: Anise is recorded in the Bible as part of a tithe payment and the oil has been used for centuries in an attempt to relieve flatulence and ease coughs and chest complaints. Today it is found in cough medicines where it is supposed to act as an expectorant (i.e. to help you expel sputum). In very large amounts, it may irritate the stomach and produce nausea and vomiting.

Annatto, bixin, norbixin (E160b)

FOOD ADDITIVE: FOOD COLOUR

Regulations: EC permitted for:
- Margarine, minarine, other fat emulsions, and fats essentially free from water, maximum level: 10 mg/kg
- Decorations and coatings, maximum level: 20 mg/kg
- Fine bakery wares, maximum level: 10 mg/kg
- Edible ices, maximum level: 20 mg/kg
- Liqueurs, including fortified beverages with less than 15% alcohol by volume, maximum level: 10 mg/l
- Flavoured processed cheese, maximum level: 15 mg/kg
- Ripened orange, yellow and broken-white cheese, unflavoured processed cheese, maximum level: 15 mg/kg
- Desserts, maximum level: 10 mg/kg
- Snacks: dry, savoury potato, cereal or starch-based snack products; extruded or expanded savoury snack products, maximum level: 20 mg/kg; other savoury snack products and savoury coated nuts, maximum level: 10 mg/kg
- Smoked fish, maximum level: 10 mg/kg
- Edible cheese rind and edible casings, maximum level: 20 mg/kg
- Red Leicester cheese, maximum level: 50 mg/kg
- Mimolette cheese, maximum level: 35 mg/kg
- Extruded, puffed and/or fruit-flavoured breakfast cereals, maximum level: 25 mg/kg.
  Directive 94/36/EC.

Acceptable Daily Intake: 0 – 0.065.

What It Is: Annatto is the fruit of the *Bixa orellana* shrub, grown in South America, India and East Africa. The fruits are pulped with water, fermented, dried and the residue contains 6–12 per cent of the yellow colour bixin, a carotene. Where the colour has to be soluble in oil, bixin is used; for water solubility, norbixin (its potassium salt) is used.

What You Need To Know: May provoke flare-up of symptoms in some people susceptible to urticaria and/or angioneurotic oedema. Scientific studies do not raise mutagenic or carcinogenic concerns.[100]

Antazoline
MEDICINAL SUBSTANCE: ANTIHISTAMINE

What It Is: An antihistamine drug. For some general information about antihistamines, see the feature article, below.

Anthocyanins (E163)
FOOD ADDITIVE: FOOD COLOUR

Regulations: EC permitted at *quantum satis* in all foods except those to which the EC only permits certain colours to be added (Appendix C, pp. 476ff) and those to which the EC forbids the adding of colours (Appendix D, pp. 482ff). Directive 94/36/EC.

Acceptable Daily Intake: No acceptable daily intake allocated.

What It Is: Most of the red or blue colours we see in flowers, leaves and fruit are due to anthocyanins – a class of some 200 or more chemical compounds, obtained from plants, often grape skin. Whether the final colour turns out to be blue or red depends upon the acidity of the foodstuff.

What You Need To Know: Very low toxicity. Scientific studies do not raise mutagenic or reproductive concerns. Improvements in visual acuity and darkness adaptation have been observed in humans receiving doses of up to 700 mg of the anthocyanins.[101]

Anthraquinone glycosides of rhubarb
MEDICINAL SUBSTANCE: LAXATIVE

What It Is: The collective name for a group of naturally derived substances which tend to have laxative and/or astringent actions. See also cascara, senna and rhubarb.

SECRET INGREDIENTS FACT FILE
ANTIHISTAMINES

As the name suggests, antihistamines are drugs that counter the effects of histamine in the body. Histamine is contained in all body tissues, and is released from cells in response to stimulation by an allergen (i.e. an allergy-provoking substance). Common allergens include dust, pollen, and animal dander, but the list is almost endless and, of course, a substance which produces allergy in one person may be entirely harmless in another. The effects of histamine release can be just as varied as the cause. Sometimes it may produce a skin rash, sneezing, watery eyes, asthma, swellings, or hay fever (often the result of pollen allergy). Histamine will also have the general effects of producing a fall in blood pressure, an increase in stomach secretions and an increase in the heart rate. Antihistamine drugs don't stop histamine from being released, but to some extent they can prevent it from reaching its final destination in the body, and so may alleviate some of its effects. It is important to understand, therefore, that antihistamines don't cure an allergy – all they can do is give some relief from the symptoms. Antihistamines have other effects, too. Many of them will produce drowsiness, which may be almost unnoticeable, or may manifest itself as deep sleep. Alcohol should be avoided while taking antihistamine since its sedative effect can be magnified. The drowsiness that antihistamines can cause may be dangerous if you drive or are in other situations which demand a high degree of mental alertness for your and other people's safety. If you are taking other depressants (tranquillizers, sleeping pills, narcotics, etc) you should check with your doctor before taking antihistamines. You should also obtain medical advice before taking them if you have an enlarged prostate, heart or liver disease, epilepsy, high blood pressure, glaucoma, thyroid problems or ulcers. Antihistamine drugs are used in a wide range of products, sometimes very effectively, but sometimes with little rationale. Here are some uses:

- Antihistamines are useful in relieving the symptoms of occasional allergy, such as hay fever. Some of them may also have a mild drying effect on the mucous membranes, which can help to reduce hay fever symptoms.
- Antihistamines can be effective when used to treat nausea, sickness and vomiting, such as travel or motion sickness. Your doctor will be able to help you choose the appropriate drug for this purpose, and s/he may also want to make sure the underlying cause of the nausea is identified. Paradoxically, antihistamines may also produce sickness and nausea as an occasional side-effect.
- They are of little use in treating the common cold. There have been claims that antihistamine drugs are effective for this purpose, but most authorities agree that there is little justification for their use in cold medications, and one authority states that 'extensive trials have shown these claims to be unsubstantiated'.[102]

The most common side-effects of over-the-counter antihistamine drugs taken orally are likely to be sedation and dryness of the mouth. Since they may irritate the stomach, it might be sensible to take them with food.

Arachis oil
MEDICINAL SUBSTANCE: LUBRICANT; MOISTURIZER
What It Is: This is also called peanut or groundnut oil, and is used in soap, as a lubricant on the skin, to moisturize, and in massages.

Argon (E938)
FOOD ADDITIVE: GAS
Regulations: EC permitted for all foodstuffs following the *quantum satis* principle. Directive 95/2/EC.
What It Is: An inert gas obtained commercially from the

distillation of liquid air, used as an inert atmosphere for food preservation.

Arsenic

⚠

FOOD ADDITIVE: CONTAMINANT

Acceptable Daily Intake: Provisional tolerable weekly intake: 0.015.

What It Is: Arsenic has been a professional poison of choice since ancient times. In the human body it accumulates in the nails and the hair, where it can be detected even in the bodies of persons long dead. There is some evidence that in very small amounts arsenic may be an essential trace nutrient, possibly with anticancer properties similar to selenium (see pp. 380ff), although paradoxically, exposure to arsenic is also known to be carcinogenic (see below).[103] Sources of human exposure may include glazes used on ceramic material, colour pigments in paints and the use of calcium supplements made from bone meal, dolomite or oyster shell. Consumption of shellfish (crustaceans) can also markedly increased arsenic levels.[104]

What You Need To Know: The International Agency for Research on Cancer has concluded that arsenic and arsenic compounds are carcinogenic to humans. This evaluation applies to the group of compounds as a whole and not necessarily to all individual compounds within the group.[105]

Classified as a human carcinogen by the US Environmental Protection Agency. Based on sufficient evidence from human data since an increased lung cancer mortality was observed in multiple human populations, exposed primarily through inhalation. In addition, increased mortality from multiple internal organ cancers (liver, kidney, lung, and bladder) and an increased incidence of skin cancer were observed in populations consuming drinking water high in inorganic arsenic.[106]

The US National Institute of Occupational Safety and Health recommends that arsenic be treated as a potential human carcinogen.[107]

Asbestos

FOOD ADDITIVE: CONTAMINANT

Acceptable Daily Intake: No tolerable intake established.

What It Is: Usually excavated from open-pit mines, asbestos rock contains fibres which can be spun into many products which utilize its unique stability, strength, and heat resistance.

What You Need To Know: The International Agency for Research on Cancer has concluded that this substance is carcinogenic to humans. There was sufficient evidence of carcinogenicity in humans, and sufficient evidence of carcinogenicity in animals.[108]

Classified as a human carcinogen by the US Environmental Protection Agency. Observation of increased mortality and incidence of cancer in occupationally exposed workers are consistent across investigators and study populations. Animal evidence for carcinogenicity via ingestion (i.e. eating) is limited, and epidemiologic data in this regard are inadequate.[109]

All types of asbestos can cause lung cancer. However, some evidence suggests that there may be differences in the potential of different asbestos types to produce disease. It has been suggested that crocidolite has the greatest potential to produce disease; chrysotile, the smallest; with amosite occupying an intermediate position.[110] There is no evidence that inhaled or ingested asbestos is completely cleared from the body. It is likely that some asbestos in the body is retained for long periods, if not for life.[111]

Potential sources of asbestos exposure in the home are: dust from mines and industry; roofing; vinyl-asbestos flooring; boiler pipe insulation; electric irons; stoves; paint; ironing-board covers; toasters and hairdryers.[112]

Ascorbic acid (E300)

FOOD ADDITIVE: ANTIOXIDANT

Regulations: EC permitted for all foodstuffs following the *quantum satis* principle (except those specified in Table 2 on

pp. 15–16 and in Appendix B on pp. 469ff). Directive 95/2/EC.
Acceptable Daily Intake: Not specified.

What It Is: Although ascorbic acid (vitamin C) can be extracted from acerola cherries, rose hips and other rich plant sources, the ascorbic acid used in today's food industry (and in vitamin supplements) is mostly chemically synthesized using glucose as a starting point. Technically, the aim is to twist the C-chain of a glucose molecule in such a way that the C-1 atom of glucose becomes the C-6 atom of ascorbic acid, and the C-6 atom of glucose becomes the C-1 atom of ascorbic acid. Ascorbic acid thus produced is chemically identical to that found in nature.

What You Need To Know: Vitamin C, or ascorbic acid, is perhaps one of the most important vitamins known to science. Long derided as only relevant to the prevention of scurvy, there is now increasing evidence that a first-class intake of vitamin C can help to prevent a wide range of human diseases. Humans are one of the few species unable to synthesize vitamin C internally, and therefore we need to be certain of a regular dietary intake. In evolutionary terms, our bodies are used to consuming far more vitamin C than we obtain from today's diet. Our close cousin the gorilla, for example, requires four to five grams of vitamin C a day (i.e. 4000 to 5000 mg). This is nearly one hundred times greater than many officially recommended intakes.

At this higher level of intake, the evidence shows that there are generally few adverse effects. Since ascorbic acid is soluble in water, excess amounts will simply pass into your urine and be excreted. Rarely, adverse reactions have been reported, including nausea, vomiting, heartburn, abdominal cramps, diarrhoea, fatigue, flushing, headache, insomnia, or sleepiness. These can all be corrected, if they occur, simply by reducing the dose.

Pregnant women are a special case. Newly born babies have sometimes been found to suffer from scurvy if their mothers have taken very large doses of vitamin C while pregnant.[113] The reason for this is simply that the infant in the womb becomes accustomed to receiving high doses of vitamin C, which are suddenly discontinued following the baby's birth. A 'discontinuation' effect then ensues, until the baby adjusts to its new, lower intake of vitamin C. In adults, the same effect can also occur if someone who is taking large doses of vitamin C suddenly stops.

It has been suggested that another possible side-effect of large doses of vitamin C may be hyperoxaluria (high levels of oxalate in the urine), leading to stones being formed in the urinary tract. Some people have a genetic tendency to develop high levels of oxalic acid in their bodies, and such people are usually advised to avoid eating food which has a high oxalate content (spinach and rhubarb are the two most common examples), and should probably also limit their intake of vitamin C. But the vast majority of people do not suffer from this genetic disorder.

It has been argued that the correct dose of vitamin C needed to control a viral infection such as the common cold is that which just falls short of causing a loose, watery bowel movement.[114] The way to establish this is to increase the vitamin C dose until it acts as a laxative, then reduce it so that the stools firm up again.

Although vitamin C is one of the best-known and safest of the food antioxidants, it is still necessary for manufacturers to understand that it must be used appropriately. For example, it should never be used in foods in which copper is present since this results in the accumulation of hydrogen peroxide, a highly reactive substance which destroys many valuable nutrients in food. The combination of copper and vitamin C in fatty foods may also initiate rancidity.[115]

Aspartame (E951)

FOOD ADDITIVE: SWEETENER

Regulations: EC permitted for the following foods up to the total maximum usable dose specified.

- Water-based flavoured drinks; energy-reduced or with no added sugar, maximum usable dose: 600 mg/l
- Milk- and milk-derivative-based or fruit-juice-based drinks, energy-reduced or with no added sugar, maximum usable dose: 600 mg/l
- Water-based flavoured desserts, energy-reduced or with no added sugar, maximum usable dose: 1 000 mg/kg; Milk- and milk-derivate-based preparations, energy-reduced or with no added sugar, maximum usable dose: 1 000 mg/kg; Fruit- and vegetable-based desserts, energy-reduced or with no added sugar, maximum usable dose: 1 000 mg/kg; Egg-based desserts, energy-reduced or with no added sugar, maximum usable dose: 1 000 mg/kg; Cereal-based desserts, energy-reduced or with no added sugar, maximum usable dose: 1 000 mg/kg; Fat-based desserts, energy-reduced or with no added sugar, maximum usable dose: 1 000 mg/kg
- Snacks: certain flavours of ready to eat, prepacked, dry, savoury starch products and coated nuts, maximum usable dose: 500 mg/kg
- Confectionery with no added sugar, maximum usable dose: 1 000 mg/kg; Cocoa- or dried-fruit-based confectionery, energy-reduced or with no added sugar, maximum usable dose: 2 000 mg/kg; Starch-based confectionery, energy-reduced or with no added sugar, maximum usable dose: 2 000 mg/kg; Cocoa-, milk-, dried-fruit- or fat-based sandwich spreads, energy-reduced or with no added sugar, maximum usable dose: 1 000 mg/kg; Chewing gum with no added sugar, maximum usable dose: 5 500 mg/kg
- Cider and perry, maximum usable dose: 600 mg/l
- Alcohol-free or with an alcohol content not exceeding 1,2% vol, maximum usable dose: 600 mg/l
- 'Biere de table/Tafelbier/Table beer' (original wort content less than 6 %) except for 'Obergariges Einfachbier', maximum usable dose: 600 mg/l
- Beers with a minimum acidity of 30 milli-equivalents expressed as NaOH, maximum usable dose: 600 mg/l
- Brown beers of the 'oud bruin' type, maximum usable dose: 600 mg/l

- Edible ices, energy-reduced or with no added sugar, maximum usable dose: 800 mg/kg
- Canned or bottled fruit, energy-reduced or with no added sugar, maximum usable dose: 1 000 mg/kg
- Energy-reduced jams, jellies and marmalades, maximum usable dose: 1 000 mg/kg
- Energy-reduced fruit and vegetable preparations, maximum usable dose: 1 000 mg/kg
- Sweet-sour preserves of fruit and vegetables, maximum usable dose: 300 mg/kg
- Sweet-sour preserves and semi-preserves of fish and marinades of fish, crustaceans and molluscs, maximum usable dose: 300 mg/kg
- Sauces, maximum usable dose: 350 mg/kg
- Mustard, maximum usable dose: 350 mg/kg
- Fine bakery products for special nutritional uses, maximum usable dose: 1 700 mg/kg
- Complete formulae for weight control intended to replace total daily food intake or an individual meal, maximum usable dose: 800 mg/kg
- Complete formulae and nutritional supplements for use under medical supervision, maximum usable dose: 1 000 mg/kg
- Liquid food supplements/dietary integrators, maximum usable dose: 600 mg/kg
- Solid food supplements/dietary integrators, maximum usable dose: 2 000 mg/kg
- Vitamins and dietary preparations, maximum usable dose: 5 500 mg/kg
- EC permitted for Chewing gum with added sugars, maximum level: 2 500 mg/kg. Directive 94/35/EC.

Acceptable Daily Intake: 0 – 40.

What It Is: A sweetening agent which is about 200 times as sweet as table sugar, aspartame is synthesized from aspartic acid and phenylalanine.

What You Need To Know: There is some concern that the amino acid phenylalanine, released during the course of normal metabolism of aspartame, may affect persons with phenylketonuria (PKU). About 1 in 10,000 humans suffers from this genetically induced metabolic defect. As a result, they cannot metabolize phenylalanine and must restrict their intake of this amino acid.[116] Two hundred and thirty-one consumer complaints associated with the food additive aspartame were analysed. No clear symptom complex that suggests a widespread public health hazard associated with aspartame use was found; however, some case reports in which the symptoms may be attributable to aspartame in commonly consumed amounts were identified.[117]

The consumption of aspartame, primarily in beverages, causes significant elevations in plasma and, probably, brain phenylalanine levels. Anecdotal reports suggest that some people suffer neurologic or behaviourial reactions in association with aspartame consumption. It has been suggested that the regulations concerning the sale of food additives should be modified to require the reporting of adverse reactions.[118]

Recent published and unpublished reports of headaches, seizures, blindness, and cognitive and behavioural changes with long-term, high-dose aspartame may be cause for concern. It is important for doctors to be aware of the present clinical and research status of aspartame.[119]

Aspirin
MEDICINAL SUBSTANCE: ANALGESIC
What It Is: Aspirin is the world's most enduringly popular 'pill-for-all-ills'. It was first synthesized in the laboratory in 1899, although the active principle of *salix alba* – the willow tree – had been chemically identified 50 years earlier, and willow bark itself has had a medicinal use in many cultures since ancient times. Sometimes called acetylsalicylic acid, aspirin is one of the group of substances known as salicylates (see salicylic acid pp. 379–80).
What You Need To Know: Aspirin is useful in relieving mild to moderate pain; in reducing fever; and helping to reduce inflammation of joints caused by arthritis. It is not so effective in relieving deeper pain coming from internal organs, but it is

generally better than paracetamol in treating pain which arises from inflammation. There is also some evidence that people with unstable angina may benefit from a daily dose of about 0.3g aspirin, since it may reduce their risk of suffering a first or further heart attack. For occasional use, the usual dose of aspirin is 0.3g to 1g repeated every four hours, up to a maximum of 4g daily. Higher doses may be prescribed on medical advice for the relief of arthritic pain.

One of the adverse effects of aspirin on the human body is its ability to irritate the lining of the stomach, sometimes producing nausea and bleeding, and it may therefore be best to take it with meals and with plenty of liquid. Hangover 'cures' featuring aspirin and designed to be taken when the stomach is upset are therefore of questionable value. Drugs such as caffeine and alcohol may also irritate the stomach, and for this reason it may not be a good idea to combine them with aspirin. Aspirin can also make it more difficult for the blood to clot. There seem to be two broad types of allergic reactions to aspirin. One involves asthma, runny nose, wheeziness and shortness of breath, and this type of reaction is often found in people who are also allergic to the food colouring tartrazine. The other reaction is characterized by itching, rashes and weals on the skin. If you get any of these or the following symptoms, stop using the drug and consult your doctor: ringing in the ears, bloody or black motions, mental confusion, and headache. You should also be aware that aspirin and other salicylates are often found in combination in many other OTC products – always read the label, and guard against accidentally dosing yourself with two or more salicylate-containing products at the same time. If you have pain that continues for more than a few days, you should not continue to treat yourself, but should get your symptoms checked by a professional.

Do not take aspirin if you suspect you may be allergic to it or to any other salicylate, and seek medical advice before taking it if you suffer from any of the following:

- Anaemia
- Asthma
- History of allergies
- Nasal polyps
- Gout
- Haemophilia
- Hodgkin's disease
- Kidney disease
- Liver disease
- Heart disease
- Ulcers or other stomach problems
- Cerebral haemorrhage

It has been determined by the Committee on Safety of Medicines that aspirin should not be given to children under 12 years of age, since it may be a contributory factor in the development of Reyes syndrome, which is an abnormal reaction to a viral infection (such as chickenpox or influenza) that damages both the brain and the liver.

Atropine
MEDICINAL SUBSTANCE: ANTISPASMODIC; ANTISECRECTORY

What It Is: Categorized as an antimuscarinic drug. It acts on both the central and peripheral nervous system. As an anti-diarrhoea agent, its effect is to reduce the movements of the intestines, slowing down the rate at which material is processed and expelled. It has a drying-up action on saliva, mucous and gastric fluids and reduces perspiration.

What You Need To Know: Reactions to it are common, and may include: skin rashes, conjunctivitis, dry mouth and difficulty in swallowing, dilation of the pupils, palpitations, and wanting to pass water but being unable to do so. See the general note about antimuscarinic drugs under the entry for homatropine methylbromide (pp. 256–7).

Azorubine, carmoisine (E122)

FOOD ADDITIVE: FOOD COLOUR

Regulations: EC permitted to be used singly or in combination with other colours in the following foods up to the total maximum level specified. For non-alcoholic flavoured drinks, edible ices, desserts, fine bakery wares and confectionery, a combination of food colours may be used up to the maximum limit indicated below, but the amount of azorubine may not exceed 50 mg/kg or mg/l.

- Non-alcoholic flavoured drinks, maximum level: 100 mg/l
- Candied fruits and vegetables, Mostarda di frutta, maximum level: 200 mg/kg
- Preserves of red fruits, maximum level: 200 mg/kg
- Confectionery, maximum level: 300 mg/kg
- Decorations and coatings, maximum level: 500 mg/kg
- Fine bakery wares (e.g. viennoiserie, biscuits, cakes and wafers), maximum level: 200 mg/kg
- Edible ices, maximum level: 150 mg/kg
- Flavoured processed cheese, maximum level: 100 mg/kg
- Desserts including flavoured milk products, maximum level: 150 mg/kg
- Sauces, seasonings (for example, curry powder, tandoori), pickles, relishes, chutney and piccalilli, maximum level: 500 mg/kg
- Mustard, maximum level: 300 mg/kg
- Fish paste and crustacean paste, maximum level: 100 mg/kg; Precooked crustaceans, maximum level: 250 mg/kg; Salmon substitutes, maximum level: 500 mg/kg; Surimi, maximum level: 500 mg/kg; Fish roe, maximum level: 300 mg/kg; Smoked fish, maximum level: 100 mg/kg;
- Snacks: dry, savoury potato, cereal or starch-based snack products: Extruded or expanded savoury snack products maximum level: 200 mg/kg; Other savoury snack products and savoury coated nuts, maximum level: 100 mg/kg
- Edible cheese rind and edible casings, maximum level: *quantum satis*
- Complete formulae for weight control intended to replace total daily food intake or an individual meal, maximum level: 50 mg/kg

- Complete formulae and nutritional supplements for use under medical supervision, maximum level: 50 mg/kg
- Liquid food supplements/dietary integrators, maximum level: 100 mg/l
- Solid food supplements/dietary integrators, maximum level: 300 mg/kg
- Soups, maximum level: 50 mg/kg
- Meat and fish analogues based on vegetable proteins, maximum level: 100 mg/kg
- Spirituous beverages (including products less than 15 % alcohol by volume), except those mentioned in Annex II or III, maximum level: 200 mg/l
- Aromatized wines, aromatized wine-based drinks and aromatized wine-product cocktails as mentioned in Regulation (EEC) No 1601/91, except those mentioned in Annex II or III, maximum level: 200 mg/l
- Fruit wines (still or sparkling) cider (except cidre bouche) and perry, aromatized fruit wines, cider and perry, maximum level: 200 mg/l. Directive 94/36/EC.

Acceptable Daily Intake: 0 – 4.

What It Is: A synthetic bluish-red monoazo dye.

What You Need To Know: The Joint FAO/WHO Expert Committee on Food Additives reviewed this substance in 1983 and concluded, on the basis of animal experiments, that azorubine is not carcinogenic. Of the four long-term studies which examined azorubine's carcinogenic potential (two on rats, two on mice) all came to the opinion that the incidence of tumours in animals exposed to azorubine was not 'significantly different' to the incidence of tumours in animals not exposed (i.e. tumours developed in both treated and untreated animals). In one study, female rats given azorubine developed endometrial stromal polyps of the uterus three times more frequently than rats not exposed to azorubine: this too was believed to be not significant, on the grounds that female rats are historically prone to develop polyps at this frequency.[120]

People who suffer from asthma, rhinitis or urticaria may find their symptoms become worse following consumption of foods or beverages containing azo dyes. Such people may be mistakenly thought to be suffering from specific food allergies.[121]

Bearberry

MEDICINAL SUBSTANCE: ASTRINGENT; ANTIMICROBIAL; DIURETIC

What It Is: The leaves of this shrub, also called Uva-Ursi, have astringent, antiseptic and diuretic action.

Beeswax, white and yellow (E901)

FOOD ADDITIVE: OTHER ADDITIVE; CARRIER

Regulations: EC permitted for the following foods:
  As glazing agents only for:
- Confectionery (including chocolate)
- Small products of fine bakery wares coated with chocolate
- Snacks
- Nuts
- Coffee beans
  Maximum level: *quantum satis*
- Dietary food supplements, maximum level: *quantum satis*
- Fresh citrus fruits, melons, apples and pears (surface treatment only), maximum level: *quantum satis*
- EC permitted as carrier. Restricted use: colours. Directive 95/2/EC.

Acceptable Daily Intake: Acceptable

What It Is: Refined wax from honeycombs.

What You Need To Know: Scientific studies do not raise carcinogenic concerns.

Beetroot red, betanin(e) (E162)

FOOD ADDITIVE: FOOD COLOUR

Regulations: EC permitted at *quantum satis* in all foods except those to which the EC only permits certain colours to be added (Appendix C, pp. 476ff) and those to which the EC forbids the adding of colours (Appendix D, pp. 482ff). Directive 94/36/EC.

Acceptable Daily Intake: Not specified.

What It Is: Obtained from the red beetroot, the principal component of which is betanine.

What You Need To Know: Scientific studies do not raise carcinogenic concerns. It should be noted that nitrate (see sodium nitrate, potassium nitrite) is a component of beet red, and the nitrate intake of infants and young children must be minimized.

Belladonna
MEDICINAL SUBSTANCE: ANTISPASMODIC; ANTISECRECTORY

What It Is: Categorized as an antimuscarinic drug, it comes from the Deadly Nightshade plant, and contains hyoscyamine and various other alkaloids, from which atropine (see p. 144) can be produced. Belladonna alkaloids may be found in some antacids, for the purpose of reducing the amount of secretions produced by the stomach.

What You Need To Know: Side-effects may include dry mouth, blurring of vision, urinary retention, constipation, and an increase in heart rate. See the general note about anti-muscarinic drugs under the entry for homatropine methylbromide (pp. 256–7).

Bentonite (E558)
FOOD ADDITIVE: CARRIER; ANTICAKING AGENT

Regulations: EC permitted as carrier. Restricted use: colours, max. 5 per cent. Directive 95/2/EC.

Acceptable Daily Intake: No acceptable daily intake allocated.

What It Is: Bentonite is mainly made up of the mineral smectite, formed by volcanic ash. Used as drilling mud in the oil industry; as a decolourizer for fats and oils; also in sugar purification and brewing. Bentonites have the unique capability of swelling when they become wet.

What You Need To Know: Biologically inert when ingested, the main health hazard posed by bentonite is to workers in processing plants, who may suffer a very high incidence of bronchial asthma, caused by the irritant action of bentonite dust on the lining of the lungs.[122] [123]

Benzalkonium chloride

MEDICINAL SUBSTANCE: ANTIMICROBIAL

What It Is: A quaternary ammonium compound, used as a wound cleanser on small or superficial wounds. It is inactivated by anionic compounds such as soap – before applying quaternary ammonium compounds to the skin for disinfection, all traces of soap should be removed.[124]

What You Need To Know: After repetitive use it sometimes may cause dermatitis.[125]

Benzo(a)pyrene

FOOD ADDITIVE: CONTAMINANT

Acceptable Daily Intake: Provisional tolerable weekly intake not established.

What It Is: A polycyclic aromatic hydrocarbon, produced by the incomplete combustion of organic material containing hydrogen and carbon – vehicle exhausts, cigarette smoke, industrial pollution. Food may become contaminated with benzo[a]pyrene by exposure, or by smoking, curing or charcoal broiling.

What You Need To Know: A well-documented carcinogen, producing local tumours after skin application, inhalation or oral administration.

Your exposure can be reduced by:

- cleaning fruit and vegetables thoroughly to remove any surface contamination
- trimming excess fat from meat prior to barbecuing to minimize 'flare ups'
- preventing food from coming into direct contact with flames.[126]

The International Agency for Research on Cancer has

concluded that this substance is probably carcinogenic to humans.[127]

Classified as a probable human carcinogen by the US Environmental Protection Agency. Human data specifically linking benzo(a)pyrene to a carcinogenic effect are lacking. There are, however, multiple animal studies in many species demonstrating it to be carcinogenic following administration by numerous routes.[128]

Research suggests that vegetables (especially those containing beta-carotene) and some fruits may exert a protective, antimutagenic effect against benzo(a)pyrene.[129]

Benzocaine
MEDICINAL SUBSTANCE: LOCAL ANAESTHETIC

What It Is: Benzocaine is used as a local anaesthetic, and may be found, for example, in products sold to reduce skin irritation, and to relieve the pain of mouth ulcers.

What You Need To Know: Local anaesthetics often have some capacity for producing allergic reactions – one report found that the benzocaine and amethocaine present in lozenges and throat sprays could produce a sensitizing reaction, and a person thus sensitized could react again whenever a local anaesthetic was administered.[130] There are also isolated examples of unfortunate people reacting very violently to benzocaine (sometimes with fatal results, as in the case of one person who died after sucking a throat lozenge containing 10 mg of benzocaine). However, when the United States Food and Drug Administration convened a panel to review the available evidence, they found that even in 'high-risk' population groups (e.g. those people who already suffered from allergic dermatitis) there were few allergic reactions to benzocaine, and they concluded that the incidence of benzocaine sensitivity is quite low. Benzocaine is relatively insoluble in water, and so is not easily absorbed from damaged skin into the system. This means that there is less risk of it passing into the bloodstream and provoking a toxic reaction than more water-soluble substances.

In some countries, benzocaine is sold as an appetite suppressant. The idea, presumably, is that the anaesthetic effect of benzocaine numbs the taste-buds on your tongue, and thus decreases your appetite. Unfortunately, the drive to eat comes not from your taste-buds, but from part of the brain called the hypothalamus, and the idea of swallowing significant amounts of a local anaesthetic (especially over a prolonged period) in order to quell your urge to eat is scientifically incorrect, not to say deranged.

Benzoic acid (E210)
FOOD ADDITIVE: PRESERVATIVE

MEDICINAL SUBSTANCE: ANTIMICROBIAL

Regulations: EC permitted to be used singly or in combination with E211, E212 and E213 only in the following foods up to the combined maximum level specified.
- Non-alcoholic flavoured drinks not including dairy-based drinks, maximum level: 150 mg/l
- Sod . . . Saft or Sodet . . . Saft, maximum level: 200 mg/l
- Alcohol-free beer in keg, maximum level: 200 mg/l
- Spirits with less than 15 % alcohol by volume, maximum level: 200 mg/l
- Low-sugar jams, jellies, marmalades and similar low calorie or sugar-free products and other fruit-based spreads, maximum level: 500 mg/kg
- Frugtgrod and Rote Grutze, maximum level: 500 mg/kg
- Aspic, maximum level: 500 mg/kg

When used singly or combined with E202 or E203, and further combined with E214, E215, E216, E217, E218 or E219 may be used in the following foods up to the combined maximum level specified.
- Jelly coatings of meat products (cooked, cured or dried); pâté, maximum level: 1 000 mg/kg
- Cereal- or potato-based snacks and coated nuts, maximum level:

1 000 mg/kg (of which a maximum of 300 mg/kg from E214, E215, E216, E217, E218 or E219)

When used singly or combined with E211, E212 or E213, and further combined with E200, E202 or E203, may be used in the following foods up to the combined maximum level specified.
- Non-alcoholic flavoured drinks not including dairy-based drinks, maximum level: 250 mg/l from E200, E202 or E203 combined plus 150 mg/l from E210, E211, E212 or E213 combined
- Liquid tea concentrates and liquid fruit and herbal infusion concentrates, maximum level: 600 mg/l
- Grape juice, unfermented, for sacramental use, maximum level: 2 000 mg/l
- Spirits with less than 15 % alcohol by volume, maximum level: 400 mg/l
- Low-sugar jams, jellies, marmalades and similar low calorie or sugar-free products and other fruit-based spreads, maximum level: 1 000 mg/kg
- Candied, crystallized and glacé fruit and vegetables, maximum level: 1 000 mg/kg
- Vegetables in vinegar, brine or oil (excluding olives), maximum level: 2 000 mg/kg
- Semi-preserved fish products including fish roe products, maximum level: 2 000 mg/kg; Salted, dried fish, maximum level: 200 mg/kg; Shrimps, cooked, maximum level: 2 000 mg/kg
- *Crangon crangon* and *Crangon vulgaris*, cooked maximum level: 6 000 mg/kg
- Non-heat-treated dairy-based desserts, maximum level: 300 mg/kg
- Liquid egg (white, yolk or whole egg), maximum level: 5 000 mg/kg
- Chewing gum, maximum level: 1 500 mg/kg
- Non-emulsified sauces, maximum level: 1 000 mg/kg
- Prepared salads, maximum level: 1 500 mg/kg
- Mustard, maximum level: 1 000 mg/kg
- Seasonings and condiments, maximum level: 1 000 mg/kg
- Liquid soups and broths (excluding canned), maximum level: 500 mg/l
- Dietetic foods intended for special medical purposes excluding foods for infants and young children as referred to in Directive 89/398/EEC (1) – dietetic formulae for weight control intended to

replace total daily food intake or an individual meal, maximum level: 1 500 mg/kg

When used singly or combined with E211, E121 or E213, further combined with E210, E202 or E203, and further combined with E214, E215, E216, E217, E218 or E219, may be used in the following foods up to the combined maximum level specified.
- Surface treatment of dried meat products, maximum level: *quantum satis*
- Confectionery (excluding chocolate), maximum level: 1 500 mg/kg (of which a maximum of 300 mg/kg from E214, E215, E216, E217, E218 or E219)
- Liquid dietary food supplements, maximum level: 2 000 mg/kg. Directive 95/2/EC.

Acceptable Daily Intake: 0 – 5.

What It Is: Naturally occurring in certain foods, including cranberries, prunes, cinnamon and cloves, benzoic acid is today produced synthetically, often by oxidizing toluene. Benzoic acid is most effective as a yeast, mould and bacterial inhibiter in food that is acidic. Sodium benzoate is the most commonly used form, because it is more soluble than the acid (which it yields) in water. There is no clear-cut consensus as to how, precisely, its preservative action functions in food. Medicinally, compound benzoic acid ointment is considered to be quite effective in the treatment of ringworm.

What You Need To Know: Rapidly absorbed and rapidly and completely excreted into the urine (within 10 – 14 hours). Can temporarily inhibit function of digestive enzymes, may deplete levels of the amino acid glycine. People who suffer from asthma, rhinitis or urticaria may find their symptoms get worse after consuming food or drink containing benzoates.[131]

The US Environmental Protection Agency was unable to classify this substance as to human carcinogenicity, there being no human data and inadequate data from animal bioassays.[132]

Benzoin gum

MEDICINAL SUBSTANCE: ANTIMICROBIAL, INHALANT, EXPECTORANT

What It Is: An aromatic resin obtained by extraction of natural benzoin obtained from various species of the tree, *Styrax*, produced in Thailand, Cambodia, South Vietnam, Sumatra and Java. Contains benzoic and cinnamic acids. Used as a protective application for irritations of skin. When mixed with glycerin and water, it may be applied locally for cutaneous ulcers, bedsores, cracked nipples, fissures of the lips and anus, also as an inhalant and as an expectorant in cough medicines.

Benzoyl peroxide

MEDICINAL SUBSTANCE: KERATOLYTIC

What It Is: Made by reacting benzoyl chloride and sodium peroxide. Main use as a source of free radicals in the plastics and rubber industry. Lesser amounts are used in non-prescription drugs.

What You Need To Know: Found in products sold to treat acne, where it acts to loosen and remove the outer layer of skin, and kills some of the underlying bacteria. It has a reputation for being a generally safe and effective treatment, and is available in a variety of different concentrations. In order to try and minimize any reaction to it, you should use it in the least concentrated form (e.g. 2.5 per cent) that seems to be effective. It causes a stinging or burning sensation for a brief time after application; with continuous use these effects mostly disappear. After 1 or 2 weeks of use there may be a sudden excess of dryness of the skin and peeling.[133] Not to be used in cases of acne rosacea, nor on very raw skin. Keep away from the eyes, lips, hair and coloured fabric. Stop using it if your skin becomes excessively dry, itchy or peeling, and seek medical advice.

Benzoyl peroxide can cause contact dermatitis. Contact

hypersensitivity has been observed in 1 per cent to 3 per cent of patients under conditions of recommended use. In one study in volunteers, a reaction occurred in 70 per cent of subjects after use of occlusive patches (bandages) containing a 5 per cent or 10 per cent concentration.[134]

The International Agency for Research on Cancer has concluded that this substance is unclassifiable as to carcinogenicity in humans. There was inadequate evidence of carcinogenicity in humans, and inadequate evidence of carcinogenicity in animals.[135]

A case-control study utilizing available medical records was carried out to investigate possible links between use of topical benzoyl peroxide for acne, and malignant melanoma. One hundred and fifty nine cases and 213 matched controls were used in the analysis which shows no significant association between the use of benzoyl peroxide and the occurrence of malignant melanoma, nor between the occurrence of acne and malignant melanoma.[136]

The carcinogenic promoting effects of benzoyl peroxide have been studied on animals. The authors of one study conclude that benzoyl peroxide is capable of promoting the formation of dermally located melanotic tumours in hamsters, and should therefore be used with caution in the long-term treatment of human skin diseases.[137]

Benzydamine hydrochloride
MEDICINAL SUBSTANCE: ANALGESIC

What It Is: Benzydamine is a topical analgesic used, as a cream, for the treatment of sprains and muscle injuries and as a mouthwash for the alleviation of throat and mouth soreness. One report concluded that its value in the treatment of soft-tissue injuries is uncertain, but it may offer temporary relief of mouth and throat symptoms.

Benzyl nicotinate

MEDICINAL SUBSTANCE: COUNTER-IRRITANT

What It Is: Benzyl nicotinate is a counter-irritant which stimulates the blood flow of the skin at the site of application, thus producing redness and an increase in skin temperature – a chemical version of the hot water-bottle. Counter-irritants are substances which, when applied to the skin, stimulate it, resulting in reduced perception of deeper-seated pain. Thus pain relief is effected by stimulating, rather than depressing, the sensory receptors – precisely the opposite effect that an anaesthetic substance would have, and rather like rubbing the site of an injury. This type of pain relief seems to have most value for the temporary relief of minor aches and pains of muscles and joints.

Beta-apo-8'-carotenal (C 30) (apocarotenal) (E160e)

FOOD ADDITIVE: FOOD COLOUR

Regulations: EC permitted to be used singly or in combination with other colours in the following foods up to the total maximum level specified.

- Non-alcoholic flavoured drinks, maximum level: 100 mg/l
- Candied fruits and vegetables, Mostarda di frutta, maximum level: 200 mg/kg
- Preserves of red fruits, maximum level: 200 mg/kg
- Confectionery, maximum level: 300 mg/kg
- Decorations and coatings, maximum level: 500 mg/kg
- Fine bakery wares (e.g. viennoiserie, biscuits, cakes and wafers), maximum level: 200 mg/kg
- Edible ices, maximum level: 150 mg/kg
- Flavoured processed cheese, maximum level: 100 mg/kg
- Desserts including flavoured milk products, maximum level: 150 mg/kg
- Sauces, seasonings (for example, curry powder, tandoori), pickles, relishes, chutney and piccalilli, maximum level: 500 mg/kg
- Mustard, maximum level: 300 mg/kg

- Fish paste and crustacean paste, maximum level: 100 mg/kg; Pre-cooked crustaceans, maximum level: 250 mg/kg; Salmon substitutes, maximum level: 500 mg/kg; Surimi, maximum level: 500 mg/kg; Fish roe, maximum level: 300 mg/kg; Smoked fish, maximum level: 100 mg/kg
- Snacks: dry, savoury potato, cereal or starch-based snack products: Extruded or expanded savoury snack products, maximum level: 200 mg/kg; Other savoury snack products and savoury coated nuts, maximum level: 100 mg/kg
- Edible cheese rind and edible casings, maximum level: *quantum satis*
- Complete formulae for weight control intended to replace total daily food intake or an individual meal, maximum level: 50 mg/kg
- Complete formulae and nutritional supplements for use under medical supervision, maximum level: 50 mg/kg
- Liquid food supplements/dietary integrators, maximum level: 100 mg/l
- Solid food supplements/dietary integrators, maximum level: 300 mg/kg
- Soups, maximum level: 50 mg/kg
- Meat and fish analogues based on vegetable proteins, maximum level: 100 mg/kg
- Spirituous beverages (including products less than 15 % alcohol by volume), except those mentioned in Annex II or III, maximum level: 200 mg/l
- Aromatized wines, aromatized wine-based drinks and aromatized wine-product cocktails as mentioned in Regulation (EEC) No 1601/91, except those mentioned in Annex II or III, maximum level: 200 mg/l
- Fruit wines (still or sparkling) cider (except cidre bouche) and perry, aromatized fruit wines, cider and perry, maximum level: 200 mg/l. Directive 94/36/EC.

Acceptable Daily Intake: 0 – 5 group acceptable daily intake as sum of the carotenoids.

What It Is: A carotene which occurs naturally in oranges and tangerines, but is normally produced synthetically for food-colouring usage.

Betaine hydrochloride

MEDICINAL SUBSTANCE: ACIDIFIER

What It Is: Used to acidify the contents of the stomach by producing hydrochloric acid when dissolved. Low stomach acid is not a complaint that can be self-diagnosed or self-treated.

Biphenyl (diphenyl) (phenyl benzene) (E230)

FOOD ADDITIVE: PRESERVATIVE

Regulations: EC permitted for surface treatment of citrus fruits. Maximum level: 70 mg/kg. Directive 95/2/EC.

Acceptable Daily Intake: 0 – 0.5.

What It Is: A fungistat used to prevent the growth of mould on grapefruit, lemons and oranges. Made by the thermal dehydrogenation of benzene.[138]

What You Need To Know: Workers impregnating fruit wrappers with diphenyl have displayed cumulative symptoms indicative of central and peripheral nerve damage and liver injury.[139] [140]

The US Environmental Protection Agency was unable to classify this substance as to human carcinogenicity, there being no human data and inadequate data from animal bioassays.[141]

Bisacodyl

MEDICINAL SUBSTANCE: LAXATIVE

What It Is: Bisacodyl produces its laxative effect by irritating the lining of the large bowel, thus producing movement culminating in the passing of a stool. It may also increase stool bulk by fluid absorption. To work, it must reach the intestine, so pills are coated with a substance that resists acid attack by the stomach, but softens when it reaches the different fluids in the intestines. For this reason, the tablets shouldn't be chewed, or taken with an antacid. It may produce abdominal cramps. Like all laxatives, it should not be taken if there is pain in the abdomen, or if there is abdominal obstruction, and prolonged use should be avoided. Avoid getting it into contact with the eyes or mucous membranes.

Bismuth aluminate

MEDICINAL SUBSTANCE: ANTIMICROBIAL; ASTRINGENT; ANTACID

What It Is: Bismuth was an ingredient in some of the older antacids, also used in various forms on the skin and for the treatment of haemorrhoids. Some countries have restricted the use of bismuth salts because of the risk of toxicity, especially when taken in large amounts by people with colostomies or ileostomies. Once widely used to treat syphilis, the availability of more modern remedies mean that many bismuth products have now been superseded.

What You Need To Know: Bismuth and its salts tend to be quite insoluble, and are thus poorly absorbed into the system, but where use is prolonged, or when it is applied in sufficient quantity to open surfaces, poisoning may result. Symptoms may include headache, ulceration, nausea, jaundice, and a distinctive blue line round the gums which may last for years (called the 'bismuth line').

Boric acid (E284)

FOOD ADDITIVE: PRESERVATIVE
MEDICINAL SUBSTANCE: ANTIMICROBIAL

Regulations: EC permitted for sturgeons' eggs (caviar). Maximum level: 4 g/kg expressed as boric acid. Directive 95/2/EC.

Acceptable Daily Intake: No acceptable daily intake allocated.

What It Is: Made by treating sodium tetraborate with hydrochloric or sulphuric acid.

What You Need To Know: Boric acid is poisonous. The lethal dose has been estimated to be 15–20 grams in adults and 5–6 grams in infants. Lesser intakes – such as those absorbed from borate-containing mouthwashes – may give rise to chronic intoxication, whose symptoms include anorexia, asthenia, confusion, menstrual disorders, and alopecia (falling hair).[142]

Borax and boric acid used in powders and ointments have resulted in serious poisonings and death.[143] If used externally it can be absorbed through wounds or grazes. Since it is only slowly excreted from the system, toxic amounts may accumulate in the body through continued use.

Boro-tannic acid complex

MEDICINAL SUBSTANCE: ANTIMICROBIAL; ASTRINGENT

What It Is: Breaks down to form boric and tannic acids, which can both be absorbed through the skin and may produce toxic effects if sufficient is absorbed. Boric acid is a weak antiseptic while tannic acid has astringent properties.

Brilliant Black BN (E151)

FOOD ADDITIVE: FOOD COLOUR

Regulations: EC permitted to be used singly or in combination with other colours in the following foods up to the total maximum level specified.

- Non-alcoholic flavoured drinks, maximum level: 100 mg/l
- Candied fruits and vegetables, Mostarda di frutta, maximum level: 200 mg/kg
- Preserves of red fruits, maximum level: 200 mg/kg
- Confectionery, maximum level: 300 mg/kg
- Decorations and coatings, maximum level: 500 mg/kg
- Fine bakery wares (e.g. viennoiserie, biscuits, cakes and wafers), maximum level: 200 mg/kg
- Edible ices, maximum level: 150 mg/kg
- Flavoured processed cheese, maximum level: 100 mg/kg
- Desserts including flavoured milk products, maximum level: 150 mg/kg
- Sauces, seasonings (for example, curry powder, tandoori), pickles, relishes, chutney and piccalilli, maximum level: 500 mg/kg
- Mustard, maximum level: 300 mg/kg

- Fish paste and crustacean paste, maximum level: 100 mg/kg; Precooked crustaceans, maximum level: 250 mg/kg; Salmon substitutes, maximum level: 500 mg/kg; Surimi, maximum level: 500 mg/kg; Fish roe, maximum level: 300 mg/kg; Smoked fish, maximum level: 100 mg/kg
- Snacks: dry, savoury potato, cereal or starch-based snack products: Extruded or expanded savoury snack products, maximum level: 200 mg/kg; Other savoury snack products and savoury coated nuts, maximum level: 100 mg/kg
- Edible cheese rind and edible casings, maximum level: *quantum satis*
- Complete formulae for weight control intended to replace total daily food intake or an individual meal, maximum level: 50 mg/kg
- Complete formulae and nutritional supplements for use under medical supervision, maximum level: 50 mg/kg
- Liquid food supplements/dietary integrators, maximum level: 100 mg/l
- Solid food supplements/dietary integrators, maximum level: 300 mg/kg
- Soups, maximum level: 50 mg/kg
- Meat and fish analogues based on vegetable proteins, maximum level: 100 mg/kg
- Spirituous beverages (including products less than 15 % alcohol by volume), except those mentioned in Annex II or III, maximum level: 200 mg/l
- Aromatized wines, aromatized wine-based drinks and aromatized wine-product cocktails as mentioned in Regulation (EEC) No 1601/91, except those mentioned in Annex II or III, maximum level: 200 mg/l
- Fruit wines (still or sparkling) cider (except cidre bouche) and perry, aromatized fruit wines, cider and perry, maximum level: 200 mg/l.

Directive 94/36/EC.

Acceptable Daily Intake: 0 – 1.

What It Is: A synthetic, violet diazo dye.

What You Need To Know: An interesting example of how acceptable daily intakes are calculated: piglets were forced to consume Brilliant Black in their feed for 90 days. They were then killed, and dissected. Those piglets who consumed the most Brilliant Black (300 mg/kg per day or more) had developed mucous-containing cysts in the mucosa of the ileum. Since none of the piglets consuming the next-lower dose (100 mg/kg day) had developed cysts, the level causing no toxicological effect was determined to be 100 mg/kg a day. By applying a safety factor of 100 to this number, the acceptable daily intake has been calculated to be of 0 – 1.0 mg/kg bw day.[144] You may wonder whether this highly artificial – and undoubtedly cruel – experiment really tells us anything useful about the long-term effect of this substance on human beings.

People who suffer from asthma, rhinitis or urticaria may find their symptoms become worse following consumption of foods or beverages containing azo dyes. Such people may be mistakenly thought to be suffering from specific food allergies.[145]

Brilliant Blue FCF (E133)

FOOD ADDITIVE: FOOD COLOUR

Regulations: EC permitted to be used singly or in combination with other colours in the following foods up to the total maximum level specified.

- Non-alcoholic flavoured drinks, maximum level: 100 mg/l
- Candied fruits and vegetables, Mostarda di frutta, maximum level: 200 mg/kg
- Preserves of red fruits, maximum level: 200 mg/kg
- Confectionery, maximum level: 300 mg/kg
- Decorations and coatings, maximum level: 500 mg/kg
- Fine bakery wares (e.g. viennoiserie, biscuits, cakes and wafers), maximum level: 200 mg/kg
- Edible ices, maximum level: 150 mg/kg
- Flavoured processed cheese, maximum level: 100 mg/kg
- Desserts including flavoured milk products, maximum level: 150 mg/kg
- Sauces, seasonings (for example, curry powder, tandoori), pickles, relishes, chutney and piccalilli, maximum level: 500 mg/kg

- Mustard, maximum level: 300 mg/kg
- Fish paste and crustacean paste, maximum level: 100 mg/kg; Precooked crustaceans, maximum level: 250 mg/kg; Salmon substitutes, maximum level: 500 mg/kg; Surimi, maximum level: 500 mg/kg; Fish roe, maximum level: 300 mg/kg; Smoked fish, maximum level: 100 mg/kg
- Snacks: dry, savoury potato, cereal or starch-based snack products: Extruded or expanded savoury snack products, maximum level: 200 mg/kg; Other savoury snack products and savoury coated nuts, maximum level: 100 mg/kg
- Edible cheese rind and edible casings, maximum level: *quantum satis*
- Complete formulae for weight control intended to replace total daily food intake or an individual meal, maximum level: 50 mg/kg
- Complete formulae and nutritional supplements for use under medical supervision, maximum level: 50 mg/kg
- Liquid food supplements/dietary integrators, maximum level: 100 mg/l
- Solid food supplements/dietary integrators, maximum level: 300 mg/kg
- Soups, maximum level: 50 mg/kg
- Meat and fish analogues based on vegetable proteins, maximum level: 100 mg/kg
- Spirituous beverages (including products less than 15 % alcohol by volume), except those mentioned in Annex II or III, maximum level: 200 mg/l
- Aromatized wines, aromatized wine-based drinks and aromatized wine-product cocktails as mentioned in Regulation (EEC) No 1601/91, except those mentioned in Annex II or III, maximum level: 200 mg/l
- Fruit wines (still or sparkling) cider (except cidre bouche) and perry, aromatized fruit wines, cider and perry, maximum level: 200 mg/l.
  Directive 94/36/EC.

Acceptable Daily Intake: 0 – 12.5.

What It Is: A synthetic, bright greenish-blue triarylmethane dye.

What You Need To Know: The International Agency for Research on Cancer has concluded that this substance is unclassifiable as to carcinogenicity in humans. There was inadequate data available in humans, and there was limited evidence of carcinogenicity in animals.[146]

Brompheniramine maleate

MEDICINAL SUBSTANCE: ANTIHISTAMINE

What It Is: An antihistamine drug. For some general information about antihistamines, see the special feature (pp. 134–5).

Bronopol

MEDICINAL SUBSTANCE: ANTIMICROBIAL

What It Is: An antibacterial agent often used as a preservative in pharmaceutical products.

Brown FK (E154)

FOOD ADDITIVE: FOOD COLOUR

Regulations: EC permitted for kippers, maximum level: 20 mg/kg. Directive 94/36/EC.

Acceptable Daily Intake: No acceptable daily intake allocated.

What It Is: A synthetic yellowish-brown dye.

What You Need To Know: In long-term experiments on mice, Brown FK has produced liver nodules, myopathy, myocarditis, and substantial pigment deposition in the heart and liver.[147]

Brown HT (Chocolate Brown HT) (E155)

FOOD ADDITIVE: FOOD COLOUR

Regulations: EC permitted to be used singly or in combination with other colours in the following foods up to the total maximum level specified. For non-alcoholic flavoured drinks, edible ices, desserts, fine bakery wares and confectionery, a combination of food colours may be used up to the maximum limit indicated below, but the amount of Brown HT may not exceed 50 mg/kg or mg/l.

- Non-alcoholic flavoured drinks, maximum level: 100 mg/l
- Candied fruits and vegetables, Mostarda di frutta, maximum level: 200 mg/kg
- Preserves of red fruits, maximum level: 200 mg/kg
- Confectionery, maximum level: 300 mg/kg
- Decorations and coatings, maximum level: 500 mg/kg
- Fine bakery wares (e.g. viennoiserie, biscuits, cakes and wafers), maximum level: 200 mg/kg
- Edible ices, maximum level: 150 mg/kg
- Flavoured processed cheese, maximum level: 100 mg/kg
- Desserts including flavoured milk products, maximum level: 150 mg/kg
- Sauces, seasonings (for example, curry powder, tandoori), pickles, relishes, chutney and piccalilli, maximum level: 500 mg/kg
- Mustard, maximum level: 300 mg/kg
- Fish paste and crustacean paste, maximum level: 100 mg/kg; Pre-cooked crustaceans, maximum level: 250 mg/kg; Salmon substitutes, maximum level: 500 mg/kg; Surimi, maximum level: 500 mg/kg; Fish roe, maximum level: 300 mg/kg; Smoked fish, maximum level: 100 mg/kg
- Snacks: dry, savoury potato, cereal or starch-based snack products: Extruded or expanded savoury snack products, maximum level: 200 mg/kg; Other savoury snack products and savoury coated nuts, maximum level: 100 mg/kg
- Edible cheese rind and edible casings, maximum level: *quantum satis*
- Complete formulae for weight control intended to replace total daily food intake or an individual meal, maximum level: 50 mg/kg
- Complete formulae and nutritional supplements for use under medical supervision, maximum level: 50 mg/kg
- Liquid food supplements/dietary integrators, maximum level: 100 mg/l
- Solid food supplements/dietary integrators, maximum level: 300 mg/kg
- Soups, maximum level: 50 mg/kg
- Meat and fish analogues based on vegetable proteins, maximum level: 100 mg/kg

- Spirituous beverages (including products less than 15 % alcohol by volume), except those mentioned in Annex II or III, maximum level: 200 mg/l
- Aromatized wines, aromatized wine-based drinks and aromatized wine-product cocktails as mentioned in Regulation (EEC) No 1601/91, except those mentioned in Annex II or III, maximum level: 200 mg/l
- Fruit wines (still or sparkling) cider (except cidre bouche) and perry, aromatized fruit wines, cider and perry maximum level: 200 mg/l. Directive 94/36/EC.

Acceptable Daily Intake: 0 – 1.5.

What It Is: A synthetic, reddish-brown diazo dye.

What You Need To Know: People who suffer from asthma, rhinitis or urticaria may find their symptoms become worse following consumption of foods or beverages containing azo dyes. Such people may be mistakenly thought to be suffering from specific food allergies.[148]

Buchu

MEDICINAL SUBSTANCE: ANTIMICROBIAL, DIURETIC

What It Is: The leaves of the shrub Barosma produce buchu oil which is used for its antiseptic and diuretic properties.

Buclizine hydrochloride

MEDICINAL SUBSTANCE: ANTIHISTAMINE

What It Is: An antihistamine drug. For some general information about antihistamines, see the special feature (pp. 134–5).

Burnt sugar

MEDICINAL SUBSTANCE: FLAVOURING

What It Is: Also called caramel. Formed by heating sugar until a brown liquid is formed, and used for flavouring and colouring purposes.

Butylated hydroxyanisole (BHA) (E320)

⚠️

FOOD ADDITIVE: ANTIOXIDANT

Regulations: EC permitted to be used similarly to propyl gallate (E310). Directive 95/2/EC.

Acceptable Daily Intake: 0 – 0.5.

What It Is: Perhaps the most extensively used synthetic anti-oxidant in the world, BHA is used mainly to preserve foods which contain animal fats, since it is relatively ineffective in unsaturated vegetable oils. It is highly soluble in fat, and has a high degree of 'carry through' (in other words, once added to a food ingredient, it is capable of surviving cooking or other processing and remaining intact in the finished food product). Used in fat-containing foods, confectionery, essential oils, food-coating materials and waxes.

What You Need To Know: The International Agency for Research on Cancer has concluded that this substance is possibly carcinogenic to humans. No data were available in humans. There was sufficient evidence of carcinogenicity in animals.[149]

In animal experiments, rats fed a diet high in BHA have developed squamous cell carcinoma. At intakes below 50 mg/kg body weight, no adverse effects were observed.[150] Advocates of BHA would argue that the increased incidence of tumours was found in the forestomach of the rat (subsequently in other rodents too) but since humans do not possess forestomachs, the rodent evidence is not relevant to humans. True, but it should be pointed out that while humans do not have forestomachs, they do indeed have types of cell similar to those found in rat forestomachs, for example in the lining of the human oesophagus. It is also true that individual carcino-gens may produce tumours at differing sites in different species. In the real world outside the laboratory, we are constantly exposed to an impossibly intricate mixture of substances, many of which may interact with each other in ways far more complex than are ever recreated in single-substance animal experiments. BHA, for example, has been shown to interact with nitrite (naturally present in many foods) to form chemicals which are known to be highly mutagenic.[151]

The human acceptable daily intake is based on the above 'no adverse effects' level of intake, divided by a 'safety factor' of 100. Although this may sound like a wide safety margin, it should be noted that one of the major problems associated with using antioxidants under commercial conditions has been the failure to achieve complete dispersion.[152] If the antioxidant is not properly dispersed throughout the foodstuff this would of course mean that the consumer could receive a considerably higher dose than that envisioned by the regulatory authorities.

Patch tests indicate that BHA can produce allergic contact dermatitis.[153]

Butylated hydroxytoluene (BHT) (E321)

FOOD ADDITIVE: ANTIOXIDANT

Regulations: EC permitted to be used similarly to propyl gallate (E310). Directive 95/2/EC.

Acceptable Daily Intake: 0 – 0.3 (1996).

What It Is: Made from p-cresol and isobutylene. Like BHA, BHT is a very popular antioxidant, used to retard oxidation in rubber, plastics and jet fuel. Because it is widely used industrially, it makes a cheap food ingredient. Typically, you can find it used where hydrogenated vegetable oils are used for pastries and other baked products, in low-fat products, fish products and packaging materials. Also widely used in fish meals and poultry feed. Often used in combination with BHA, since they together have greater antioxidant powers than either chemical alone (synergy).

What You Need To Know: BHT produces toxicity at a lower intake than any other synthetic antioxidant. A number of studies have shown that at high doses in experimental animals it can cause extensive internal and external haemorrhaging.[154] This may be due to its anti-vitamin K effect.[155]

The International Agency for Research on Cancer has concluded that this substance is unclassifiable as to carcinogenicity in humans. No data were available in humans, and there was limited evidence of carcinogenicity in animals.[156] See the previous comment (BHA) concerning variability of dose received due to inadequate dispersal of the antioxidant in the food product.

Cade oil

MEDICINAL SUBSTANCE: OINTMENT

What It Is: Made from the juniper tree, and sometimes found in products used to treat psoriasis and eczema. Its value may lie in the fact that it contains phenol (see pp. 336–7) derivatives, although it is thought to be less corrosive than phenol.

What You Need To Know: An irritant to the conjunctiva and may cause chemosis of cornea; care should be taken to keep it out of the eyes.

Cadmium

FOOD ADDITIVE: CONTAMINANT

Acceptable Daily Intake: Provisional tolerable weekly intake 0.007.

What It Is: Cadmium does not occur naturally in a free state, and its compounds are almost always found together with zinc compounds, so that the two metals are always mined together. Most cadmium is obtained as a by-product in the preparation of zinc. It contaminates the water supply when the electroplating and PVC industries discharge effluent into the ground water. Landfill sites used to dump industrial waste can also slowly leach out their cadmium into the surrounding ground water. Galvanized metal pipes can also be a significant source of cadmium pollution, particularly in soft water areas.

What You Need To Know: Cadmium and its salts are highly toxic. There is no known dietary requirement for it, and intakes can lead to various health problems, including kidney damage and high blood pressure. Some areas of the UK (for example, Shipham in Somerset) have high levels of cadmium in their soil, which may cause high levels in vegetables grown there. Significant levels of cadmium have also been found in shellfish products from the south coast of England (eating one crab could give you all the provisional tolerable weekly intake above). One study has shown that 1 in 10 Belgians have levels of cadmium in their bodies that adversely affect their kidney function.[157]

Many non-fatal cases of food poisoning have followed ingestion of acid food kept for brief periods in cadmium-coated containers, such as ice cube trays and metal jugs.[158]

Cadmium accumulates in many body tissues and is very slowly eliminated – half-lives of 10–30 years have been reported for muscles, kidneys and liver.[159]

The International Agency for Research on Cancer has concluded that cadmium and cadmium compounds are carcinogenic to humans. There is sufficient evidence in humans for the carcinogenicity of cadmium and cadmium compounds. There is sufficient evidence in experimental animals for the carcinogenicity of cadmium compounds. There is limited evidence in experimental animals for the carcinogenicity of cadmium metal.[160]

The US Environmental Protection Agency has classified this substance as a probable human carcinogen. Limited evidence from occupational epidemiologic studies of cadmium is consistent across investigators and study populations. There is sufficient evidence of carcinogenicity in rats and mice by inhalation and intramuscular and subcutaneous injection. Seven studies in rats and mice wherein cadmium salts (acetate, sulphate, chloride) were administered orally have shown no evidence of carcinogenic response. Human carcinogenicity data: limited.[161]

SECRET INGREDIENTS FACT FILE
HOW TO REDUCE YOUR CADMIUM INTAKE

- Run the tap for a few minutes at the start of the day and never use water from the hot tap for consumption.
- Don't smoke – cigarettes can contain significant amounts of it.
- Cut out tea and coffee – drinking five cups of either per day can double your daily intake of cadmium.
- Ensure your diet contains a good source of zinc, to counter the effects of cadmium toxicity.
- A reverse-osmosis water-treatment system will reduce cadmium levels.

Caffeine

MEDICINAL SUBSTANCE: STIMULANT

What It Is: Unlike most of the other substances in this book, caffeine is taken mainly for pleasure. The effects it produces include stimulation of the cortex of the brain, clearer thinking, greater alertness, and improved physical coordination. Caffeine is the most widely used stimulant drug in the world – present in diuretics, tonics, headache tablets, and a galaxy of other pills and potions, not to mention tea, coffee, cocoa, colas and many other soft drinks. Its physical effects include stimulation of the heart and respiration, dilation of the coronary arteries, increased circulation, constriction of the blood vessels in the brain, a rise in blood pressure and increased output of adrenalin and noradrenalin. Like other members of the group of drugs called the xanthines, it acts on the central nervous system, the kidneys, the muscular wall of the heart and it also has a diuretic (urine-producing) effect. If taken in sufficient quantities, it can be fatal – the short-term lethal dose of caffeine in adults appears to be about 5 to 10 g (start worrying after your 65th cup).[162] At much lower doses, however, it can have unpleasant effects.

What You Need To Know: Excessive consumption may lead to the development of something called caffeinism, a disorder which is characterized by increasing anxiety, coupled with headaches, depression and listlessness. Psychological dependence on the drug often makes withdrawal difficult to achieve. As we get older, tea or coffee drinkers may start to experience insomnia or irregular heartbeats. Unwanted effects may include nervousness, irritability, and restlessness. Some symptoms can even be mistaken for psychological illness.

Because caffeine increases secretions from the stomach, it may be implicated in the development of stomach ulcers, and people who suffer from this complaint should consider reducing their consumption. Caffeine can also reduce the amount of thiamin (vitamin B1) in your body, and it has been linked to the development of osteoporosis. There have also been suggestions that caffeine consumption may be linked to birth defects such as cleft palate, heart abnormalities and missing fingers and toes. People with heart ailments are sometimes advised to reduce their caffeine intake, as should pregnant women since caffeine can cross the placenta (no drug can be proved to be safe beyond all doubts if taken during pregnancy). One recent study followed the health of 2000 men for 20 years, and found that those who drank more than 6 cups of coffee a day were 71 per cent more likely to die of coronary heart disease than those who drank only one cup a day (but the study made no distinction between regular and decaffeinated coffee).[163]

Because caffeine is all around us, it is very easy to accumulate significant doses without ever realizing we're 'hooked'. Caffeine is often found in analgesic preparations where it is claimed it has an adjuvant effect – there is research to show that if an analgesic contains no caffeine, a 40 per cent greater dose of the analgesic is required to produce the same pain-relieving effect. However, evaluation of pain intensity and comparative analgesic effect is necessarily subjective, and may be open to considerable individual variation. While some studies support this 'adjuvant' effect, others do not. One authority states that 'the rationale for fixed combinations of caffeine and analgesics is questionable'.[164] Another authority states that caffeine 'does not contribute to the analgesic or anti-inflammatory effect of the preparation and may possibly aggravate the gastric irritation caused by aspirin. Moreover, in excessive dosage or on withdrawal caffeine may itself induce headache'.[165]

The International Agency for Research on Cancer has concluded that this substance is unclassifiable as to carcinogenicity in humans. There is inadequate evidence for its carcinogenicity in humans. There is inadequate evidence for its carcinogenicity in animals. NB: There is some evidence of an inverse relationship between coffee drinking and cancer of the large bowel; but coffee drinking could not be classified as to its carcinogenicity to other organs.[166]

SECRET INGREDIENTS FACT FILE
KICKING CAFFEINE

If you are a serious coffee-drinker and you want to cut it out (and why ever would you want to do that?) then you're going to find it much harder than you might suppose. Here are some straws to clutch at:

- Read the labels. Caffeine is all around you. For example, caffeine is sometimes found as an adjuvant in over-the-counter analgesics, and many brands of soft drinks include quite a dose. You're going to have to learn to just say no!

- Try replacing caffeine-containing beverages with grain-based beverages such as Barley Cup and Yannoh, herbal teas, or fruit juices.

- We can't see the point in decaffeinated coffee. It's too close to the real thing for you to forget what you're missing, but not similar enough to give you the buzz you crave.

- If you habitually need a strong black coffee to kick you into gear in the mornings, try installing an exercise machine just next to your bed, and use it first thing. It may sound brutal, but a cross-country ski machine warms you up nice and slowly, and after about 10 minutes or so you'll get the same sort of buzz you used to get from the Java. Well, not exactly the same, but pretty close.

- If you visit people where you're routinely offered a tea or coffee, get into the habit of carrying a couple of your favourite herbal tea bags with you. It doesn't matter what they think of you, at least it'll remove the temptation to say 'Yes' to the inevitable offer of coffee.

- If none of this works – and we're not making any promises that it will – at least you can console yourself with the knowledge that coffee drinkers are much less likely to commit suicide than abstainers.[167] And espresso drinkers are simply the nicest people on the entire planet . . .

Cajuput oil

MEDICINAL SUBSTANCE: COUNTER-IRRITANT; STIMULANT

What It Is: This oil is used internally as a stimulant and to kill parasites. It has a warming effect, whether taken internally or applied to the skin, and is often found in products which are applied as counter-irritants.

Calamine

See Zinc oxide.

Calcium 5'-ribonucleotides (E634)

FOOD ADDITIVE: FLAVOUR ENHANCER

Regulations: EC permitted to be used similarly to guanylic acid (E626). Directive 95/2/EC.

Acceptable Daily Intake: Not specified.

What It Is: See the description of flavour enhancers under monosodium glutamate (pp. 317–8).

What You Need To Know: Scientific studies do not raise carcinogenic concerns.[168]

Calcium acetate (E263)

FOOD ADDITIVE: PRESERVATIVE; STABILIZER; ACIDITY REGULATOR; CARRIER

Regulations: EC permitted for all foodstuffs following the *quantum satis* principle (except those specified in Table 2 on pp. 15–16 and in Appendix B on pp. 469ff). EC permitted as carrier. Restricted use: none. Directive 95/2/EC.

Acceptable Daily Intake: Not specified.

What It Is: Calcium salt of acetic acid (see pp. 106–7). Often substituted for acetic acid in certain food uses, e.g. in bread and other baked goods to prevent ropiness and discourage mould growth without killing the active yeast. Also used as an antifoam additive in antifreeze, and in dying, tanning and curing skins.

Calcium alginate (E404)

FOOD ADDITIVE: THICKENING AGENT; STABILIZER

Regulations: EC permitted for all foodstuffs following the *quantum satis* principle (except those specified in Table 2 on pp. 15–16 and in Appendix B on pp. 469ff). Directive 95/2/EC.

Acceptable Daily Intake: Not specified.

What It Is: See Alginic acid and its sodium, potassium, calcium and ammonium salts (see p. 113).

Calcium aluminium silicate (E556)

FOOD ADDITIVE: ANTICAKING AGENT

Regulations: EC permitted to be used similarly to silicon dioxide (E551). Directive 95/2/EC.

Acceptable Daily Intake: Not specified.

Calcium ascorbate (E302)

FOOD ADDITIVE: ANTIOXIDANT

Regulations: EC permitted for all foodstuffs following the *quantum satis* principle (except those specified in Table 2 on pp. 15–16 and in Appendix B on pp. 469ff). Directive 95/2/EC.

Acceptable Daily Intake: Not specified.

What It Is: Calcium salt of ascorbic acid (see pp. 137–9); used similarly.

What You Need To Know: Scientific studies do not raise carcinogenic, mutagenic or reproductive concerns. Since oxalate is the major metabolite of ascorbate, the use of calcium ascorbate in large amounts might increase the likelihood of crystalluria and the formation of calcium oxalate stones.

Calcium benzoate (E213)

FOOD ADDITIVE: PRESERVATIVE

Regulations: EC permitted to be used similarly to benzoic acid (E210). Directive 95/2/EC.

Acceptable Daily Intake: 0 – 5.

What It Is: Calcium salt of benzoic acid (see pp. 151–3)

Calcium carbonate (E170)

FOOD ADDITIVE: FOOD COLOUR; CARRIER; ANTICAKING AGENT;
STABILIZER

MEDICINAL SUBSTANCE: ANTACID

Regulations: EC permitted at *quantum satis* in all foods except those to which the EC only permits certain colours to be added (Appendix C, pp. 476ff) and those to which the EC forbids the adding of colours (Appendix D, pp. 482ff). EC permitted as carrier. Restricted use: none. EC permitted as food additive for all foodstuffs following the *quantum satis* principle (except those specified in Table 2 on pp. 15–16 and in Appendix B on pp. 469ff). Directive 94/36/EC.

Acceptable Daily Intake: Not specified.

What It Is: Calcium carbonate occurs extensively in nature as chalk, limestone, marble and feldspar. Eggshells are 94 per cent calcium carbonate. Most of the world's production goes into paint, plastics, carpet backing, putty and rubber. When used as a food colour it gives an opaque white appearance, and is sometimes used in sugar confectionery instead of titanium dioxide.

What You Need To Know: Increased intake of calcium decreases absorption of magnesium.[169] Dose related constipation is common when 20 to 40 g is taken daily; haemorrhoids, painful, bleeding anal fissures may occur. Acute appendicitis has been produced by impacted calcium carbonate fecoliths.[170]

Calcium carbonate is a strong, fast-acting alkali used in antacids. Like other calcium salts, it can tend to cause constipation and flatulence. It is soluble and may therefore be absorbed into the bloodstream. Prolonged administration of calcium carbonate may result in hypercalcemia (the 'milk-alkali syndrome'), where larger than normal quantities of calcium accumulate in the blood, producing confused behaviour, anorexia, abdominal pain and weak muscles, possibly leading to the development of kidney stones and impaired kidney function. This is more likely if milk is taken at the same time as the antacid. Treatment involves reducing dietary calcium intake. The 'acid-rebound' effect, where the stomach actually increases its production of hydrochloric acid to cope with the strong alkali, may also occur with this substance.

Calcium chloride (E509)

FOOD ADDITIVE: FIRMING AGENT; CARRIER

Regulations: EC permitted for all foodstuffs following the

quantum satis principle (except those specified in Table 2 on pp. 15–16 and in Appendix B on pp. 469ff).

EC permitted as carrier. Restricted use: none. Directive 95/2/EC.

Acceptable Daily Intake: Not specified.

What It Is: Manufactured in several ways: (1) refining natural brine (2) reacting calcium hydroxide with ammonium chloride (3) reacting hydrochloric acid with calcium carbonate. Used as a road de-icer; as an antifreeze and refrigerating solution; in fire extinguishers; as a wood preservative; for fireproofing fabrics; as a firming agent for fruit and as a source of calcium.

What You Need To Know: Calcium chloride is a neutral, water soluble salt which in solution is essentially innocuous, but solid particles can have a powerful irritant action on the skin and mucous membranes. Cases have been reported, amongst workers packing dry calcium chloride, of peeling of facial skin, eye discharge, occasional nose bleeding and perforation of the nasal septum.[171] Calcium chloride does not biodegrade, and in countries where calcium chloride is used instead of salt to melt snow on roads there have been serious losses among wild animals drinking from slush at the roadside.[172]

Calcium citrates (i) monocalcium citrate (ii) dicalcium citrate (iii) tricalcium citrate (E333)

FOOD ADDITIVE: ACIDITY REGULATOR; FIRMING AGENT; SEQUESTRANT

Regulations: EC permitted for all foodstuffs following the *quantum satis* principle (except those specified in Table 2 on pp. 15–16 and in Appendix B on pp. 469ff). Directive 95/2/EC.

Acceptable Daily Intake: Not specified.

What It Is: Calcium salt of citric acid (see pp. 202–4) Used as a raising agent and nutritional supplement in the baking industry, and also to keep peppers, potatoes, tomatoes and lima beans firm during processing.

Calcium diglutamate (E623)

FOOD ADDITIVE: FLAVOUR ENHANCER; SALT SUBSTITUTE

Regulations: EC permitted to be used similarly to glutamic acid (E620). Directive 95/2/EC.

Acceptable Daily Intake: Not specified.

What It Is: Calcium salt of glutamic acid (see pp. 244–5).

Calcium disodium ethylene diamine tetra-acetate (Calcium disodium EDTA) (E385)

FOOD ADDITIVE: ANTIOXIDANT; PRESERVATIVE; SEQUESTRANT

Regulations: EC permitted for the following foods:

- Emulsified sauces, maximum level: 75 mg/kg
- Canned and bottled pulses, legumes, mushrooms and artichokes, maximum level: 250 mg/kg
- Canned and bottled crustaceans and molluscs, maximum level: 75 mg/kg
- Canned and bottled fish, maximum level: 75 mg/kg
- Minarine, maximum level: 100 mg/kg
- Frozen and deep-frozen crustaceans, maximum level: 75 mg/kg

Directive 95/2/EC.

Acceptable Daily Intake: 0 – 2.5.

What It Is: Therapeutically used as a chelating agent for lead in cases of lead poisoning, calcium disodium EDTA readily binds with this and other metals. In the food industry, it can therefore be used to sequester (i.e. remove from activity) metals that would otherwise increase the rate of oxidation and spoilage.

What You Need To Know: Relatively low toxicity, poorly absorbed from the gastrointestinal tract and rapidly excreted (50 per cent is excreted in urine within an hour, over 95 per cent within 24 hours).[173]

Calcium ferrocyanide (E538)

FOOD ADDITIVE: ANTICAKING AGENT

Regulations: EC permitted to be used similarly to sodium ferro-cyanide (E535). Directive 95/2/EC.

Acceptable Daily Intake: 0 – 0.025.

What It Is: See Sodium ferrocyanide.

Calcium gluconate (E578)

FOOD ADDITIVE: ACIDITY REGULATOR; FIRMING AGENT;
SEQUESTRANT

Regulations: EC permitted for all foodstuffs following the *quantum satis* principle (except those specified in Table 2 on pp. 15–16 and in Appendix B on pp. 469ff). Directive 95/2/EC.

Acceptable Daily Intake: 0 – 50.

What It Is: Made by neutralizing gluconic acid with lime or calcium carbonate, and used in sewage purification, in coffee powders to prevent caking, as a source of calcium in vitamin tablets and a gelling agent in foods. The main use of calcium gluconate is as a dietary supplement in cases of calcium deficiency.

Calcium guanylate (E629)

FOOD ADDITIVE: FLAVOUR ENHANCER

Regulations: EC permitted to be used similarly to guanylic acid (E626). Directive 95/2/EC.

Acceptable Daily Intake: Not specified.

What It Is: See Guanylic acid.

Calcium hydrogen sulphite (E227)

FOOD ADDITIVE: COMBINED PRESERVATIVE AND FIRMING AGENT

Regulations: EC permitted to be used similarly to sulphur dioxide (E220). Directive 95/2/EC.

Acceptable Daily Intake: 0 – 0.7 group acceptable daily intake for sulphur dioxide and sulphites expressed as sulphur dioxide.

What It Is: A sulphiting agent similar to sulphur dioxide.

What You Need To Know: The International Agency for Research on Cancer has concluded that sulphites are unclassifiable as to carcinogenicity in humans. There was inadequate evidence for their carcinogenicity in humans, and there was inadequate evidence of carcinogenicity in animals.[174] Also see sulphur dioxide (see pp. 422–7)

Calcium hydroxide (E526)
FOOD ADDITIVE: NEUTRALIZING AGENT; BUFFER; FIRMING AGENT
Regulations: EC permitted for all foodstuffs following the *quantum satis* principle (except those specified in Table 2 on pp. 15–16 and in Appendix B on pp. 469ff). Directive 95/2/EC.
Acceptable Daily Intake: Not specified.
What It Is: Also known as slaked lime or caustic lime, it is made by hydrating lime (calcium oxide). Many industrial uses include lubricants, drilling fluid, pesticides, fireproofing coatings, manufacture of paper pulp, rubber vulcanization, dehairing hides, water treatment and in mortar, plaster, cement and other binding and paving materials.
What You Need To Know: Workers' industrial contact with calcium hydroxide is one of the commonest causes of severe chemical burns of the eye, but in the small amounts likely to be present in foodstuffs it should pose no hazard to consumers.

Calcium inosinate (E633)
FOOD ADDITIVE: FLAVOUR ENHANCER
Regulations: EC permitted to be used similarly to guanylic acid (E626). Directive 95/2/EC.
Acceptable Daily Intake: Not specified.
What It Is: See the description of flavour enhancers under monosodium glutamate (see pp. 317–8).

Calcium lactate (E327)
FOOD ADDITIVE: BUFFER; DOUGH CONDITIONER; YEAST FOOD
Regulations: EC permitted for all foodstuffs following the

quantum satis principle (except those specified in Table 2 on pp. 15–16 and in Appendix B on pp. 469ff). Directive 95/2/EC.
Acceptable Daily Intake: Not specified.
What It Is: Calcium salt of lactic acid (see p. 272). Can preserve the texture and stability of canned fruit and vegetables during processing (e.g. the rigours of the canning process could easily make apple slices degenerate into a soggy mess – calcium lactate reacts with the natural pectin the fruit contains to form calcium pectate, which is less water-soluble and therefore helps to prevent the food's structural collapse). Also used in angel food cake, whipped toppings and meringues to bulk up the foam. Since it contains approximately 14 per cent calcium, it can also be used to nutritionally-fortify foods. Also used in dentifrices and as a blood coagulant in the treatment of haemorrhages.

Calcium malates (i) calcium malate (ii) calcium hydrogen malate (E352)

FOOD ADDITIVE: SEASONING AGENT; BUFFERING AGENT
Regulations: EC permitted for all foodstuffs following the *quantum satis* principle (except those specified in Table 2 on pp. 15–16 and in Appendix B on pp. 469ff). Directive 95/2/EC.
Acceptable Daily Intake: Not specified.
What It Is: Calcium salts of malic acid (see p. 291).

Calcium oxide (E529)

FOOD ADDITIVE: ALKALI; DOUGH CONDITIONER; YEAST FOOD
Regulations: EC permitted for all foodstuffs following the *quantum satis* principle (except those specified in Table 2 on pp. 15–16 and in Appendix B on pp. 469ff). Directive 95/2/EC.
Acceptable Daily Intake: Not specified.
What It Is: Also known as lime, originally made by burning limestone.
What You Need To Know: A strongly caustic alkali which may

cause severe irritation of the skin and mucous membranes of those occupationally exposed, but unlikely to pose a hazard in food products.

Calcium phosphates (i) monocalcium phosphate (ii) dicalcium phosphate (iii) tricalcium phosphate (E341)

FOOD ADDITIVE: BUFFER; ANTICAKING AGENT; CARRIER

Regulations: EC permitted to be used similarly to phosphoric acid (E338).

EC permitted as carrier. Restricted use: none. Directive 95/2/EC.

Acceptable Daily Intake: Maximum tolerable daily intake 70.

What It Is: Calcium salts of phosphoric acid (see pp. 341ff). Monocalcium phosphate (MCP) revolutionized the baking industry in 1939, when a process was developed by which a coating of alkali or heavy metal phosphate was applied to anhydrous MCP during manufacture. Since water could only penetrate the coating quite slowly, this gave time for the dough to be prepared before the acidic MCP started to react with sodium bicarbonate, releasing the gas carbon dioxide which gives bakery products their volume and lightness. Today, a range of slow-acting leavening agents is available, some of which include dicalcium phosphate (DCP), used in products which particularly require slow baking (it only releases its acid when a temperature of 60°C is reached). Tricalcium phosphate (TCP) is used as an anticaking agent in table salt and as a bleaching agent in flour.

What You Need To Know: See phosphoric acid.

Calcium propionate (E282)

FOOD ADDITIVE: PRESERVATIVE

Regulations: EC permitted to be used similarly to propionic acid (E280). Directive 95/2/EC.

Acceptable Daily Intake: Not specified.
What It Is: Calcium salt of propionic acid (see pp. 368–9).

Calcium silicate (E552)

FOOD ADDITIVE: ANTICAKING AGENT

Regulations: EC permitted to be used similarly to silicon dioxide (E551). Directive 95/2/EC.
Acceptable Daily Intake: Not specified.
What It Is: Manufactured by combining lime and diatomaceous earth under carefully controlled conditions, used to enable table salt, baking powder and other foods to flow smoothly.

Calcium sorbate (E203)

FOOD ADDITIVE: PRESERVATIVE

Regulations: EC permitted to be used similarly to sorbic acid (E200). Directive 95/2/EC.
Acceptable Daily Intake: 0 – 25.
What It Is: Calcium salt of sorbic acid (see pp. 408–11)

Calcium stearoyl-2-lactylate (E482)

FOOD ADDITIVE: EMULSIFIER; STABILIZER

Regulations: EC permitted to be used similarly to sodium stearoyl-2-lactylate (E481). Directive 95/2/EC.
Acceptable Daily Intake: 0 – 20.
What It Is: Calcium salt of the reaction product of lactic and stearic acids, hydrolized in the body to stearic and lactic acids, which are normal constituents of the human diet. Used as a dough conditioner in bakery products (it increases its gas retention properties, thus reducing the proofing time and increasing the loaf volume) and as an egg-white whipping aid.

Calcium sulphate (E516)

FOOD ADDITIVE: YEAST FOOD; DOUGH CONDITIONER;
SEQUESTRANT; FIRMING AGENT; CARRIER

Regulations: EC permitted for all foodstuffs following the *quantum satis* principle (except those specified in Table 2 on pp. 15–16 and in Appendix B on pp. 469ff). EC permitted as carrier. Restricted use: none. Directive 95/2/EC.

Acceptable Daily Intake: Not specified.

What It Is: Manufactured either from natural sources (gypsum rock) or by precipitating calcium chloride and a soluble sulphate, when heated to 200°C (calcined) it becomes plaster of Paris, whose many uses include the ability to stimulate new bone growth when used in reconstructive surgery.

Calcium sulphite (E226)

FOOD ADDITIVE: PRESERVATIVE

Regulations: EC permitted to be used similarly to sulphur dioxide (E220). Directive 95/2/EC.

Acceptable Daily Intake: 0 – 0.7.

What It Is: A sulphiting agent similar to sulphur dioxide (see pp. 422–7).

What You Need To Know: The International Agency for Research on Cancer has concluded that there is inadequate evidence that sulphites are carcinogenic in animal studies or in humans, and sulphites are therefore not classifiable as to their carcinogenicity in humans.[175]

Calcium tartrate (E354)

FOOD ADDITIVE: ACIDITY REGULATOR

Regulations: EC permitted for all foodstuffs following the *quantum satis* principle (except those specified in Table 2 on pp. 15–16 and in Appendix B on pp. 469ff). Directive 95/2/EC.

Acceptable Daily Intake: No acceptable daily intake allocated.

What It Is: Calcium salt of tartaric acid (see p. 433).

Camphor

MEDICINAL SUBSTANCE: COUNTER-IRRITANT

What It Is: True camphor oil is steam-distilled from Formosan and Japanese varieties of the camphor tree. May also be produced synthetically. An old remedy, this ingredient is occasionally found as an ingredient in some topical analgesics, where it acts as a counter-irritant. It is also included in some products for its pleasantly medicinal smell. It should be kept well away from young children – many cases of camphor poisoning have occurred, usually after children have drunk liquid camphor-containing products. Like menthol, it may produce a severe reaction with spasm of the air passage if applied to the nostrils, especially of an infant or young child.

Candelilla wax (E902)

FOOD ADDITIVE: GLAZING AGENT; COMPONENT OF CHEWING GUM BASE; SURFACE FINISHING AGENT; CARRIER FOR FLAVOUR

Regulations: EC permitted to be used similarly to beeswax, white and yellow (E901). Directive 95/2/EC.

Acceptable Daily Intake: Acceptable.

What It Is: Manufactured from the candelilla plant found in northern Mexico and the southern United States

What You Need To Know: Scientific studies do not raise carcinogenic, mutagenic or reproductive concerns.[176]

Canthaxanthin (E161g)

FOOD ADDITIVE: FOOD COLOUR

Regulations: EC permitted for Saucisses de Strasbourg, maximum level: 15 mg/kg. Directive 94/36/EC.

Acceptable Daily Intake: 0 – 0.05 (temporary 1996).

What It Is: An intensely red-coloured carotene, present in nature but produced synthetically for food industry use. It has no vitamin A activity. Recently restricted for use in foodstuffs, it was previously used to impart artificial colour to pale, factory-farmed egg yolks, and to give an artificially pink tint to the flesh of similarly intensively reared salmon.

What You Need To Know: The main health concern with this substance is its tendency to form crystals in the retina of the eye. Long-term ingestion may cause liver damage. Scientific studies do not raise carcinogenic concerns.[177]

Capsicum oleoresin

MEDICINAL SUBSTANCE: COUNTER-IRRITANT

What It Is: Made from dried chilli peppers, such as tabasco peppers or African chillies, capsicum is used on the skin as a powerful counter-irritant in products sold to try and relieve deep-seated pain such as arthritis. Even the smallest amount will produce severe pain if it comes into contact with the eyes or other sensitive areas, and it may produce severe inflammation of the stomach and diarrhoea if swallowed. It may also stain clothing.

Caraway oil

MEDICINAL SUBSTANCE: FLAVOURING

What It Is: Caraway oil is extracted from the caraway fruit, and is used for its flavour and aroma.

Carbamide (urea) (E927B)

FOOD ADDITIVE: TEXTURIZER IN CHEWING GUM;
YEAST NUTRIENT

Regulations: EC permitted for chewing gum without added sugars, maximum level: 30 g/kg. Directive 95/2/EC.

Acceptable Daily Intake: Acceptable.

What It Is: Found in urine and other body fluids (urea is the excretory end product of protein metabolism). Urea was, in fact, the first organic compound to be synthesized, and is today manufactured by the dehydration of ammonium carbonate, which is synthesized from ammonia and carbon dioxide. Most urea production is used in fertilizers, some is used as a livestock nutrient, and the rest for resins and other industrial uses. It can be used topically to moisturize, soften and smooth hardened, rough or dry skin, and it may aid in removing old dry skin.

Carbon black

FOOD ADDITIVE: FOOD COLOUR

Acceptable Daily Intake: Decision postponed.

What It Is: Small particle-size carbon, possibly obtained in a variety of ways: by charring bones, meat, blood, etc; by incomplete combustion of natural gas; by burning various fats, oils, resin, etc, under suitable conditions; or made from wood and vegetables.

What You Need To Know: Depending on the process of manufacture there are variations in the chemical composition of carbon black. It typically contains 88–99.5 per cent of carbon; 0.3–11 per cent of oxygen; 0.1–1 per cent of hydrogen; up to 1 per cent inorganic materials; a small amount of tarry matter and traces of sulphur.[178] Tiny particles of vegetable carbon may contain some molecules of carcinogenic substances, but these are held so tightly that they are not released by hot or cold water, gastric juices or blood plasma.[179]

The standardized morbidity for carbon black workers, in comparison with that for other workers, suggests that carbon black may be a carcinogen. This possibility is rendered more likely, although no quantitative value for the increase can be assigned, by the apparent finding that carbon black may cause leukaemia. These two suggestions of malignant neoplastic activity at least raise suspicions of an excess cancer risk associated with exposure to carbon black.[180] The original incrimination of carbon black as a carcinogenic agent is due to the presence of impurities. In European carbon black up to 1 per cent by weight of 3,4-benzpyrene has been found, while American carbon black is practically free of this substance.[181]

Carbon blacks:

The International Agency for Research on Cancer has

concluded that carbon blacks are unclassifiable as to carcinogenicity in humans. There was insufficient evidence in humans and insufficient evidence in animals.[182]

The US National Institute of Occupational Safety and Health recommends that carbon black be regulated as a potential human carcinogen.[183]

Carbon black extracts:
The International Agency for Research on Cancer has concluded that carbon black extracts are possibly carcinogenic to humans. There was sufficient evidence in animals.[184]

Carbon dioxide (E290)

FOOD ADDITIVE: CARBONATING AGENT; PACKING GAS;
PRESERVATIVE; FREEZING AGENT; EXTRACTION SOLVENT

Regulations: EC permitted for all foodstuffs following the *quantum satis* principle. Directive 95/2/EC.

Acceptable Daily Intake: Not specified.

What It Is: Carbon dioxide is both a natural and an artificial component of many foods, and it fulfils many functions. Beer, for example, naturally generates carbon dioxide during its fermentation, but manufacturers generally inject considerably more (up to four times the beer's liquid volume) to give the product the sort of fizz that they believe consumers require. As dry ice, it is used in the low-temperature storage and transportation of perishable products. As a gas, it can be used to create an atmosphere in which fruits and vegetables are stored, since it delays plant respiration and thus retards ripening and spoilage. At high concentrations, it can be used as an antimicrobial agent to inactivate moulds and some bacteria but not yeasts; in lower concentrations, it can actually stimulate spore germination and aid bacterial growth.

What You Need To Know: Exposure of humans to atmospheres of more than 10 per cent carbon dioxide causes unconsciousness; more than 30 per cent (in the presence of 20 per cent oxygen) can cause death.[185] Inhalation of smaller amounts of carbon dioxide over long periods of time may also be dangerous. There is also experimental evidence showing that carbon dixoide exposure can significantly reduce fertility.

Carboxy methyl cellulose, Sodium carboxy methyl cellulose (E466)

FOOD ADDITIVE: THICKENING AGENT; STABILIZER; CARRIER

Regulations: EC permitted for all foodstuffs following the *quantum satis* principle (except those specified in Table 2 on pp. 15–16 and in Appendix B on pp. 469ff).
EC permitted as carrier. Restricted use: none. Directive 95/2/EC.

Acceptable Daily Intake: Not specified.

What It Is: Commonly referred to as cellulose gum, this substance was first developed in Germany during the First World War as a gelatin substitute. It is made by treating cellulose (from wood pulp or cotton) with an alkali (sodium hydroxide) and then reacting it with sodium monochloroacetate. Food-grade CMC is then washed with an alcohol-water mixture to remove chemical residue. It is used to retard ice growth in ice-cream, in puddings to prevent liquid drops forming on the surface, and as a thickener and bulking agent in cakes and baked goods.

Carnauba wax (E903)

FOOD ADDITIVE: GLAZING AGENT; COMPONENT OF CHEWING GUM; CARRIER FOR FLAVOUR; SURFACE TREATING AGENT

Regulations: EC permitted to be used similarly to beeswax, white and yellow (E901). Directive 95/2/EC.

Acceptable Daily Intake: 0 – 7.

What It Is: Obtained from the leaves and buds of the Brazilian wax palm.

What You Need To Know: Scientific studies do not raise carcinogenic or reproductive concerns.[186]

Carotenes (i) mixed carotenes (ii) beta-carotene (E160a)

FOOD ADDITIVE: FOOD COLOUR

Regulations: EC permitted at *quantum satis* in all foods except those to which the EC only permits certain colours to be added (Appendix C, pp. 476ff) and those to which the EC forbids the adding of colours (Appendix D, pp. 482ff). Directive 94/36/EC.

Acceptable Daily Intake: 160ai (beta carotene [synthetic]) 0 – 5. Natural carotenes: no acceptable daily intake allocated.

What It Is: Carotenes are widespread natural pigments found in plants (in green leaves as well as in orange carrots). Many people don't realize that carotenes are found in animals, too: yellow or red birds' plumage is often due to a carotene compound, as is the skin colour in chickens and the yellow of an egg yolk. In fish, carotenes are responsible for colouring the pink flesh of salmon and trout, as well as shrimps, crabs and lobsters. In the food industry, carotenes were first mass-produced in order to add butter-like colour to margarine (which would otherwise have been an unappetizing grey). The first carotene pigments were obtained from natural sources (see Annatto pp. 132–3) but today, they are mostly synthesized – which creates an interesting controversy: is the 'nature identical' beta-carotene synthesized from acetone identical in every respect to the form found in a carrot? In plants it almost always occurs together with chlorophyll.

What You Need To Know: Carotenes are not known to cause any acute toxic problems. Absorbing large quantities may cause a yellowing of the skin (known as carotenemia) and typically develops in people who consume two quarts of tomato juice daily for several years.[187]

A review of the published scientific literature on the possible adverse effects of carotenes suggests that beta-carotene administration may prevent genetic damage caused by mutagenic substances, and that large doses of pure beta-carotene do not cause embryotoxicity in rodents. In addition, studies of individuals with congenitally high levels of plasma carotenoids and babies born carotenemic because of their mothers' intake of large amounts of carotenoid containing foods during pregnancy reveal no abnormalities attributable to the carotenoid molecule.[188]

There is considerable evidence showing that a diet high in foods rich in natural sources of beta-carotene can have a profoundly beneficial effect on the incidence of diseases such as cancer, for example:

- A Hawaiian study found that people consuming the least beta-carotene are three times more likely to develop lung cancer compared to people whose diets are rich in it.[189]
- A survey conducted in Maryland collected blood samples from 26,000 people, and analysed each sample if the donor developed cancer. The results showed that low levels of serum beta-carotene were again strongly associated with lung cancer and melanoma, a deadly form of skin cancer.[190]
- An Indian study on fishermen who chewed tobacco on a daily basis involved giving beta-carotene to those suffering from oral leukoplakia (smoker's tongue, precancerous lesions which look like leathery patches). The beta-carotene actually healed the lesions, but when treatment was stopped, the cell abnormalities reappeared.[191]
- In 1959, blood samples were taken from 2,974 Swiss men and tested for levels of carotene. Deaths from cancer were recorded for the next 12 years, and it was found that levels of carotene were significantly lower in those who died from all cancers (particularly lung cancer) than in the 2,421 survivors.[192]

Set against findings such as these are some recent widely-reported studies:

- 'Claims that anti-oxidant vitamins such as beta-carotene

and vitamin E might help to prevent cancer and heart disease should be viewed with scepticism, according to the New England Journal of Medicine ... there was a higher incidence of lung cancer among men who took beta-carotene than among those who did not. Anti-oxidant vitamins may have harmful as well as beneficial effects, says the study from the National Public Health Institute, Helsinki, Finland.'[193]

Two other studies support the Finnish data. In the Physicians' Health Study, more than 22,000 male US physicians were randomly assigned to take either beta-carotene (50 mg every other day) or a placebo for 12 years. Most of the participants in the trial were non-smokers. The supplements seemed to have no significant effects – either beneficial or harmful – on rates of cancer in this relatively healthy, low-risk population. In the other study, 17,000 people at high risk of lung cancer (because they smoked or because they had been exposed to asbestos) were either given a combination of beta-carotene (30 mg/day) and vitamin A (retinol, 25,000 IU/day) or a placebo. The trial had been scheduled to continue for six years, but treatment was discontinued in January 1996, after only four years, when interim results showed possible adverse effects similar to those observed in Finland.[194]

These studies have caused much consternation, including a media backlash against all forms of beta-carotene. An intelligent interpretation of the results, however, seems to reveal the following:

- None of the negative studies used a natural source of beta-carotene, nor a mixed carotenoid supplement
- It has been shown that natural beta-carotene is stored and used more efficiently by the body than synthetic beta-carotene[195]
- Alpha-carotene (naturally present with beta-carotene in green and yellow vegetables, but not present with synthetic

beta-carotene) is a more powerful anticarcinogen than beta-carotene[196]

This suggests the conclusion that there is a major difference between the way the body responds – and in particular, the way cancers respond – to food sources which are rich in *natural* beta-carotene, and *synthetically produced* beta-carotene. So while it may be a good idea to shelve the synthetic beta-carotene supplements, there is no reason to worry about natural beta-carotene in foods. People who eat more fruits and vegetables, especially those rich in carotenes, have a considerably lower risk of most cancers.

Carrageenan (E407)

FOOD ADDITIVE: CARRIER; THICKENING AGENT;
GELLING AGENT; STABILIZER

Regulations: EC permitted as carrier. Restricted use: none.
EC permitted for all foodstuffs following the *quantum satis* principle (except those specified in Table 2 on pp. 15–16 and in Appendix B on pp. 469ff). Directive 95/2/EC.

Acceptable Daily Intake: Not specified.

What It Is: Named after the Irish town of Carragheen where it was first exploited, carrageenan is obtained from the red seaweeds Chondrus and Gigartina, by being heated in an alkaline solution for about four hours. The crude extract is then chemically and physically purified. Although bleached, dried Irish Moss has been used in food and herbal preparations for many centuries, industrially processed carrageenan has only been produced on a large scale since the Second World War, when Japanese-sourced agar became impossible to obtain.

Carrageenan doesn't just thicken foods: it also reacts with certain proteins (e.g. casein present in milk) to form a thin gel without making the product taste or appear more viscous. This can be used, for example, to make a milkshake appear to be 'thick with chocolate' when, in fact, very little of the flavouring substance has actually been used. It will greatly extend the shelf life of non-refrigerated canned desserts, and it is also used in soups, sauces, syrups and toppings – often to give a product that nefarious quality 'mouthfeel'. When applied as a gel, it has been shown in laboratory tests to prevent human immuno-deficiency virus (HIV) from infecting cells of the type that line the vagina.

What You Need To Know: The International Agency for Research on Cancer has concluded that this substance is unclassifiable as to carcinogenicity in humans, but that degraded carrageenan is possibly carcinogenic to humans.[197]

Cascara

MEDICINAL SUBSTANCE: LAXATIVE

What It Is: A laxative made from the bark of the Californian Buckthorn. Similar in its effects to senna (another anthraquinone), it may cause red colouration of the urine. Powerful stimulant laxatives such as cascara are seldom necessary. Like all laxatives, it should not be used regularly.

Catechu

MEDICINAL SUBSTANCE: ASTRINGENT

What It Is: This plant extract is made from the shrub *Acacia catechu* and is an astringent (drying agent).

Caustic sulphite caramel (caramel colour class II) (E150b)

FOOD ADDITIVE: FOOD COLOUR

Regulations: EC permitted at *quantum satis* in all foods except those to which the EC only permits certain colours to be added (Appendix C, pp. 476ff) and those to which the EC forbids the adding of colours (Appendix D, pp. 482ff). Directive 94/36/EC.

Acceptable Daily Intake: No acceptable daily intake allocated.

What It Is: Prepared by the controlled heat treatment of carbo-hydrates with sulphite-containing compounds

What You Need To Know: Scientific studies do not raise carcinogenic concerns.[198]

Cedar wood oil

MEDICINAL SUBSTANCE: PERFUME

What It Is: An essential oil, which possesses a strong antiseptic aroma. In the past, it has been used to produce abortion, in some cases with a fatal outcome.[199]

Cellulose (microcrystalline or powdered) (E460)

FOOD ADDITIVE: CARRIER; EMULSIFIER; ANTICAKING AGENT;
STABILIZER; DISPERSING AGENT

Regulations: EC permitted as carrier. Restricted use: none.
EC permitted for all foodstuffs following the *quantum satis* principle (except those specified in Table 2 on pp. 15–16 and in Appendix B on pp. 469ff). Directive 95/2/EC.

Acceptable Daily Intake: Not specified.

What It Is: Cellulose is the most abundant organic compound on earth, because it occurs in all plants as the main constituent of cell walls. Although insoluble, it can be chemically converted to water-soluble gums (e.g. guar gum, locust bean gum, methylcellulose, etc). Microcrystalline cellulose is made by the controlled hydrolysis of wood pulp with hydrochloric acid; the resulting fine white powder can be used as an anticaking agent for shredded cheese, or (in the microcrystalline form) to stabilize food during high-temperature processing and as an ingredient in reduced-fat foods.

Cetalkonium chloride

MEDICINAL SUBSTANCE: ANTIMICROBIAL

What It Is: Like benzalkonium chloride, cetalkonium chloride is another quaternary ammonium compound. Used in mouth and throat preparations as an antiseptic, it may occasionally irritate the skin, and some people may become allergic to it after repeated use. Don't use in a douche or enema, and keep away from the eyes.

Cetrimide

MEDICINAL SUBSTANCE: ANTIMICROBIAL; DETERGENT

What It Is: A quaternary ammonium compound, used as an antiseptic and detergent in skin preparations. Strong solutions may produce chemical burns – there is a case on record of a child receiving a large burn on the chest after a shampoo containing cetrimide at 12 per cent strength was accidentally spilt.[200] Don't use in a douche or enema. May occasionally irritate the skin, and some people may become allergic to it after repeated use. Keep away from the eyes.

Cetylpyridinium chloride

MEDICINAL SUBSTANCE: ANTIMICROBIAL

What It Is: A quaternary ammonium compound with similar uses to cetrimide (see above).

Chalk

See calcium carbonate.

Chamomile

MEDICINAL SUBSTANCE: EMETIC; FLAVOURING

What It Is: Used as a bitter. In large doses it produces vomiting, in smaller doses it has the effect of soothing gut spasms and is slightly sedative.

Chlorbutol

MEDICINAL SUBSTANCE: LOCAL ANAESTHETIC; ANTIMICROBIAL

What It Is: Also called chlorbutanol or chlorobutanol. It has been used on the surface of the skin as an anaesthetic, and also against bacteria and fungi.

What You Need To Know: Has been widely used as a very effective preservative in eyedrops, usually in 0.5 per cent concentration, without producing clinically recognized ocular disturbance, even though applied several times a day for several years.[201]

Solutions containing 0.4 per cent chlorobutanol under contact lenses, left on the eye for several minutes, have been known to cause keratitis epithelialis, with fogging of vision, haloes around lights, and foreign-body type of discomfort beginning within an hour and becoming worse. Eyes have recovered spontaneously and completely in a day or two.[202]

Chlorobutanol has been employed as sedative and hypnotic. Probable oral lethal dose for an adult human is between 1 teaspoon and 1 oz.[203]

Chlorhexidine hydrochloride

MEDICINAL SUBSTANCE: ANTIMICROBIAL

What It Is: An antimicrobial agent that kills a wide range of bacteria. When used as a mouthwash it may discolour the teeth, temporarily upset the taste buds, and may also cause the lining of the mouth to peel. Brushing the teeth may help to remove any resulting discolouration.

Chlorocresol

MEDICINAL SUBSTANCE: ANTIMICROBIAL

What It Is: Chlorocresol is an antimicrobial, similar to phenol (see pp. 336–7) in its effects, but less toxic. Used as an external germicide, also as a preservative for glues, gums, paints, inks, textiles and leather goods.

What You Need To Know: Chlorocresol is an occasional human contact sensitizer. Consecutive human patch tests with chlorocresol showed 11 reactions among 1462 patients tested, but none were explainable and reproducible during re-test and provocative-use tests.[204]

Very little toxicological data are available. One source has rated p-chloro-m-cresol as very toxic, with a probable lethal dose to humans of 50 to 500 mg/kg.[205]

Chloroform

MEDICINAL SUBSTANCE: ANAESTHETIC; FLAVOURING

What It Is: Chloroform used to be used as an anaesthetic, but was implicated in liver and kidney damage. It has been used as an ingredient in mouthwashes.

What You Need To Know: The International Agency for Research on Cancer has concluded that this substance is possibly carcinogenic to humans. There was inadequate evidence of carcinogenicity in humans. There was sufficient evidence of carcinogenicity in animals.[206]

The US Environmental Protection Agency classified this substance as a probable human carcinogen. Based on increased incidence of several tumour types in rats and three strains of mice. Human carcinogenicity data: inadequate. Animal carcinogenicity data: sufficient.[207]

[Restrictions on the retail sale or supply of products containing chloroform are imposed by the Medicines (Chloroform Prohibition) Order 1979 (S.I.1979/382, amended by S.I. 1980/263)]

Chlorophylls and chlorophyllins: (i) chlorophylls (ii) chlorophyllins (E140)

FOOD ADDITIVE: FOOD COLOUR

Regulations: EC permitted at *quantum satis* in all foods except those to which the EC only permits certain colours to be added (Appendix C, pp. 476ff) and those to which the EC forbids the adding of colours (Appendix D, pp. 482ff). Directive 94/36/EC.

Acceptable Daily Intake: Not specified.

What It Is: A green colouring generally obtained from grasses such as alfalfa, which is first dried and powdered, then mixed with a solvent such as alcohol or acetone, which is finally removed under vacuum leaving the chlorophyl. To produce a bright green colour, it is combined with copper.[208]

Chloropropanols

FOOD ADDITIVE: CONTAMINANT

Acceptable Daily Intake: These substances are undesirable contaminants in food, and levels in hydrolized vegetable proteins should be reduced to the lowest technologically achievable.

What It Is: Processing of defatted vegetable proteins by traditional hydrochloric acid hydrolysis leads to the formation of significant amounts of 3-chloro-1,2-propanediol and 1,3-dichloro-2-propanol (chloropropanols). However, manufacturing techniques have been improved, enabling the reduction of the level of 3-chloro-1,2-propanediol to less than 2 mg/kg and that of 1,3-dichloro-2-propanol to less than 0.02 mg/kg in hydrolized vegetable proteins.

What You Need To Know:

3-chloro-1,2-propanediol

Capable of crossing blood-brain barrier, blood-testis barrier, distributed widely in body fluids after ingestion. Has been found to depress male fertility in rats, although this is reversible when intake stops. Can be metabolized to make oxalic acid, which causes kidney damage. A long-term study in rats suggests that it has a carcinogenic effect.

1,3-dichloro-2-propanol

A long-term study in rats suggests that it has a carcinogenic effect, including induction of benign and malignant tumours of the liver, kidney, thyroid gland and mouth in mid and high doses.[209]

Chlorothymol

MEDICINAL SUBSTANCE: ANTIMICROBIAL

What It Is: Chlorothymol is a mild antiseptic, related to phenol (see pp. 336–7) which may provoke irritation if applied to mucous membranes or sensitive skin. It is thought to be less toxic than phenol or thymol (see p. 438).

Chloroxylenol

MEDICINAL SUBSTANCE: ANTIMICROBIAL

What It Is: An antimicrobial which is related to phenol, although thought to be less toxic. It may occasionally produce skin reactions with repeated use.

Chlorpheniramine maleate

MEDICINAL SUBSTANCE: ANTIHISTAMINE

What It Is: An antihistamine drug. For some general information about antihistamines, see the special feature (pp. 134–5).

Choline salicylate

MEDICINAL SUBSTANCE: ANALGESIC

What It Is: Choline salicylate is one of the salicylate family, similar in its effect to aspirin (see pp. 142–4), but very soluble in water.

What You Need To Know: It should not be used at the same time as aspirin.

Chondrus

MEDICINAL SUBSTANCE: DEMULCENT

What It Is: Also called carrageenan (see pp. 194–5) or Irish Moss, it is found in some cough syrups, presumably for its demulcent (i.e. soothing) properties.

Cineole

MEDICINAL SUBSTANCE: EXPECTORANT; COUNTER-IRRITANT

What It Is: Also known as eucalyptol, it is an aromatic liquid

which is the main constituent (about 70 per cent) of oil of eucalyptus (see p. 235). Cineole is found in some topical analgesics
which try to relieve deep-seated pain by provoking a 'counter
irritation' on the surface of the skin. In diluted form, it may
sometimes be used as an expectorant.

What You Need To Know: Fatalities have followed doses as
small as 3.5 ml, though recovery has occurred after a dose of
20 and even 30 ml.[210]

Cinnamon oil

MEDICINAL SUBSTANCE: FLAVOURING

What It Is: Sweet-smelling and made from the bark of the
cinnamon tree, cinnamon oil is now generally used as a
flavouring. It is slightly antiseptic and astringent, and is
reputed to relieve flatulence and prevent vomiting.

Citric acid (E330)

FOOD ADDITIVE: ACIDULANT; ANTIOXIDANT; SEQUESTRANT;
SYNERGIST; FLAVOURING AGENT

Regulations: EC permitted for all foodstuffs following the
quantum satis principle (except those specified in Table 2 on
pp. 15–16 and in Appendix B on pp. 469ff). Directive 95/2/EC.

Acceptable Daily Intake: Not specified.

What It Is: The most versatile and widely used organic acid in
foodstuffs and pharmaceutical products, citric acid occurs
plentifully in nature (it was first isolated from lemon juice as
long ago as 1784). Although some citric acid is still obtained
from natural sources (e.g. pineapple waste), most is today
manufactured by fermentation from a mould (*Aspergillus
niger*) which is grown in a sugar and salt solution. It has been
utilized as a food additive for over a hundred years, and has a
wide ranges of uses:

• Its tangy sharp taste makes it an ideal flavouring agent for many fruit drinks, water ices and popular carbonated beverages.

- In cheese, it can be used as an acidulant to assist in the clotting of milk – the enzyme rennin (see p. 375), usually obtained from the gastric secretions of slaughtered calves, will not produce satisfactory clotting unless a suitably acidic environment is present in the milk. Traditionally, this was naturally achieved as a result of the lactic acid produced by bacteria in the milk (souring). However, this process can be both too slow and too unpredictable for the modern cheese industry, which often therefore resorts to the chemical acidification of milk.

- It creates an acidic environment in food products which discourages the growth of certain bacteria, yeasts and moulds (e.g. salmonella in chicken).

- It often works synergistically with other antioxidants (e.g. ascorbic acid) to enhance their effectiveness (e.g. citric protects the ascorbic acid content of frozen fruit; with tocopheróls, it retards rancidity in beef patties).

- In a similar way, it functions as a chelating agent (sequestrant) which can chemically bind with undesirable substances in processed foods, and thus neutralize them. For example, canned pears are prone to pink discolouration, partially caused by the presence of copper, iron and zinc. Citrate added to the product will bind with the metals, and largely prevent this 'unsightly' blemish. Since these metals often speed up the process of oxidation (catalysts), their removal by chelation also serves an antioxidant function. Sequestrants are often used for this kind of purpose, i.e. to preserve the numerous properties identified in the consumer's mind with wholesome food, including colour, flavour and texture.

Citric acid is such a popular food additive precisely because it can fulfil all these roles in a foodstuff simultaneously.

What You Need To Know: Frequent or excessive intake of citric acid may cause erosion of teeth and local irritation. This may also occur with lemon juice, which contains about 7 per cent citric acid.[211]

Citric acid esters of mono- and diglycerides of fatty acids (E472C)

FOOD ADDITIVE: EMULSIFIER; STABILIZER; DOUGH CONDITIONER; ANTIOXIDANT; SYNERGIST; CARRIER

Regulations: EC permitted for all foodstuffs following the *quantum satis* principle (except those specified in Table 2 on pp. 15–16 and in Appendix B on pp. 469ff).

EC permitted as carrier. Restricted use: colours and fat-soluble antioxidants. Directive 95/2/EC.

Acceptable Daily Intake: Not specified.

What It Is: Consists of mixed esters of glycerol with citric acid (see above) and fatty acids occurring in food oils and fats. Forms a milky dispersion in water, and is only partially soluble in oils and fats. Main use in foods is as an anti-spatter agent in margarine, an emulsifier in various oil/water emulsions, and as a fat replacement in high-fat foods.

What You Need To Know: In 1992 the British government's Food Advisory Committee recommended that this substance continue to be permitted for use in food, subject to the provision of chronic toxicity/carcinogenicity and teratology/fertility studies, or unless clear evidence could be provided that these products could be metabolized to normal dietary components; such data to be provided within three years.

Their concern reflected the possibility that this substance (and E472b, for which a similar request was made) might not fully break down in the human gastrointestinal tract to normal dietary components, raising the possibility that there could be the absorption of novel chemical forms with the potential to elicit toxic effects.[212]

Clioquinol

MEDICINAL SUBSTANCE: ANTIMICROBIAL

What It Is: Was the active ingredient in intestinal anti-infective products such as 'Entero-Vioform'.

What You Need To Know: When taken internally as a gastro-intestinal disinfectant, clioquinol was implicated in the development of a condition known as 'Subacute Myelo-Opticoneuropathy' (abbreviated to SMON) which affects the spinal cord, optic nerve and peripheral nerves. Symptoms included diarrhoea, difficulty in normal walking and vision, abnormal reflexes and mental disturbances. The syndrome was first diagnosed in Japan, where 100,000 people between the years 1955 and 1970 were believed to have contracted it. Between 10 and 15 per cent of SMON victims in Japan are incapable of looking after themselves. An estimated 3 to 6 per cent have died of the disease.[213] There have been many similar cases of subacute myelo-opticoneuropathy scattered in various parts of the world affecting adults, with convincing histories relating clioquinol to disturbances of vision, with varying degrees of spinal cord involvement. Visual disturbances have ranged from impairment of discrimination of colours to blindness from optic atrophy. In a number of cases there has been improvement of vision after administration of clioquinol was stopped. No treatment has been effective other than stopping administration of clioquinol.[214]

A neurotoxicity dose response curve for clioquinol can be constructed as follows: 750 mg/day for 4 weeks or less: little risk of toxic reactions; 750–1 500 mg/day for less than 2 weeks: 1 per cent have neurologic symptoms; 750–1 500 mg/day for over 2 weeks: 35 per cent develop symptoms; 1 800 mg/day for 5 days one patient developed symptoms. At higher doses onset of toxic reactions may begin within 24 hours.[215]

Clioquinol generally appears to be well tolerated following topical application to the skin. Local irritation, rash, and sensitivity reactions have been reported occasionally.[216]

Clotrimazole
MEDICINAL SUBSTANCE: ANTIMICROBIAL

What It Is: An anti-fungal drug used against such infections as athlete's foot, ringworm, genital thrush, etc. There are few reported side-effects, although it is possible that skin allergy may develop. Athlete's foot is caused by the fungus commonly known as ringworm and is characterized by peeling, softening and cracking of the skin under and between the toes. The symptoms are itchiness and burning, with reddening of the skin which in severe cases may crack and become further infected. Cross-infection to other parts of the body may occur. It is treated by anti-fungal agents and prevented from recurring by elimination of the moist conditions in which it flourishes. Treatment is usually long-term, and is best carried out under the supervision of a doctor (especially if you are diabetic).

Clove oil
MEDICINAL SUBSTANCE: FLAVOURING

What It Is: Used as a flavouring, to treat the pain of toothache, and mildly antiseptic. Its main constituent is eugenol (see p. 236). It has a warming effect and is found in products which are applied to the skin as counter-irritants.

Coal tar
MEDICINAL SUBSTANCE: ANTIPRURITIC

What It Is: The black residue obtained by the destructive distillation of coal. Coal tar is not a single chemical entity – official sources do not specify its composition, and its therapeutic effect depends on a myriad of carbonized and volatile constituents. Because of the lack of specifications for coal tar, a Joint Industry Coal Tar Project is attempting to develop a standard of quality that will lead to an effective, uniform coal tar product with the smallest quantity of undesirable components.[217] It has been used to treat bronchitis, diarrhoea and diseases of the urinary organs, but is now mostly used on the skin to prevent itching, and to treat chronic skin disorders. Over-the-counter coal tar preparations actually contain only small amounts of refined or purified coal tar extracts.

What You Need To Know: There is some disagreement as to how effective coal tar preparations are in the treatment of dandruff, seborrheic dermatitis, or psoriasis. One authority states that there are few well-controlled studies demonstrating their efficacy.[218] Another maintains that it is a treatment of proved efficacy.[219] Considered to be a safe treatment, coal tar can be used either in refined form, or as a cruder extract (e.g. crude coal tar in petroleum jelly) which is generally considered to be a more effective treatment.[220] The potential severity of side-effects from tar in the treatment of psoriasis is less than that from some other treatments (e.g. topical corticosteroids).[221] It may sensitize the skin to sunlight, and it may produce skin itching (although it is also used to treat itching). Coal tar preparations may produce dermatitis, sometimes severe, when used for prolonged periods.[222]

The International Agency for Research on Cancer has concluded that coal tar is carcinogenic in humans. There was sufficient evidence of carcinogenicity in humans, and sufficient evidence of carcinogenicity in animals.[223]

The US Environmental Protection Agency has classified coal tar as carcinogenic to humans. Studies of coke oven workers have shown increased risk of mortality from cancer of the lung, trachea and bronchus; cancer of the kidney; cancer of the prostate; and cancer of all sites combined. In animals, extracts and condensates of coke oven emissions were found to be carcinogenic in both inhalation studies and skin-painting bioassays. The mutagenicity of whole extracts and condensates, as well as their individual components, provides supportive evidence for carcinogenicity. Carcinogenicity data: sufficient.[224]

In a review of the literature for the possible occurrence of cancer in patients treated with coal tar, only 13 cases of skin cancer (most in the anogenital region) attributable to coal tar were reported during the period of 1900–1966; two of these patients had also been treated with arsenic. It has been suggested that psoriasis may selectively protect against skin cancer.[225] Studies of patients with psoriasis who are treated with coal tar do not indicate an increased incidence of skin cancer.[226]

Cochineal, carminic acid, carmines (E120)

FOOD ADDITIVE: FOOD COLOUR

Regulations: EC permitted to be used singly or in combination with other colours in the following foods up to the total maximum level specified.

- Non-alcoholic flavoured drinks, maximum level: 100 mg/l
- Candied fruits and vegetables, Mostarda di frutta, maximum level: 200 mg/kg
- Preserves of red fruits, maximum level: 200 mg/kg
- Confectionery, maximum level: 300 mg/kg
- Decorations and coatings, maximum level: 500 mg/kg
- Fine bakery wares (e.g. viennoiserie, biscuits, cakes and wafers), maximum level: 200 mg/kg
- Edible ices, maximum level: 150 mg/kg
- Flavoured processed cheese, maximum level: 100 mg/kg
- Desserts including flavoured milk products, maximum level: 150 mg/kg
- Sauces, seasonings (for example, curry powder, tandoori), pickles, relishes, chutney and piccalilli, maximum level: 500 mg/kg
- Mustard, maximum level: 300 mg/kg
- Fish paste and crustacean paste, maximum level: 100 mg/kg; Pre-cooked crustaceans, maximum level: 250 mg/kg; Salmon substitutes, maximum level: 500 mg/kg; Surimi, maximum level: 500 mg/kg; Fish roe, maximum level: 300 mg/kg; Smoked fish, maximum level: 100 mg/kg
- Snacks: dry, savoury potato, cereal or starch-based snack products; Extruded or expanded savoury snack products, maximum level: 200 mg/kg

- Other savoury snack products and savoury coated nuts, maximum level: 100 mg/kg
- Edible cheese rind and edible casings, maximum level: *quantum satis*
- Complete formulae for weight control intended to replace total daily food intake or an individual meal, maximum level: 50 mg/kg
- Complete formulae and nutritional supplements for use under medical supervision, maximum level: 50 mg/kg
- Liquid food supplements/dietary integrators, maximum level: 100 mg/l
- Solid food supplements/dietary integrators, maximum level: 300 mg/kg
- Soups, maximum level: 50 mg/kg
- Meat and fish analogues based on vegetable proteins, maximum level: 100 mg/kg
- Spirituous beverages (including products less than 15 % alcohol by volume), except those mentioned in Annex II or III, maximum level: 200 mg/l
- Aromatized wines, aromatized wine-based drinks and aromatized wine-product cocktails as mentioned in Regulation (EEC) No 1601/91, except those mentioned in Annex II or III, maximum level: 200 mg/l
- Fruit wines (still or sparkling) cider (except cidre bouche) and perry, aromatized fruit wines, cider and perry, maximum level: 200 mg/l. Directive 94/36/EC.

Acceptable Daily Intake: 0 – 5.

What It Is: Obtained from aqueous extracts of cochineal, which consists of the dried bodies of the female insect *Dactylopius coccus Cosat.* The main commercial source is Tenerife in the Canary Islands. It takes 70,000 insects to make one pound of colour. Carminic acid is the main colour constituent of cochineal, from which carmine is derived.

Cocillana

MEDICINAL SUBSTANCE: EMETIC; EXPECTORANT

What It Is: Cocillana is made from the bark of the guarea tree, powdered or as an extract. It induces vomiting, has been used to relieve flatulence and is said to be expectorant in its action.

Codeine

MEDICINAL SUBSTANCE: ANALGESIC; COUGH SUPPRESSANT

What It Is: Codeine is a narcotic pain reliever and cough suppressant. It is present in opium from 0.7 to 2.5 per cent, depending on the source, and is obtained by partial synthesis from morphine.

What You Need To Know: In over-the-counter analgesics, codeine is usually present with other pain killers (such as paracetamol or aspirin) for the simple reason that the amount of codeine itself needed to relieve pain is more than the amount that is allowed in over-the-counter products.

There is no doubt that codeine is an effective cough suppressant. Cough suppressants can be useful in terminal illnesses (such as lung cancer) in which case the patient will be under the care of a physician. They may also be useful to soothe coughing so that sleep can be obtained. Otherwise, their use is open to question. One authority states that 'The drawbacks of prescribing cough suppressants are rarely outweighed by the benefits of treatment.'[227]

People with asthma or emphysema, for example, may need to cough in order to keep their airways clear. Cough suppressants containing codeine or similar substances should not be used on children without medical advice. Side-effects may include constipation (which is why it may be included in small amounts in some anti-diarrhoea medicines) nausea, palpitation, dizziness and drowsiness, although they are unlikely to be a problem with the small doses of codeine present in OTC medicines. Adults may occasionally become short of breath or their heart may beat more slowly; in children, codeine may have the opposite effect and produce over-excitement. In either case, consult your doctor. If you become drowsy you should not drive a car or operate hazardous machinery, and codeine should not be taken with alcohol. Codeine may increase the effects of sedatives and certain other drugs being taken at the same time. Consult your doctor before taking codeine if you are taking other medicines, or if you have:

- Asthma or breathing difficulties
- Colitis
- Prostate or urinary problems
- Adrenal or thyroid problems
- Heart problems

Being an opium-related narcotic, codeine could be habit-forming. Since the late 1970s, an oral drug combination locally known as a 'hit' or 'loads' including codeine has been responsible for a large number of deaths in the 15–29 age group in New Jersey, Chicago and Los Angeles, where it is considered an oral substitute for heroin.[228]

Coltsfoot
MEDICINAL SUBSTANCE: DEMULCENT

What It Is: This plant has been used over the centuries for its soothing effect on inflamed or irritated lung tissue, as found in asthma, colds, coughs and bronchitis. It is sometimes called 'Son before the Father' because its flowers appear before its leaves.

Copper
FOOD ADDITIVE: CONTAMINANT

Acceptable Daily Intake: Provisional maximum tolerable daily intake: 0.05 – 0.5.

What It Is: Copper was the first metal to be used by humans (5000 BC or earlier). Over 1,000 different copper alloys have been created, the best-known being brass. Although it is an essential component of the body's enzyme systems, a normal diet probably provides all the necessary dietary intake. Albinos lack the normal form of the copper-containing enzyme tyrosinase, essential to the synthesis of the pigment melanin.

What You Need To Know: The reaction of soft water with the copper pipes that are used in some household plumbing systems contributes to the copper levels in water at the tap.[229] Gastrointestinal irritation, seldom serious, can result following the drinking of carbonated water or citrus fruit juices which have been in contact with copper vessels, pipes, tubing or valves. Such beverages are acidic enough to dissolve irritant quantities of copper.[230] Dietary copper intake varies widely according to the type of food consumed, the condition of the soil, and the amount present in drinking water. Copper is an essential trace element, but can have adverse effects when consumed, accidentally or deliberately, in large quantities – 200 mg per kg body weight is generally considered to be the lethal human dose. The estimated safe and adequate daily intake of copper for adults lies between 2 and 3 mg, except for those suffering from Wilson's disease (a genetic disease in which copper is accumulated in body tissues, particularly the brain and liver).[231]

Copper itself probably has little toxicity, although there are conflicting reports in medical literature.[232] It is debatable whether chronic copper poisoning exists in human beings. Many cases of illness formerly attributed to copper are now believed to have been probably due to admixture with other metals, especially lead.[233]

Copper has a contraceptive effect when present in the uterus. It is added to some intrauterine contraceptive devices in order that their overall size can be reduced, thus reducing the associated side-effects such as pain and bleeding.[234]

The US Environmental Protection Agency was unable to classify this substance as to human carcinogenicity. There are no human data, inadequate animal data from assays of copper compounds, and equivocal mutagenicity data. Human carcinogenicity data: none. Animal carcinogenicity data: inadequate.[235]

Copper complexes of chlorophylls and chlorophyllins (i) copper complexes of chlorophylls (ii) copper complexes of chlorophyllins (E141)

FOOD ADDITIVE: FOOD COLOUR

Regulations: EC permitted at *quantum satis* in all foods except those to which the EC only permits certain colours to be added (Appendix C, pp. 476ff) and those to which the EC forbids the adding of colours (Appendix D, pp. 482ff). Directive 94/36/EC.
Acceptable Daily Intake: 0 – 15.
What It Is: See Chlorophylls.

Coriander oil

MEDICINAL SUBSTANCE: FLAVOURING

What It Is: Coriander oil is sometimes used in popular medicines to disguise the flavour and odour of less pleasant ingredients, and has traditionally been used as an antiflatulent.

Creosote

MEDICINAL SUBSTANCE: ANTIMICROBIAL; EXPECTORANT ⚠

What It Is: Creosote has traditionally been made by distilling tar extracted from beech wood (the beech tree had many uses in the past, beech-nuts provided human food in times of famine, an oily butter substitute was extracted and used in Central Europe, and the German army even resorted to smoking its leaves during the First World War). Creosote contains phenols, and was once used in a similar way to phenol itself.

What You Need To Know: The International Agency for Research on Cancer has concluded that creosote derived from coal tars is probably carcinogenic to humans. There was limited evidence of carcinogenicity in humans. There was sufficient evidence of carcinogenicity in animals.[236]

The US Environmental Protection Agency classified creosote derived from coal tar as a probable human carcinogen. Limited evidence of the association between occupational creosote contact and subsequent tumour formation, sufficient evidence of local and distant tumour formation after dermal application to mice, and some evidence of mutagenic activity as well as the well-documented carcinogenicity of other coal tar products to humans. Human carcinogenicity data: limited. Animal carcinogenicity data: sufficient.[237]

Cubeb

MEDICINAL SUBSTANCE: FLAVOURING

What It Is: Cubeb oil is extracted from the unripe fruit of the Java Pepper (*Piper Cubeba*), and was once used as a treatment for gonorrhoea.

Curcumin (E100)

FOOD ADDITIVE: FOOD COLOUR

Regulations: EC permitted to be used singly or in combination with other colours in the following foods up to the total maximum level specified.
- Non-alcoholic flavoured drinks, maximum level: 100 mg/l
- Candied fruits and vegetables, Mostarda di frutta, maximum level: 200 mg/kg
- Preserves of red fruits, maximum level: 200 mg/kg
- Confectionery, maximum level: 300 mg/kg
- Decorations and coatings, maximum level: 500 mg/kg
- Fine bakery wares (e.g. viennoiserie, biscuits, cakes and wafers), maximum level: 200 mg/kg
- Edible ices, maximum level: 150 mg/kg
- Flavoured processed cheese, maximum level: 100 mg/kg
- Desserts including flavoured milk products, maximum level: 150 mg/kg
- Sauces, seasonings (for example, curry powder, tandoori), pickles, relishes, chutney and piccalilli, maximum level: 500 mg/kg

- Mustard, maximum level: 300 mg/kg
- Fish paste and crustacean paste, maximum level: 100 mg/kg; Pre-cooked crustaceans, maximum level: 250 mg/kg; Salmon substitutes, maximum level: 500 mg/kg; Surimi, maximum level: 500 mg/kg; Fish roe, maximum level: 300 mg/kg; Smoked fish, maximum level: 100 mg/kg
- Snacks: dry, savoury potato, cereal or starch-based snack products: Extruded or expanded savoury snack products, maximum level: 200 mg/kg
- Other savoury snack products and savoury coated nuts, maximum level: 100 mg/kg
- Edible cheese rind and edible casings, maximum level: quantum satis
- Complete formulae for weight control intended to replace total daily food intake or an individual meal, maximum level: 50 mg/kg
- Complete formulae and nutritional supplements for use under medical supervision, maximum level: 50 mg/kg
- Liquid food supplements/dietary integrators, maximum level: 100 mg/l
- Solid food supplements/dietary integrators, maximum level: 300 mg/kg
- Soups, maximum level: 50 mg/kg
- Meat and fish analogues based on vegetable proteins, maximum level: 100 mg/kg
- Spirituous beverages (including products less than 15 % alcohol by volume), except those mentioned in Annex II or III, maximum level: 200 mg/l
- Aromatized wines, aromatized wine-based drinks and aromatized wine-product cocktails as mentioned in Regulation (EEC) No 1601/91, except those mentioned in Annex II or III, maximum level: 200 mg/l
- Fruit wines (still or sparkling) cider (except cidre bouche) and perry, aromatized fruit wines, cider and perry, maximum level: 200 mg/l. Directive 94/36/EC.

Acceptable Daily Intake: 0 – 1 (1996).

What It Is: Curcumin occurs naturally in the root of the herb turmeric, and is its main colouring component. It is isolated by steam distillation.

What You Need To Know: Like turmeric, curcumin has anti-carcinogenic properties, being able to inhibit cancer initiation, promotion and progression. When applied to the skin, it can inhibit skin tumours and can cure scabies (again, applied to the skin). It also has anti-inflammatory properties (perhaps due to its free radical scavenging activity). It has a beneficial effect on ulcers, and can protect against some forms of liver damage. Daily doses of 500 mg curcumin in humans taken for one week resulted in a significant decrease of total blood cholesterol, and an increase in HDL ('good') cholesterol.[238]

Cyclamic acid and its Na and Ca salts (E952)

FOOD ADDITIVE: SWEETENER

Regulations: EC permitted for the following foods up to the total maximum usable dose specified.

- Water-based flavoured drinks, energy-reduced or with no added sugar, maximum usable dose: 400 mg/l; Milk- and milk-derivative-based or fruit-juice-based drinks, energy-reduced or with no added sugar, maximum usable dose: 400 mg/l
- Water-based flavoured desserts, energy-reduced or with no added sugar, maximum usable dose: 250 mg/kg; Milk- and milk-derivative-based preparations, energy-reduced or with no added sugar, maximum usable dose: 250 mg/kg; Fruit- and vegetable-based desserts, energy-reduced or with no added sugar, maximum usable dose: 250 mg/kg; Egg-based desserts, energy-reduced or with no added sugar, maximum usable dose: 250 mg/kg; Cereal-based desserts, energy-reduced or with no added sugar, maximum usable dose: 250 mg/kg; Fat-based desserts, energy-reduced or with no added sugar, maximum usable dose: 250 mg/kg
- Confectionery with no added sugar, maximum usable dose: 500 mg/kg; Cocoa- or dried-fruit-based confectionery, energy-reduced or with no added sugar, maximum usable dose: 500 mg/kg; Starch-based confectionery, energy-reduced or with no added sugar, maximum usable dose: 500 mg/kg
- Cocoa-, milk-, dried-fruit- or fat-based sandwich spreads, energy-reduced or with no added sugar, maximum usable dose: 500 mg/kg

- Chewing gum with no added sugar, maximum usable dose: 1500 mg/kg
- Edible ices, energy-reduced or with no added sugar, maximum usable dose: 250 mg/kg
- Canned or bottled fruit, energy-reduced or with no added sugar, maximum usable dose: 1000 mg/kg
- Energy-reduced jams, jellies and marmalades, maximum usable dose: 1000 mg/kg; Energy-reduced fruit and vegetable preparations, maximum usable dose: 250 mg/kg
- Fine bakery products for special nutritional uses, maximum usable dose: 1600 mg/kg
- Complete formulae for weight control intended to replace total daily food intake or an individual meal, maximum usable dose: 400 mg/kg
- Complete formulae and nutritional supplements for use under medical supervision, maximum usable dose: 400 mg/kg
- Liquid food supplements/dietary integrators, maximum usable dose: 400 mg/kg
- Solid food supplements/dietary integrators, maximum usable dose: 500 mg/kg. Directive 94/35/EC.

Acceptable Daily Intake: 0 – 11.

What It Is: An artificial sweetener produced by reacting cyclohexylamine and sulphamic acid or chlorosulphonic acid. A bitter taste becomes noticeable when the amount present in foods approaches 0.5 per cent. This is generally overcome by mixing it with a suitable proportion of saccharin (see pp. 377ff).

What You Need To Know: In the United States, cyclamates were removed from a list of substances recognized as safe in food and drink in 1969, because of their carcinogenic effects on animals.[239] Some skin conditions (e.g., pruritus, dermographia, urticaria, angioneurotic edema) have been attributed to intake of cyclamates.[240]

After consumption, cyclamate is eliminated largely unchanged in humans and animals except for a small amount (about 0.7 per cent of the dose) which is converted by intestinal flora into cyclohexyamine. The teratogenic, mutagenic, and carcinogenic potentials of cyclohexylamine lack uniform, experimental agreement, although cyclohexylamine is generally rated as 'moderately toxic or very toxic' by most authorities.[241] [242]

The International Agency for Research on Cancer has concluded that cyclamates are unclassifiable as to carcinogenicity in humans.[243]

DDT

FOOD ADDITIVE: CONTAMINANT

Acceptable Daily Intake: Not specified.

What It Is: The first organochlorine pesticide, particularly lethal against many insects but virtually inactive against mites and ticks. It kills by acting as a nerve poison – it causes hyperactivity and convulsions. The paralysis and death that ensues are thought to occur from exhaustion.[244] Rachel Carson's *Silent Spring* (1962) focused public attention on the persistence of DDT in the environment, its accumulation in the food chain and its impact on dramatically declining numbers of many species of birds (it causes the laying of infertile or deformed eggs).

What You Need To Know: DDT can be biodegraded by a number of micro-organisms present in water, sediments and soils; although it can take a long time for them to do their job – reported half-lives for DDT in soils range from two years to more than 15 years.[245]

The International Agency for Research on Cancer has concluded that this substance is possibly carcinogenic to humans. There is inadequate evidence in humans for the carcinogenicity of DDT. There is sufficient evidence in experimental animals for the carcinogenicity of DDT.[246]

The US Environmental Protection Agency classified this substance as a probable human carcinogen, based on observation of tumours (generally of the liver) in seven studies in various mouse strains and three studies in rats. DDT is structurally similar to other probable carcinogens, such as DDD and DDE. Human carcinogenicity data: inadequate. Animal carcinogenicity data: sufficient.[247]

Delta-tocopherol (E309)

FOOD ADDITIVE

Regulations: EC permitted for all foodstuffs following the *quantum satis* principle (except those specified in Table 2 on pp. 15–16 and in Appendix B on pp. 469ff). Directive 95/2/EC. **What It Is:** See Alpha-tocopherol (pp. 121–2).

Dequalinium chloride

MEDICINAL SUBSTANCE: ANTIMICROBIAL

What It Is: Dequalinium chloride is another quaternary ammonium compound (the group that includes cetrimide and benzalkonium chloride). It is active against fungal infections but has limited activity against bacteria, and its effectiveness may be restricted in the presence of natural body fluids. It is found in some lozenges and pastilles intended to be used for mild oral fungal infections (which should be diagnosed by a doctor).

Dextromethorphan

MEDICINAL SUBSTANCE: COUGH SUPPRESSANT

What It Is: Dextromethorphan is a cough suppressant similar to pholcodine (see p. 340). It may be superior to codeine (see pp. 210–11) as a suppressant since it seems to have fewer side-effects and is not narcotic. Dextromethorphan should be used with care by people with liver disease.

Diastase

MEDICINAL SUBSTANCE: ENZYME

What It Is: An enzyme which is produced when seeds germinate, able to convert carbohydrate into maltose and dextrose. Enzymes are included in some antacids and indigestion remedies, although the rationale for their inclusion in these products is open to question.

Dichlorophen
MEDICINAL SUBSTANCE: ANTIMICROBIAL
What It Is: An antifungal agent sometimes used as a germicide in soaps.

Diethylamine salicylate
MEDICINAL SUBSTANCE: COUNTER IRRITANT
What It Is: Used in topical analgesics where it acts as a counter-irritant, and may also provide some aspirin-like analgesia if absorbed through the skin.

Dill
MEDICINAL SUBSTANCE: FLAVOURING
What It Is: An aromatic and flavouring herb, dill oil being distilled from its seeds. It has been used to relieve flatulence and stomach pains.

Dimethicone
MEDICINAL SUBSTANCE: ANTI-FLATULENT; LUBRICANT
What It Is: Dimethicone (dimethyl polysiloxane, polydimethyl siloxane) is found in some indigestion remedies, and in water-repellant creams for use on the skin. Internally, it is generally accepted to be non-toxic. Its mode of action is physical – it seems to be able to make small bubbles of gas form into larger ones, which can then be more easily expelled. Some common ingredients of antacids (especially aluminium hydroxide) may interfere with dimethicone's ability to do this.

Dimethyl dicarbonate (E242)
FOOD ADDITIVE: PRESERVATIVE; COLD STERILIZING AGENT
Regulations: EC permitted for non-alcoholic flavoured drinks, alcohol-free wine, liquid-tea concentrate, maximum level:

250 mg/l ingoing amount, residues not detectable. Directive 95/2/EC.

Acceptable Daily Intake: Acceptable.

What It Is: Quickly decomposes in water to form methanol and carbon dioxide.

Dimethyl polysiloxane (simethicone) (E900)

FOOD ADDITIVE: ANTIFOAMING AGENT; ANTICAKING AGENT

Regulations: EC permitted for the following foods:

- Jam, jellies and marmalades as defined in Directive 79/693/EEC and similar fruit spreads, including low calorie products, maximum level: 10 mg/kg
- Soups and broths, maximum level: 10 mg/kg
- Oils and fats for frying, maximum level: 10 mg/kg
- Confectionery (excluding chocolate), maximum level: 10 mg/kg
- Non-alcoholic flavoured drinks, maximum level: 10 mg/l
- Pineapple juice, maximum level: 10 mg/l
- Canned and bottled fruit and vegetables, maximum level: 10 mg/kg
- Chewing gum, maximum level: 100 mg/kg
- (*pro memoria*) Wine in accordance with Regulation (EEC) No 1873/84 authorizing the offer or disposal for direct human consumption of certain imported wines which may have undergone oenological processes not provided for in Regulation (EEC) No 337/79
- Sod . . . saft, maximum level: 10 mg/l
- Batters, maximum level: 10 mg/kg

Directive 95/2/EC.

Acceptable Daily Intake: 0 – 1.5.

What It Is: Silicon constitutes about 28 per cent of the earth's crust, and is an important trace mineral in bone formation and mineralization. Silicon reacted with methyl chloride produces siloxanes, which can be further processed to form dimethyl polysiloxanes. Simethicone is a mixture of dimethyl polysiloxanes and silica gel. Used as a water repellent, also in protective creams and lotions, defoaming agent and lubricant.

What You Need To Know: Practically inert physiologically and essentially non-toxic in food use. Clinical studies have shown silicones to be non-irritant when applied to skin.[248]

Problems have arisen in recent years with the use of polydimethylsiloxane (PDMS) linear polymers, the silicone used in silicone gel breast implants. Implants were once believed to be inert, however in 1978 it was demonstrated that implants 'bleed' silicone gel through the implant shell.[249] Because of the lack of studies actually proving the safety of implants, the United States Food and Drug Administration, in its 1992 review of medical devices, decided that the implants should be removed from the market except for use in surgical reconstruction as part of clinical trials.[250] Subsequent studies have shown that, when used in this way, silicones are neither biologically nor chemically inert in the human body.[251]

Dioxins

⚠️

FOOD ADDITIVE: CONTAMINANT

What It Is: The generic term given to polychlorinated dibenzo-p-dioxins and dibenzofurans. This group of organic chemicals consists of accidental by-products created in the process of manufacturing certain herbicides, bactericides, wood preservatives, and other products. Concern over dioxins arose initially because one particular dioxin, TCDD, was found to produce clinical effects (chloracne) in workers exposed to it through industrial accidents; some scientists believe it to be the most toxic of all synthetic chemicals. TCDD was a contaminant of the defoliant Agent Orange, which was sprayed on fields and jungles during the Vietnam War. They are now ubiquitous environmental contaminants and can generally be detected to some degree in all foods.

What You Need To Know: The International Agency for Research on Cancer has concluded that TCDD is possibly carcinogenic to humans. No data were available in humans, and there was limited evidence of carcinogenicity in animals.[252]

Cancer may not be the most serious health risk from dioxins at common exposure levels. Findings from the US Environmental Protection Agency (EPA) indicate that very low exposure levels may produce subtle effects on foetal development and on the immune system.[253] It has been found that dioxin may act to reduce the number of B cells (immune cells that develop in the bone marrow, then circulate throughout the blood and lymph, fighting off invaders) and reduce the number of T cells (immune cells that develop in the thymus, then circulate throughout the body, attacking invaders). It may also prevent the immune system from developing properly in an unborn child, with lifelong consequences. Comments the director of research at the EPA Health Effects Laboratory: 'Dioxin appears to be a carcinogen in fish, rodents, and other mammals, including humans. But dioxin can also modulate [modify] the immune system resulting in an inability to fight disease. It is a very powerful immunosuppressant. But it can also upregulate [excite] the immune system so that you start becoming hypersensitive, developing autoimmunity and allergies. Depending upon the stage [of growth] of the animal and the species, sometimes you observe immunosuppression and in other cases you observe upregulation.'[254]

Biochemical studies have shown that dioxins can act as powerful 'environmental hormones'. Like natural hormones, they can cross cell membranes and bind to a receptor protein, eventually activating genes which control a wide range of biological functions. Tiny doses of these 'false signals' can thus have powerful effects on many of the most fundamental life processes, including proliferation and differentiation of cells and the reproduction, development, metabolism, and immune function. Sadly, it can take many decades for these subtle but profound effects to register statistically. In 1976, an explosion at a chemical plant in Seveso, Italy, sent a cloud of dioxin-contaminated herbicide 2,4,5-T over the surrounding countryside. Some claimed that this dioxin-exposure had produced little evidence of ill-health. In 1993, however, the first study showed that people with moderate exposure to dioxin had 2.8 times the liver cancer risk of the unexposed population, and 3.7 times to 5.7 times the risk of leukaemia and lymphoma.[255] Commented Linda Birnbaum, the EPA's director of environmental toxicology: 'This, together with other studies, clearly supports that dioxin has the potential to cause cancer in people, just as it does in every animal it's been tested on,' she said. 'The weight of evidence is becoming overwhelming.'

Virtually all human exposures to dioxins occur through the food supply, particularly consumption of animal products.[256] Significant quantities are passed from mother to child during the most sensitive stages of development: across the placenta and via mother's milk.[257] The daily dose received by the average nursing infant in the United States is 10 to 20 times greater than the average adult exposure, which means that babies receive about 10 per cent of their entire lifetime exposure to these compounds during the first year of life.[258]

Apart from accidents such as that at Seveso, environmental dioxins can be produced by incinerators as products of incomplete combustion when chlorinated organic substances are burned. PVC, which is 59 per cent chlorine by weight, is the only major plastic that contains chlorine. Removal of PVC from the waste stream might significantly reduce the generation of dioxin. In Britain, the Ministry of Agriculture, Fisheries and Food states that 'there appears to be no risk to human health from the levels of dioxins in the UK diet'.[259]

Diperodon hydrochloride
MEDICINAL SUBSTANCE: LOCAL ANAESTHETIC
What It Is: Diperodon is a local anaesthetic used to provide temporary pain relief.

Diphenhydramine hydrochloride

MEDICINAL SUBSTANCE: ANTIHISTAMINE

What It Is: An antihistamine drug. For some general information about antihistamines, see the special feature (pp. 134–5). One manufacturer includes diphenhydramine hydrochloride in their analgesic product to relieve symptoms of tension pain. It is also used as a cough suppressant.

Diphenylpyraline hydrochloride

MEDICINAL SUBSTANCE: ANTIHISTAMINE

What It Is: An antihistamine drug. For some general information about antihistamines, see the special feature (pp. 134–5).

Diphosphates
(i) Disodium diphosphate
(ii) Trisodium diphosphate
(iii) Tetrasodium diphosphate
(iv) Dipotassium diphosphate
(v) Tetrapotassium diphosphate
(vi) Dicalcium diphosphate
(vii) Calcium dihydrogen diphosphate (E450)

FOOD ADDITIVE: BUFFERING AGENT; SEQUESTRANT; LEAVENING AGENT

Regulations: EC permitted to be used similarly to phosphoric acid (E338). Directive 95/2/EC.

Acceptable Daily Intake: Maximum tolerable daily intake 70, expressed as phosphorous from all sources.

What It Is: Salts of pyrophosphoric acid, a polymer of phosphoric acid (see pp. 341ff). Some of these are rarely used in food, but disodium diphosphate (SAPP) may be used as a leavening agent in doughnuts and biscuits, as a delayed-action

225

acid release agent in baking powders, and to bind with (sequester) metals which would otherwise oxidize or taint processed foods, such as potatoes and canned fish. Tetrasodium diphosphate (TSPP) is a coagulant, emulsifier and sequestrant sometimes used in cheese to reduce its meltability and fat separation; also used to prevent crystal formation in tuna.

What You Need To Know: See Phosphoric acid.

Dipotassium guanylate (E628)

FOOD ADDITIVE: FLAVOUR ENHANCER

Regulations: EC permitted to be used similarly to guanylic acid (E626). Directive 95/2/EC.

Acceptable Daily Intake: Not specified.

What It Is: See Guanylic acid.

Dipotassium inosinate (E632)

FOOD ADDITIVE: FLAVOUR ENHANCER

Regulations: EC permitted to be used similarly to guanylic acid (E626). Directive 95/2/EC.

Acceptable Daily Intake: Not specified.

What It Is: See the description of flavour enhancers under monosodium glutamate (see pp. 317–8).

Disodium 5'-ribonucleotides (E635)

FOOD ADDITIVE: FLAVOUR ENHANCER

Regulations: EC permitted to be used similarly to guanylic acid (E626). Directive 95/2/EC.

Acceptable Daily Intake: Not specified.

What It Is: See the description of flavour enhancers under monosodium glutamate (pp. 317–8).

What You Need To Know: Scientific studies do not raise carcinogenic concerns.[260]

Disodium guanylate (E627)
FOOD ADDITIVE: FLAVOUR ENHANCER
Regulations: EC permitted to be used similarly to guanylic acid (E626). Directive 95/2/EC.
Acceptable Daily Intake: Not specified.
What It Is: See Guanylic acid.

Disodium inosinate (E631)
FOOD ADDITIVE: FLAVOUR ENHANCER
Regulations: EC permitted to be used similarly to guanylic acid (E626). Directive 95/2/EC.
Acceptable Daily Intake: Not specified.
What It Is: See the description of flavour enhancers under monosodium glutamate (pp. 317–8).

Distarch phosphate (E1412)
FOOD ADDITIVE: STABILIZER; THICKENING AGENT; BINDER; CARRIER
Regulations: EC permitted for all foodstuffs following the *quantum satis* principle (except those specified in Table 2 on pp. 15–16 and in Appendix B on pp. 469ff).
EC permitted as carrier. Restricted use: none. Directive 95/2/EC.
Acceptable Daily Intake: Not specified.
What It Is: A chemically modified starch, made by reacting starch with phosphorous oxychloride or sodium trimetaphosphate, which results in a starch whose strengthened molecular bonds help it to better resist food processing, cooking, acidic conditions, etc.

Dithranol
MEDICINAL SUBSTANCE: PSORIASIS
What It Is: Dithranol is the active ingredient of chrysophanic acid, known to be an effective treatment for psoriasis for more than 100 years.[261]

What You Need To Know: There are many forms of psoriasis, and many types of treatments, which is why diagnosis and treatment should be carried out under the supervision of a medically qualified person. Where the psoriasis takes the form of a small number of large plaques, dithranol can be an appropriate treatment. The more numerous the lesions and the smaller they are, the more difficult the use of dithranol becomes, and tar and topical corticosteroids become more suitable.[262] Side-effects can include skin irritation and staining of the skin and clothes. The use of dithranol in the so-called 'short contact mode', in which the preparation is left on the skin for only 15 to 45 minutes every 24 hours, is just as effective as longer treatments.[263] Dithranol should not be used near the eyes, on flexor surfaces, or in inflammatory forms of the disease.[264]

The International Agency for Research on Cancer has concluded that this substance is unclassifiable as to carcinogenicity in humans.[265]

Docusate Sodium
MEDICINAL SUBSTANCE: LAXATIVE

What It Is: Also known as dioctyl sodium sulphosuccinate, this substance is used as a wetting agent in industrial, pharmaceutical, cosmetic and food applications.

What You Need To Know: May be used in some products sold to treat constipation, which it does by softening hard, dry stools thus allowing them to be penetrated by water and fats. Stool-softener laxatives are useful for people who need to avoid straining – such as those with an episiotomy wound, painful haemorrhoids, fissures, hernias, or heart attack patients.[266]

Docusate sodium may also increase the absorption – and hence the potential toxicity – of other drugs being taken at the same time. For example, greater intestinal damage has reportedly occurred when aspirin and docusate sodium are taken together, compared to aspirin alone.[267]

Dodecyl gallate (E312)

FOOD ADDITIVE: ANTIOXIDANT

Regulations: EC permitted to be used similarly to propyl gallate (E310). Directive 95/2/EC.

Acceptable Daily Intake: 0 – 0.5 (temporary).

What It Is: See Propyl gallate (pp.369–70).

Doxylamine succinate

MEDICINAL SUBSTANCE: ANTIHISTAMINE

What It Is: An antihistamine drug. For some general information about antihistamines, see their separate entry (pp. 134–5).

Ephedrine

MEDICINAL SUBSTANCE: DECONGESTANT

What It Is: Originally derived from the Chinese shrub, *Ephedra distachia*, ephedrine is a sympathomimetic drug, whose general effects include:

- Stimulation of the heart's force and contraction
- Stimulation of the central nervous system (including increased alertness, faster breathing, reduced appetite)
- Changes (usually rises) in blood pressure and blood sugar level
- Constriction of skin and gut blood vessels
- Relaxation of other blood vessels (e.g. in the bronchial muscles)

It can be used to decongest the nose (either by applying it directly into the nostrils, or by taking it orally) and has been used to relax the bronchial muscles during an asthmatic attack (prescription substances now exist which are preferable for this purpose).

What You Need To Know: When ephedrine is used in the nose as a decongestant and applied as drops or as a spray, 'rebound congestion' may occur – in other words, the symptoms may return after initial medication, sometimes more acutely than previously.[268] If this happens, do not increase the dose in an attempt to prolong the treatment, as this may only make matters worse. Do not use products which contain ephedrine or other sympathomimetics without medical advice if you are diabetic, have hypertension, have prostate or thyroid problems, suffer from glaucoma, or if you have heart or circulatory impairments, or if you are currently taking other medicines (especially amphetamines, medication for high blood pressure or heart problems, treatment for asthma, hay fever or other allergies, or antidepressants). The central nervous stimulating effects of ephedrine may result in nervousness, anxiety, headache, nausea, palpitations, difficulty in passing water and difficulty in sleeping. Paranoid psychosis, delusions and hallucinations have been reported following ephedrine overdosage.[269]

Particularly when used in combinations with phenylpropanolamine (see pp. 338ff) and caffeine, ephedrine has been associated with stroke secondary to intracranial hemorrhage, seizures, mania, and psychosis.[270] [271] Combinations of ephedrine and caffeine have been documented to have sideeffects substantially greater than those from the consumption of either substance alone or of a placebo.[272] [273] [274] [275]

Note: abuse of ephedrine has produced psychic dependence (characterized by compulsion, obsession, and preoccupation) and mental disorders. Advisory committees to the US Food and Drug Administration (FDA) have recommended that ephedrine no longer be available for self-medication (i.e. not for sale without a prescription) based on their use in the production of illicit drugs and on their misuse and abuse as stimulants and for weight loss.[276] The FDA has also warned that people who take dietary supplements that contain ephedrine (such as the Chinese herb *ma huang*) may put themselves at risk of heart attacks, strokes and other health problems.[277]

Epsom salts
See Magnesium sulphate.

Erythorbic acid (E315)
FOOD ADDITIVE: ANTIOXIDANT

Regulations: EC permitted for:
- Semi-preserved and preserved meat products, maximum level: 500 mg/kg expressed as erythorbic acid
- Preserved and semi-preserved fish products, Frozen and deep-frozen fish with red skin, maximum level: 1500 mg/kg expressed as erythorbic acid. Directive 95/2/EC.

Acceptable Daily Intake: Not specified.

What It Is: A stereoisomer of ascorbic acid (see pp.137–9) which, unlike ascorbic acid (vitamin C), does not occur naturally in food. It has very little vitamin C activity itself, and – due to its close chemical relationship to ascorbic acid – may interfere with a number of the biological functions of ascorbic acid, e.g. by decreasing the tissue uptake of ascorbic acid and thus lowering the vitamin C stores in the body.[278] Experiments have shown that it is more readily oxidized than ascorbic acid, and this property may therefore be exploited by manufacturers to protect the vitamin C content of foods.

Erythrosine (E127)
FOOD ADDITIVE: FOOD COLOUR

Regulations: EC permitted for cocktail cherries and candied cherries, maximum level: 200 mg/kg; Bigarreaux cherries in syrup and in cocktails, maximum level: 150 mg/kg. Directive 94/36/EC.

Acceptable Daily Intake: 0 – 0.1.

What It Is: A synthetic, bright bluish-red xanthene dye.

What You Need To Know: A potential dietary source of iodine. Animal studies have shown that erythrosine may hyperstimulate the thyroid gland, leading to the development of thyroid tumours.[279] Risk estimate: based on data from the studies submitted to the United States Food and Drug Administration, one in 100,000 people may develop thyroid tumours from consuming erythrosine in food products.[280]

Ether

MEDICINAL SUBSTANCE: ANAESTHETIC; FLAVOURING

What It Is: In the early part of the nineteenth century, 'ether-frolics' or 'laughing-gas parties' became a popular pastime among young people. At one of these parties, a certain Dr Crawford W. Long noted that jubilant party participants could sustain injuries without feeling any pain. On 30 March 1842, he administered ether to permit the painless removal of a cystic tumour on the back of a man's neck. In 1846 Dr William Morton, a dentist, used ether for the painless extraction of a tooth – and was so encouraged by his results that he requested an opportunity to anaesthetize a patient undergoing major surgery at Massachusetts General Hospital. His request was granted and on 16 October 1846, he publicly staged the first successful demonstration of surgical anaesthesia in history.[281] It has some disadvantages in use, such as its potential to produce nausea and vomiting, and the risk of fire or explosion. Today, other, more modern anaesthetics are often used instead. In over-the-counter medicines it probably has little more purpose than to impart a medicinal-type odour. It can also be used as a solvent for waxes, fats, oils, perfumes, alkaloids and gums, and as a chemical reagent.

Ethyl ester of beta-apo-8'-carotenic acid (C 30) (E160f)

FOOD ADDITIVE: FOOD COLOUR

Regulations: EC permitted to be used singly or in combination with other colours in the following foods up to the total maximum level specified.
• Non-alcoholic flavoured drinks, maximum level: 100 mg/l

- Candied fruits and vegetables, Mostarda di frutta, maximum level: 200 mg/kg
- Preserves of red fruits, maximum level: 200 mg/kg
- Confectionery, maximum level: 300 mg/kg
- Decorations and coatings, maximum level: 500 mg/kg
- Fine bakery wares (e.g. viennoiserie, biscuits, cakes and wafers), maximum level: 200 mg/kg
- Edible ices, maximum level: 150 mg/kg
- Flavoured processed cheese, maximum level: 100 mg/kg
- Desserts including flavoured milk products, maximum level: 150 mg/kg
- Sauces, seasonings (for example, curry powder, tandoori), pickles, relishes, chutney and piccalilli, maximum level: 500 mg/kg
- Mustard, maximum level: 300 mg/kg
- Fish paste and crustacean paste, maximum level: 100 mg/kg; Pre-cooked crustaceans, maximum level: 250 mg/kg; Salmon substitutes, maximum level: 500 mg/kg; Surimi, maximum level: 500 mg/kg; Fish roe, maximum level: 300 mg/kg; Smoked fish, maximum level: 100 mg/kg
- Snacks: dry, savoury potato, cereal or starch-based snack products: Extruded or expanded savoury snack products, maximum level: 200 mg/kg; Other savoury snack products and savoury coated nuts, maximum level: 100 mg/kg; Edible cheese rind and edible casings, maximum level: *quantum satis*
- Complete formulae for weight control intended to replace total daily food intake or an individual meal, maximum level: 50 mg/kg
- Complete formulae and nutritional supplements for use under medical supervision, maximum level: 50 mg/kg
- Liquid food supplements/dietary integrators, maximum level: 100 mg/l
- Solid food supplements/dietary integrators, maximum level: 300 mg/kg
- Soups, maximum level: 50 mg/kg
- Meat and fish analogues based on vegetable proteins, maximum level: 100 mg/kg
- Spirituous beverages (including products less than 15 % alcohol by volume), except those mentioned in Annex II or III, maximum level: 200 mg/l
- Aromatized wines, aromatized wine-based drinks and aromatized

wine-product cocktails as mentioned in Regulation (EEC) No 1601/91, except those mentioned in Annex II or III, maximum level: 200 mg/l

- Fruit wines (still or sparkling) cider (except cidre bouche) and perry, aromatized fruit wines, cider and perry, maximum level: 200 mg/l. Directive 94/36/EC.

Acceptable Daily Intake: 0 – 5 group acceptable daily intake as sum of the carotenoids.

What It Is: Similar to Beta-apo-8'-carotenal (see pp. 156–7).

Ethyl methyl cellulose (E465)

FOOD ADDITIVE: THICKENING AGENT; EMULSIFIER; STABILIZER; FOAMING AGENT; CARRIER

Regulations: EC permitted for all foodstuffs following the *quantum satis* principle (except those specified in Table 2 on pp. 15–16 and in Appendix B on pp. 469ff).

EC permitted as carrier. Restricted use: none. Directive 95/2/EC.

Acceptable Daily Intake: Not specified.

What It Is: One of many derivatives of cellulose (see p. 196)

Ethyl p-hydroxybenzoate (E214)

FOOD ADDITIVE: PRESERVATIVE

Regulations: EC permitted to be used either singly or with E215, E216, E217, E218 and E219, but only when combined with E200, E202 or E203. May only be used in the following foods up to the combined maximum level specified.

- Jelly coatings of meat products (cooked, cured or dried); Paté, maximum level: 1 000 mg/kg
- Cereal- or potato-based snacks and coated nuts, maximum level: 1000 mg/kg (of which a maximum of 300 mg/kg from E214, E215, E216, E217, E218 or E219)

When used singly or combined with E215, E216, E217, E218 or E219, further combined with E200, E202 or E203 and further combined with E210, E211, E212 or E213, may be used in the following foods up to the combined maximum level specified.

- Surface treatment of dried meat products, maximum level: *quantum satis*
- Confectionery (excluding chocolate), maximum level: 1 500 mg/kg (of which a maximum of 300 mg/kg from E214, E215, E216, E217, E218 or E219)
- Liquid dietary food supplements, maximum level: 2 000 mg/kg. Directive 95/2/EC.

Acceptable Daily Intake: 0 – 10 as sum of ethyl, methyl and propyl esters of p-hydroxybenzoic acid.

What It Is: Also known as ethyl-paraben, made by combining para-hydroxybenzoic acid with ethanol. A closely related compound to benzoic acid (see pp. 151–3), but more soluble in water, and a more effective preservative than benzoic acid in food which tends towards the alkali.

What You Need To Know: May cause occasional hypersensitivity, usually manifested as dermatitis.[282]

Ethyl salicylate
MEDICINAL SUBSTANCE: COUNTER-IRRITANT

What It Is: The salicylic acid ester of alcohol, once used internally for rheumatism and sometimes now used on the skin as a counter-irritant.

Eucalyptus
MEDICINAL SUBSTANCE: FLAVOURING

What It Is: Distilled from the leaves of the tree of the same name, eucalyptus oil contains cineole (see pp. 201–2) which has some antiseptic properties. It is used as a flavouring agent and expectorant.

Eugenol

MEDICINAL SUBSTANCE: FRAGRANCE

What It Is: The main constituent (about 80 per cent) of clove oil, from which it can be obtained. Mainly used as a fragrance and flavouring agent, as an analgesic in dental materials and non-prescription drug products, as an insect attractant.

What You Need To Know: The International Agency for Research on Cancer has concluded that this substance is unclassifiable as to carcinogenicity in humans. There was no adequate data in humans, and limited evidence in animals.[283]

Euphorbia

MEDICINAL SUBSTANCE: COUNTER-IRRITANT

What It Is: There are nearly one thousand members of the *Euphorbiaceae* plant family. Many of them produce a milky juice which is a violent irritant and can be poisonous – it has been used to destroy animals.[284] An oil-like latex from *Euphorbia lathyris*, a shrub that grows in semi-arid regions, can be converted to a fuel similar to petrol.[285]

Fatty acid esters of ascorbic acid
(i) Ascorbyl palmitate
(ii) Ascorbyl stearate (E304)

FOOD ADDITIVE: ANTIOXIDANT

Regulations: EC permitted for all foodstuffs following the *quantum satis* principle (except those specified in Table 2 on pp. 15–16 and in Appendix B on pp. 469ff). Directive 95/2/EC.

Acceptable Daily Intake: Ascorbyl palmitate 0 – 1.25; Ascorbyl stearate 0 – 1.25; or sum of both.

What It Is: Ascorbyl palmitate is manufactured by reacting ascorbic acid (see pp.137–9) with sulphuric acid followed by re-esterification with palmitic acid. Unlike ascorbic acid, this substance is somewhat fat-soluble and is therefore used for its antioxidant qualities in fatty or oily foodstuffs, often in combination with other antioxidants such as tocopherols. Sometimes used in combination with nitrite in cured meat products to discourage the production of carcinogenic nitrosamines, and to inhibit growth of botulism bacteria. Ascorbyl stearate is similarly manufactured (using stearic acid) and has similar properties.

Ferric oxide
MEDICINAL SUBSTANCE: PIGMENT

What It Is: Also known as iron (iii) oxide, burnt sienna or burnt umber. Mainly used as a pigment in paints, plastics, inks, rubber and glass; in building materials, magnets and magnetic tapes; in animal feeds and fertilizers; and as a pharmaceutical aid in preparations for application to the skin.

What You Need To Know: The International Agency for Research on Cancer has concluded that this substance is unclassifiable as to carcinogenicity in humans. There was inadequate evidence in humans, and evidence suggesting lack of carcinogenicity in animals.[286]

Ferrous gluconate (E579)
FOOD ADDITIVE: COLOURING ADJUNCT

Regulations: EC permitted for olives darkened by oxidation, maximum level: 150 mg/kg as Fe. Directive 95/2/EC.

Acceptable Daily Intake: 0.8 provisional maximum tolerable daily intake for iron from all sources.

What It Is: Ferrous gluconate contains 12 per cent iron and is also used as a nutrient or dietary supplement in the prevention and treatment of iron deficiency, and as a trace mineral added to animal feed.

What You Need To Know: Large amounts of ferrous salts of iron are toxic but, in adults, deaths are rare. Most deaths occur in children, especially between 12 and 24 months – as little as 1 to 2 grams of iron may cause death, but 2 to 10 grams is usually ingested in fatal cases.[287] Iron poisoning is the most common cause of child poisoning deaths in the United States.[288] In one typical year, over 23,000 poisoning cases involving children and iron supplements were reported to poison control centres, of which 13 were fatal.[289] The number of tablets associated with a toxic dose varies, depending on the form and amount of iron used – consumption of as few as five or six tablets of a high-potency iron preparation could be fatal for a 10kg (22lb) child. It is particularly important that pregnant women who take iron supplements should keep the pills away from toddlers.

Ferrous lactate (E5850)
FOOD ADDITIVE: COLOURING ADJUNCT; NUTRIENT
Regulations: EC permitted to be used similarly to ferrous gluconate (E579). Directive 95/2/EC.
Acceptable Daily Intake: 0.8 provisional maximum tolerable daily intake for iron from all sources.
What It Is: Made by reacting calcium lactate with ferrous sulphate, or by direct action of lactic acid on iron; filings; contains approximately 20 per cent metallic iron.
What You Need To Know: See Ferrous gluconate.

Fluoride
See Sodium fluoride.

Formaldehyde
MEDICINAL SUBSTANCE: PRESERVATIVE
FOOD ADDITIVE: CONTAMINANT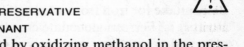
What It Is: Manufactured by oxidizing methanol in the presence of a silver catalyst. Aqueous formaldehyde is known as formalin. Uses include general preservative, disinfectant and antiseptic functions; in the manufacture of phenolic resins, artificial silk and cellulose esters; in slow-release fertilizers; in embalming solutions; as a tissue fixative; and as a component of particle board and plywood.
What You Need To Know: The US Environmental Protection

Agency has classified this substance as a probable human carcinogen. Human data include nine studies that show statistically significant associations between site-specific respiratory neoplasms and exposure to formaldehyde or formaldehyde-containing products. An increased incidence of nasal squamous cell carcinomas was observed in long-term inhalation studies in rats and in mice. The classification is supported by in vitro genotoxicity data and formaldehyde's structural relationships to other carcinogenic aldehydes such as acetaldehyde.[290]

The International Agency for Research on Cancer has concluded that formaldehyde is probably carcinogenic to humans. There is limited evidence in humans for the carcinogenicity of formaldehyde. There is sufficient evidence in experimental animals for the carcinogenicity of formaldehyde.[291]

The US National Institute of Occupational Safety and Health recommends that formaldehyde be regulated as a potential human carcinogen.[292]

In a survey of 57 embalmers who were exposed to formaldehyde in the air, at a concentration below 2 parts per million, there was a high incidence of symptoms of irritant effects on the eyes, nose and throat. Other respiratory effects included cough, chest tightness, wheezing and shortness of breath. On the basis of the results, 10 per cent were acute bronchitics, and 30 per cent were chronic bronchitics.[293] Effects in women attributed to formaldehyde exposure include menstrual disorders and secondary sterility.[294] Significantly greater rates of asthma and chronic bronchitis have been found in children from houses with formaldehyde levels above 60 parts per billion than in those less exposed, especially in children also exposed to environmental tobacco smoke.[295] Release of formaldehyde vapours in mobile homes has been associated with headache and lung and skin irritation.[296]

Humans can be exposed to formaldehyde in many ways. It is

formed by the incomplete combustion of many organic substances, making exhaust pollution and coal and wood smoke
one possible source. Others include emissions from resins in
particle board, plywood, foam insulation, resin-treated fabrics
and paper. Urea-formaldehyde and melamine-formaldehyde
resins are incorporated into tea-bag tissues to prevent their dis-
integration in water. When Britain's Ministry of Agriculture,
Fisheries and Food sampled 181 tea bags, 12 gave detectable
levels of formaldehyde.[297] The Department of Health considered that the results did not give rise to any toxicological
concerns. Formaldehyde has been implicated in many cases of
sick-building syndrome.[298] Indoor air pollution has worsened
in recent decades for two reasons. First, the replacement of
solid wood in building construction and furniture with pressed-
wood products and fibreboard, facilitates the emission of trace
levels of organic chemicals. Second, air inside energy-efficient
houses is often of very poor quality, since efficient insulation
eliminates external draughts and fresh air.

SECRET INGREDIENTS FACT FILE
HOW TO CLEAN YOUR AIR NATURALLY

NASA became interested in indoor air pollution when a study
identified 107 volatile organic chemicals in the air inside the
Skylab space station. Their scientists have found that the
presence of spider plants can rapidly decrease environmental formaldehyde levels: from 14 to 2 parts per million in
6 hours and below the detection limit of 2 ppm within 24
hours. Recent research suggests that philodendrons can
be even more effective than spider plants at removing
formaldehyde.

Frangula
MEDICINAL SUBSTANCE: LAXATIVE
What It Is: Frangula is the dried bark of the buckthorn tree,
Rhamnus frangula, and it acts as an irritant laxative.

Fumaric acid (E297)

FOOD ADDITIVE: ACIDULANT; FLAVOURING AGENT

Regulations: EC permitted for:
- (*pro memoria*) Wine in accordance with Regulation (EEC) No 1873/84 authorizing the offer or disposal for direct human consumption of certain imported wines which may have undergone oenological processes not provided for in Regulation (EEC) No 337/79
- Fillings and toppings for fine bakery wares, maximum level: 2,5 g/kg
- Sugar confectionery, maximum level: 1 g/kg
- Gel-like desserts, Fruit-flavoured desserts, Dry powdered dessert mixes, maximum level: 4 g/kg
- Instant powders for fruit based drinks, maximum level: 1 g/l
- Instant tea powder, maximum level: 1 g/l
- Chewing gum, maximum level: 2 g/kg

Directive 95/2/EC.

Acceptable Daily Intake: Not specified.

What It Is: Fumaric acid is found naturally in many plants (is named after the genus *Fumaria*). Made by fermenting glucose or molasses: relatively insoluble in water and so generally used in dry powdered food products.[299] Also used as a fortifier in paper size resins, and to remove stains from dentures.

What You Need To Know: Generally well-tolerated in humans.[300] Used experimentally to treat psoriasis. Some evidence that this substance has anti-cancer properties.[301]

Gamma-tocopherol (E308)

FOOD ADDITIVE: ANTIOXIDANT

Regulations: EC permitted for all foodstuffs following the *quantum satis* principle (except those specified in Table 2 on pp. 15–16 and in Appendix B on pp. 469ff). Directive 95/2/EC.

Acceptable Daily Intake: 0.15 – 2 group acceptable daily intake for tocopherols.

What It Is: See Alpha-tocopherol.

Garlic oil

MEDICINAL SUBSTANCE: FLAVOURANT

What It Is: This ancient and versatile member of the onion family has been used not only for the delicious (but pungent) flavour it can impart to food, but also as an expectorant and disinfectant. Garlic is said to increase perspiration and the flow of urine, and it has had many healing and preventative powers attributed to it, featuring in olden times as a tuberculosis and plague remedy.

Gelatine

FOOD INGREDIENT

What It Is: Obtained from animal skin and bones, both slaughterhouse by-products. Gelatine for food use is made primarily from pigskin (often bought by the manufacturer direct from the slaughterhouse, usually in the form of frozen blocks of skin) and cattle hides (often bought from leather tanneries). Gelatine can also be produced from cattle bones, but since this is a more complex and costly process, the gelatine thus produced is generally used in the photographic and pharmaceutical industries. Pigskin and cattle hides contain large amounts of collagen, a protein that is the principle constituent of connective tissue in all animals (it gives strength and support to our tissues and organs). Gelatine is obtained from collagen by hydrolysis (acid treatment, alkali treatment or high pressure steam extraction). The resulting gelatine finds many uses in the food industry, including table jellies, confectionery, meat products and chilled dairy products; in fact, more gelatine is sold to the food industry than any other gelling agent.[302] Unlike other vegetable-based thickening and gelling agents in this book (e.g. agar, carrageenan) gelatine has been classified by the European Commission as a food in its own right and is therefore not subject to the usual E number prefix.

Gellan gum (E418)
FOOD ADDITIVE: THICKENING AGENT; STABILIZER;
GELLING AGENT
Regulations: EC permitted for all foodstuffs following the
quantum satis principle (except those specified in Table 2 on
pp. 15–16 and in Appendix B on pp. 469ff). Directive 95/2/EC.
Acceptable Daily Intake: Not specified.
What It Is: Produced by bacterial fermentation.
What You Need To Know: May produce a laxative effect at high
intakes. Scientific studies do not raise carcinogenic concerns.

Ginger
MEDICINAL SUBSTANCE: FLAVOURING
What It Is: Ginger (Zingiber) is grown in many parts of the
world, including the West Indies, Spain, Africa and China. It
has been a plant of some commercial importance for many
centuries, valued for both its culinary and medicinal qualities.
The dried root is a flavouring agent and has been used to relieve
flatulence.

Gluconic acid (E574)
FOOD ADDITIVE: ACIDITY REGULATOR; RAISING AGENT
Regulations: EC permitted for all foodstuffs following the
quantum satis principle (except those specified in Table 2 on
pp. 15–16 and in Appendix B on pp. 469ff). Directive 95/2/EC.
Acceptable Daily Intake: Not specified.
What It Is: The main acid naturally present in honey, gluconic
acid is today manufactured by the chemical, electrolytic or
bacterial oxidation of glucose.

Glucono-delta-lactone (E575)
FOOD ADDITIVE: ACIDULANT; LEAVENING AGENT; SEQUESTRANT
Regulations: EC permitted for all foodstuffs following the
quantum satis principle (except those specified in Table 2 on
pp. 15–16 and in Appendix B on pp. 469ff). Directive 95/2/EC.

Acceptable Daily Intake: Not specified.

What It Is: Used in the baking industry as an acid which, when added to sodium bicarbonate, increases the amount of carbon dioxide produced in the dough and so adds volume and lightness to the final product. Glucono-delta-lactone is the bakers' acid of choice for this purpose, since it leaves the minimum aftertaste.[303]

What You Need To Know: Non-toxic.[304] It is metabolized in the body to lactone and gluconic acid, both natural breakdown products of glucose (sugar) metabolism. Scientific studies do not raise carcinogenic, mutagenic or reproductive concerns. Dose in excess of 20 grams may have a laxative effect.

Glutamic acid (E620)

FOOD ADDITIVE: FLAVOUR ENHANCER; SALT SUBSTITUTE

Regulations: EC permitted for the following foods:
Foodstuffs in general (except those referred to in Article 2 (3)). Maximum level: 10 g/kg individually or in combination with E621, E622, E623, E624 or E625; Condiments and seasonings, maximum level: *quantum satis.* Directive 95/2/EC.

Acceptable Daily Intake: Not specified.

What It Is: The predominant amino acid in most proteins, commercially produced by bacterial fermentation, and the basis for the flavour potentiator monosodium glutamate (see pp. 317–8).

What You Need To Know: Glutamate functions in the brain as an excitatory neurotransmitter – it is released from the terminals of one neuron and binds to receptors on the surface of adjacent neurons. Such excitatory amino acids exist in high concentration in every part of the brain, and play a vital role in almost all brain processes. In recent years, researchers have proposed that too much glutamate activation of receptors can kill nerve cells (excitotoxicity).[305] To what degree dietary glutamate may function as an excitotoxin is still controversial, but there may be vulnerable subgroups within the population who are particularly susceptible to dietary excitotoxins which, it has been suggested, may be involved in neurodegenerative diseases such as Alzheimer's, Parkinson's, and Huntington's.[306]

Glutaraldehyde

MEDICINAL SUBSTANCE: ANTIMICROBIAL

What It Is: Effective against many forms of bacteria, their spores and some fungi and viruses. It has been used with some success to inactivate the wart virus. Also used to sterilize medical instruments which cannot be heat-treated (thermometers, rubber or plastic equipment), and as embalming fluid.

What You Need To Know: It is thought to be less intensely irritating to the skin than formaldehyde, but it can still produce sensitization (allergic contact dermatitis) and will severely irritate the eyes if accidentally brought into contact with them. Since it evaporates quite slowly, only small amounts are likely to be inhaled from a cold water solution.[307] Warts are not cancerous growths. If something on your skin makes you worried about skin cancer, you should ask your doctor to check it out (you should also get any mole or birthmark looked at if it suddenly starts growing, bleeding, or if the surrounding area changes in some way). Warts can be surgically removed, or they can be removed by using a wart paint as a caustic or keratolytic agent. Reputedly, warts can also be charmed away by folk healers, or even hypnotized away. Warts will often disappear by themselves, given time, but professional advice should be taken before attempting self-treatment.

Glycerine

See Glycerol.

Glycerol (E422)

FOOD ADDITIVE: HUMECTANT; BODYING AGENT; SOLVENT; PLASTICIZER

Regulations: EC permitted for all foodstuffs following the

quantum satis principle (except those specified in Table 2 on pp. 15–16 and in Appendix B on pp. 469ff).

EC permitted as carrier. Restricted use: none. Directive 95/2/EC.

Acceptable Daily Intake: Not specified.

What It Is: A sweet-tasting polyol, or polyhydric alcohol, first discovered in 1779 when it was extracted from olive oil. Glycerol naturally occurs in all animal and vegetable fats and oils, but rarely in the free state – it is usually present as a triglyceride when it is combined with such fatty acids as stearic, oleic, palmitic and lauric. The uses of glycerol number in the thousands, and almost every major industry uses glycerol in some form, but the largest amounts go into the manufacture of synthetic resins and gums, drugs, cosmetics and toothpaste – it was also (but no longer) the original antifreeze for car radiators, today reflected in its use as a 'freeze point depressor' in the manufacture of soft-scoop ice creams. It is also one of the raw materials in the manufacture of the explosive nitroglycerine. Strictly, the term glycerol applies only to the chemical compound 1,2,3,-propanetriol, and the term glycerine applies to the purified commercial products normally containing 95 per cent or more glycerol. It is either produced by synthesis from propylene, or can recovered from the by-products of soap manufacturing. May be used as a moisturizing ingredient in cosmetic products, as a laxative agent in suppositories, and as a demulcent to soothe sore throats.

When used as a direct food additive, its hygroscopic (water-attracting) properties will help to maintain the correct degree of moisture in foods, it acts as a solvent for flavourings, it controls the rate of crystallization in sweets and candies, and its viscosity lends body to a product. It can be used as a food-grade lubricant for machinery, and as a heat-transfer medium in direct contact with foods for quick freezing. In combination with fatty acids (usually hydrogenated soya bean oil) it forms

monoglycerides, the most commonly used food emulsifier.
What You Need To Know: Mostly incorporated into body fat, relatively small amounts are excreted. Few adverse effects following intake of the amount likely to be found in food – larger amounts may cause mild headache, dizziness, nausea, vomiting, thirst (dehydration), and diarrhoea.[308]

Glycerol esters of wood rosins (E445)
FOOD ADDITIVE: DENSITY ADJUSTMENT AGENT FOR
FLAVOURING OILS IN BEVERAGE
Regulations: EC permitted for non-alcoholic flavoured cloudy drinks, maximum level: 100 mg/l. Directive 95/2/EC.
Acceptable Daily Intake: no acceptable daily intake allocated.
What It Is: Made from wood rosin harvested from the stumps of the longleaf pine tree.
What You Need To Know: A highly stable chemical structure (stable ester bond) means that it passes through the intestinal tract largely unabsorbed, and is mostly excreted.[309]

Glyceryl triacetate (triacetin) (E1518)
FOOD ADDITIVE: CARRIER; HUMECTANT
Regulations: EC permitted as carrier. Restricted use: none. Directive 95/2/EC.
Acceptable Daily Intake: Not specified.
What It Is: Made by reacting glycerol with acetic acid. Used in the manufacture of cigarette filters, a component in binders for solid rocket fuels, a fungicide (it releases acetic acid), and a fixative in perfumery.
What You Need To Know: Appears to be innocuous when swallowed, inhaled or in contact with the skin, but may cause slight irritation to sensitive individuals.[310]

Glycine and its sodium salt (aminoacetic acid) (E640)

FOOD ADDITIVE: FOOD ADDITIVE; CARRIER

Regulations: EC permitted for all foodstuffs following the *quantum satis* principle (except those specified in Table 2 on pp. 15–16 and in Appendix B on pp. 469ff).

EC permitted as carrier. Restricted use: none. Directive 95/2/EC.

Acceptable Daily Intake: None allocated.

What It Is: The simplest amino acid, and the principal amino acid in sugar cane. Made either from cane, gelatine, silk fibroin or prepared synthetically.

Gold (E175)

FOOD ADDITIVE: FOOD COLOUR

Regulations: EC permitted for external coating of confectionery, maximum level: *quantum satis.*

EC permitted for decoration of chocolates, maximum level: *quantum satis*; Liqueurs, maximum level: *quantum satis.* Directive 94/36/EC.

Acceptable Daily Intake: No acceptable daily intake allocated.

What It Is: After mining, the ore is treated with a cyanide solution, and the dissolved gold cyanate is recovered by precipitation with zinc dust, aluminium, or by hydrolysis. Most gold production goes into jewellery and the arts (52 per cent) followed by industrial and electronic uses (35 per cent), dental (12 per cent) and small bars for investment (1 per cent).[311]

What You Need To Know: Gold compounds can suppress or prevent, but not cure, arthritis and synovitis.[312] Gold metal dust is not toxic to mammals via oral intake.[313] It has a low degree of chemical activity and is not attacked by acids, air or oxygen, although it can be tarnished by sulphur.

Green S (E142)

FOOD ADDITIVE: FOOD COLOUR

Regulations: EC permitted to be used singly or in combination with other colours in the following foods up to the total maximum level specified.

- Non-alcoholic flavoured drinks, maximum level: 100 mg/l
- Candied fruits and vegetables, Mostarda di frutta, maximum level: 200 mg/kg
- Preserves of red fruits, maximum level: 200 mg/kg
- Confectionery, maximum level: 300 mg/kg
- Decorations and coatings, maximum level: 500 mg/kg
- Fine bakery wares (e.g. viennoiserie, biscuits, cakes and wafers), maximum level: 200 mg/kg
- Edible ices, maximum level: 150 mg/kg
- Flavoured processed cheese, maximum level: 100 mg/kg
- Desserts including flavoured milk products, maximum level: 150 mg/kg
- Sauces, seasonings (for example, curry powder, tandoori), pickles, relishes, chutney and piccalilli, maximum level: 500 mg/kg
- Mustard, maximum level: 300 mg/kg
- Fish paste and crustacean paste, maximum level: 100 mg/kg; Pre-cooked crustaceans, maximum level: 250 mg/kg; Salmon substitutes, maximum level: 500 mg/kg; Surimi, maximum level: 500 mg/kg; Fish roe, maximum level: 300 mg/kg; Smoked fish, maximum level: 100 mg/kg
- Snacks: dry, savoury potato, cereal or starch-based snack products: Extruded or expanded savoury snack products, maximum level: 200 mg/kg; Other savoury snack products and savoury coated nuts, maximum level: 100 mg/kg
- Edible cheese rind and edible casings, maximum level: *quantum satis*
- Complete formulae for weight control intended to replace total daily food intake or an individual meal, maximum level: 50 mg/kg
- Complete formulae and nutritional supplements for use under medical supervision, maximum level: 50 mg/kg
- Liquid food supplements/dietary integrators, maximum level: 100 mg/l

- Solid food supplements/dietary integrators, maximum level: 300 mg/kg
- Soups, maximum level: 50 mg/kg
- Meat and fish analogues based on vegetable proteins, maximum level: 100 mg/kg
- Spirituous beverages (including products less than 15% alcohol by volume), except those mentioned in Annex II or III, maximum level: 200 mg/l
- Aromatized wines, aromatized wine-based drinks and aromatized wine-product cocktails as mentioned in Regulation (EEC) No 1601/91, except those mentioned in Annex II or III, maximum level: 200 mg/l
- Fruit wines (still or sparkling) cider (except cidre bouche) and perry, aromatized fruit wines, cider and perry, maximum level: 200 mg/l. Directive 94/36/EC.

Acceptable Daily Intake: No acceptable daily intake allocated.

What It Is: A synthetic, bluish-green triarylmethane dye.

What You Need To Know: When the Joint FAO/WHO Expert Committee on Food Additives considered this substance in 1974, they withdrew the previously designated temporary acceptable daily intake on the basis that the scientific studies which they had previously requested had not been conducted.[314]

Guaiacol

MEDICINAL SUBSTANCE: EXPECTORANT

What It Is: Made by distillation of wood tar or coal tar, or synthetically. Used as a local anaesthetic; antioxidant; anti-gumming agent in hydrocarbon solvents; anti-skinning agent in surface coatings; expectorant; and flavouring agent for non-alcoholic beverages and foods.

What You Need To Know: It has similar pharmacological properties to phenol (see pp. 336–7) but appears to be about a third as toxic.[315] A nine-year-old girl died after swallowing 5 ml, and doses of more than 2 grams are hazardous when applied to the skin, especially if in prolonged contact. Severely injurious to the eyes. Medical use as an expectorant in large doses can cause cardiovascular collapse and clinical doses may cause gastro-intestinal irritation.[316]

Guaiphenesin

MEDICINAL SUBSTANCE: EXPECTORANT

What It Is: Also known as glyceryl guaicolate and guaicol glycerol ether, guaiphenesin is obtained by condensing guaiacol with glycerol in the presence of dehydrating agents and used as an expectorant in cough medicines.

What You Need To Know: When taken in normal expectorant doses, gastro-intestinal upset is rare.[317]

Guanylic acid (E626)

FOOD ADDITIVE: FLAVOUR ENHANCER

Regulations: EC permitted for the following foods:

Foodstuffs in general (except those referred to in Article 2 (3)), maximum level: 500 mg/kg individually or in combination with E627, E628, E629, E630, E631, E632, E633, E634 or E635, expressed as guanylic acid.

Seasonings and condiments, maximum level: *quantum satis*. Directive 95/2/EC.

Acceptable Daily Intake: Not specified.

What It Is: Manufactured by the enzymatic degradation of RNA (ribonucleic acid) obtained mainly from yeast.

What You Need To Know: A flavour 'potentiator' that is 50 to 100 times stronger than monosodium glutamate (MSG) (see pp. 317–8). Guanylic acid is a nucleotide often combined with MSG to powerful effect: one gram of a 50/50 mixture of guanylic acid and MSG combined has the same flavour-intensifying effect as 100 grams of MSG alone! Unlike MSG, guanylic acid is also used by food technologists to give a product positive 'mouthfeel'.[318] Scientific studies do not raise carcinogenic concerns.[319]

Guar gum (E412)

FOOD ADDITIVE: THICKENING AGENT; STABILIZER; CARRIER

Regulations: EC permitted for all foodstuffs following the *quantum satis* principle (except those specified in Table 2 on pp. 15–16 and in Appendix B on pp. 469ff). May not be used to produce dehydrated foodstuffs intended to rehydrate on ingestion.

EC permitted as carrier. Restricted use: none. Directive 95/2/EC.

Acceptable Daily Intake: Not specified.

What It Is: Made from the ground seedpod of the guar plant, *cyamopsis tetragonolobus*, guar has the unique ability amongst gums to hydrate rapidly in cold water. In the food industry, this property is particularly exploited in high speed production lines (e.g. ice-cream processing). Also used to bind water, prevent ice crystal growth, improve 'mouth-feel' and slow down the rate at which ice-cream and ices melt. Pharmaceutically, guar gum is used to bind tablets and enables them to disintegrate on contact with moisture.

What You Need To Know: Has also been used as a slimming 'aid', intended to be taken with water because it swells up in the stomach, thus producing a feeling of fullness and, theoretically, a decreased appetite. However, there have been safety fears about its use in this manner, since it could swell up in the gullet causing a dangerous, choking obstruction or rupture the eosophagus.

Hamamelis

MEDICINAL SUBSTANCE: ASTRINGENT

What It Is: Also known as witch hazel, it is extracted from the leaves, which contain tannic acid, (see p. 432), of the spotted alder. Hamamelis was used by the North American Indians to treat swellings, injuries and bruises. It is used to relieve the pain of piles, skin irritations, and bruises.

Helium (E939)
FOOD ADDITIVE: PROCESSING AID

Regulations: EC permitted for all foodstuffs following the *quantum satis* principle. Directive 95/2/EC.

What It Is: Made by extraction from helium-bearing natural gas. Many uses include a cooling medium for nuclear reactors and a gas for supersonic wind tunnels and various cryogenic applications.

What You Need To Know: An inert gas, its solubility in body fluid is extremely limited.[320] Divers breathing oxygen-helium mixture have successfully descended under compression to depths as great as 686 metres.[321]

Heparin
MEDICINAL SUBSTANCE: ANTICOAGULENT

What It Is: an anticoagulent (a substance that inhibits blood clotting) isolated from mammalian tissue. Has been used in products intended to be applied to the surface of the skin for the purpose of reducing swelling and inflammation (e.g. in cases of haemorrhoids). Haemorrhoids (piles) are veins that have become distended (varicosed) in the rectum. This is often the result of chronic constipation and the straining to produce a motion which this causes. One way of avoiding haemorrhoids might be to avoid constipation (e.g. by increasing the fibre in your diet). Medical advice should be sought on the best method of treating haemorrhoids – this may involve trying to correct the underlying cause, if it can be identified.

Hexachlorophene
MEDICINAL SUBSTANCE: ANTIMICROBIAL

What It Is: Also known as hexachlorophane, made by combining 2,4,5-trichlorophenol with formaldehyde in the presence of concentrated sulphuric acid. Has been used as a topical (i.e. applied to the surface of the skin) anti-infective, an antibacterial agent for soaps and even toothpastes, and a disinfectant against fungi.

What You Need To Know: Can produce serious toxic effects if absorbed. Twenty-five severe malformations, such as eye and central nervous system defects have been reported among 460 live births to Swedish hospital personnel exposed to hexachlorophene soap (0.3–3 per cent) 10–16 times a day during pregnancy, compared with no severe malformations seen in a control group of 233 live births from unexposed mothers.[322]

Absorption of hexachlorophene is markedly increased when skin surfaces are burnt or raw. It should not be used on large areas of skin or open wounds, nor on mucous membranes. Poisoning by hexachlorophene leads to circulatory failure, body temperature fluctuations and central nervous symptoms, including headache, twitching, convulsions and death. Some infants treated with high doses of hexachlorophene have died; premature infants and newborns appear to be most susceptible. The spongiform brain changes seen in animals were also observed in infants who died from overexposure to hexachlorophene.[323]

In 1972 in France a talcum powder which accidentally contained higher than ordinary concentration of hexachlorophene was applied repeatedly to small children, mostly in the presence of severe nappy rash, causing severe illness in 204 children, and death in 36.[324]

Cardiovascular disturbances, convulsions, and respiratory arrest have been reported following accidental ingestion of hexachlorophene detergent emulsion by young children or application of high concentration (6 per cent) to children.[325]

In the United States, it has been banned from over-the-counter products.[326] The International Agency for Research on Cancer has concluded that this substance is unclassifiable as to carcinogenicity in humans. No data were available in humans, and there was inadequate evidence of carcinogenicity in animals.[327]

Hexamethylene tetramine (hexamine) (E239)

FOOD ADDITIVE: PRESERVATIVE

Regulations: EC permitted for provolone cheese, maximum level: 25 mg/kg residual amount, expressed as formaldehyde. Directive 95/2/EC.

Acceptable Daily Intake: 0 – 0.15.

What It Is: Made by combining formaldehyde and ammonia. Mostly production is used as a curing agent for phenolic resins; also used as an ingredient in the explosive cyclonite; has lesser uses as an absorber of poisonous gases and fuel tablets for camping stoves. It hydrolizes to formaldehyde (see pp. 238–40), which possesses broad-spectrum antimicrobial properties, and also binds to protein, thereby acting as setting agent in the cheese product for which it is permitted.

Hexetidine

MEDICINAL SUBSTANCE: ANTIMICROBIAL

What It Is: An antiseptic used in some mouthwashes and on the surface of the skin against fungi (such as *candida albicans*, the yeast that causes thrush).

Hexyl nicotinate

MEDICINAL SUBSTANCE: COUNTER-IRRITANT

What It Is: The nicotinates are counter-irritants which also stimulate the blood flow of the skin at the site of application, thus producing redness and an increase in skin temperature – a chemical version of the hot-water bottle.

Hexylresorcinol

MEDICINAL SUBSTANCE: ANTIMICROBIAL

What It Is: Once used as a worming agent and as a spermicide in contraceptive creams, greatly diluted hexylresorcinol is sometimes found in cough and sore throat sweets where it acts as an antiseptic and may produce a feeling of numbness of the tongue.

What You Need To Know: Since it can irritate the gastro-intestinal tract, people with peptic ulcers or stomach problems should use it with caution.

Histamine hydrochloride
MEDICINAL SUBSTANCE: COUNTER-IRRITANT
What It Is: Histamine is used as a counter-irritant on the surface of the skin where it may have the same effect as the nicotinates (i.e. to stimulate blood flow and cause redness and a feeling of warmth). Histamine occurs naturally in the body and its release from cells is partly responsible for the symptoms of allergy (hence the use of antihistamine drugs to control allergic symptoms).

Homatropine methylbromide
MEDICINAL SUBSTANCE: ANTISPASMODIC; ANTISECRETORY
What It Is: Categorized as an antimuscarinic drug, with anti-spasmodic (i.e. relieves spasm, as in stomach cramp) and antisecretory (i.e. diminishes secretions such as saliva) proper-ties. Because it reduces stomach secretions and also reduces the frequency of peristaltic contractions, it is sometimes found in diarrhoea remedies. It has also been formulated in products intended to relieve period pain.
What You Need To Know: Antimuscarinics reduce secretions from the nose, mouth, pharynx and lungs, and relax the smooth muscles of the lungs. Some doctors advise against using antimuscarinics in asthmatic patients because of the drying effect of the drugs.[328]

Homatropine methylbromide is a quaternary ammonium compound which, unlike many other antimuscarinics, does not readily penetrate the central nervous system and is therefore less likely to produce side-effects such as restlessness or irri-tability.

Other side-effects associated with antimuscarinics include dry mouth, blurred vision, dilated pupils, light-induced discomfort (especially with scopolamine), urine retention, irregular heartbeats and palpitation, and constipation. There is a general lack of information from well-controlled studies to support the use of antimuscarinics in most conditions, and since their adverse effects often limit or preclude their use, they have generally been replaced by other more effective and/or less toxic therapies.[329]

Antimuscarinics should not be used or should only be used with caution in a number of situations, including: angle-closure glaucoma; autonomic neuropathy; diarrhoea (which may be an early symptom of incomplete intestinal obstruction); eosophageal reflux; fever (they reduce sweating and increase risk of hyperthermia); gastro-intestinal infections (they reduce the speed at which the toxin is eliminated); heart disease; high blood pressure; hyperthyroidism; liver or kidney disease; myasthenia gravis; stomach ulcer; ulcerative colitis; urinary tract problems. Children, the elderly, those already on medication and pregnant women should only use them after professional advice.

Horehound

MEDICINAL SUBSTANCE: EXPECTORANT
What It Is: The herb horehound (*Marrubium vulgare*) is also known as Gypsy wort and Madwort, and has been used for centuries as an expectorant. 'It helpeth to expectorate tough phlegm from the chest,' said herbalist Nicholas Culpeper in the early 17th century. 'It is given to women to bring down their courses, to expel the afterbirth, and to them that have sore and long travails.'

Hydrochloric acid (E507)

FOOD ADDITIVE: ACID
Regulations: EC permitted for all foodstuffs following the *quantum satis* principle (except those specified in Table 2 on pp. 15–16 and in Appendix B on pp. 469ff). Directive 95/2/EC.

Acceptable Daily Intake: Not specified.

What It Is: Mainly obtained as a byproduct in the manufacture of organic chemicals, with many industrial uses: 28 per cent of total production is used in steel picking; 26 per cent in chemical manufacturing; 23 per cent in oil and gas well acidizing; and 13 per cent in food processing; (10 per cent miscellaneous).[330] Hydrochloric acid (hydrogen chloride) is a natural constituent of human gastric juices (we produce between one and a half and three litres of gastric juice every day). It has been used at great dilutions in a few over-the-counter products, mainly for non-therapeutic reasons.

What You Need To Know: Concentrated solution will cause severe burns and possibly death. Workplace contact can cause dermatitis and chronic bronchitis.[331] Apart from workplace exposure, combustion of fuels and refuse incineration produce hydrochloric acid. Exposure to vapours not concentrated enough to cause taste or eye irritation, can still cause sneezing, laryngitis, chest pain, hoarseness, and a feeling of suffocation.[332]

Upper limit of safety for human exposure to hydrochloric acid has been estimated to be about 45 mg/cu m (30 parts per million), but even this might be harmful if daily exposures were continued over periods longer than 1 month.[333] The US Occupational Safety and Health Administration has directed that an employee's exposure to hydrochloric acid gas shall at no time exceed the ceiling value of 7 mg/cu m (5 parts per million).[334]

The International Agency for Research on Cancer has concluded that this substance is unclassifiable as to carcinogenicity in humans. There is inadequate evidence for the carcinogenicity in humans of hydrochloric acid. There is inadequate evidence for the carcinogenicity in experimental animals of hydrochloric acid.[335]

Note: accidental mixing of formaldehyde and hydrochloric acid could result in generation of bis(chloromethyl)ether, a potent human carcinogen.[336]

Hydrocodone

MEDICINAL SUBSTANCE: COUGH SUPPRESSANT

What It Is: A synthetic alkaloid similar to codeine (see pp. 210–11) which causes suppression of the cough reflex by a direct effect on the cough centre in the medulla of the brain. It also has a drying effect on the lungs, and tends to increase the thickness of phlegm.

What You Need To Know: Thought to be a more powerful anti-tussive and analgesic drug than codeine on a weight-for-weight basis.[337] Adverse effects include lightheadedness, dizziness, sedation, nausea, vomiting, constipation and itching. Prolonged use of hydrocodone may lead to dependence of the morphine type. It is more likely than codeine to produce dependence.[338]

Hydrocortisone

MEDICINAL SUBSTANCE: SKIN DISORDERS

What It Is: Hydrocortisone (cortisol) is a hormone which is naturally produced in the human adrenal glands. Hormones are the body's chemical messengers, operating in complex and inter-connected ways to regulate the chemical processes involved in living. Hydrocortisone is involved in regulating the body's carbohydrate-protein metabolism and, amongst other actions, has powerful anti-inflammatory and anti-allergic effects. This is why hydrocortisone is successfully used on the skin to treat the symptoms of inflammation and allergy. Hydrocortisone belongs to the large steroid family of compounds, and because it is produced in the adrenal cortex, is called a corticosteroid. Corticosteroids can be extracted from the adrenal glands, or may be manufactured synthetically in the laboratory. As therapeutic agents, corticosteroids are used by the medical profession in many ways – to prevent organ transplant rejection, to treat severe attacks of life-threatening asthma, to treat a wide variety of blood disorders, and to suppress inflammation, symptoms of allergy, itching, rheumatoid arthritis, etc. They are generally administered by injection, infusion or by mouth, and the course of treatment should be medically supervised. Patients on steroid therapy must carry cards giving details of their dosage and possible complications – stopping treatment suddenly, for example, could be dangerous.

What You Need To Know: The first thing to realize before using hydrocortisone on the skin is that corticosteroids treat the symptom, not the cause – when you stop using them, the condition might return.[339] Hydrocortisone should not be used against bacterial, viral or fungal infections.

Hydrocortisone is one of the less active corticosteroids, and less likely than many others to cause adverse reactions. They may however occur, and include: delayed wound healing and increased liability to infection (especially when a dressing is used – the anti-inflammatory activity of the drug can hide the signs of infection); thinning of the skin; increased hair growth; the development of acne and the development or worsening of ulcerative skin conditions (more likely if there is impaired blood circulation).[340] Children, the elderly, those already on medication and pregnant women should only use corticosteroids after professional advice. Safe use of topical corticosteroids during pregnancy has not been established.[341]

Hydrogen peroxide

MEDICINAL SUBSTANCE: ANTISEPTIC AND CLEANSING AGENT

What It Is: An important industrial chemical with a multitude of uses: 30 per cent of total production is used in textiles; 28 per cent in plasticizers and other chemicals; 9 per cent for glycerine; 8 per cent for bleaching pulp and paper; and the balance for a range of uses from fuelling rockets to removing ear wax (dilute 1.5 per cent solution). Also used to cleanse wounds and local infections.

What You Need To Know: A very unstable compound that breaks down to form oxygen and water. When used as a skin cleanser in topical solution, contact with tissues that contain the enzyme catalase releases oxygen that destroys some micro-organisms. However, the antibacterial activity of hydrogen peroxide is relatively weak and slow, and it exhibits poor tissue and wound penetration. Concentrated solutions of hydrogen peroxide have a bleaching effect on hair and can injure tissue.[342] Breathing hydrogen peroxide at a concentration of seven parts per million in air causes lung irritation.[343] Hydrogen peroxide solution as a mouthwash, even in half strength, can irritate the tongue and surrounding skin and can cause 'hairy tongue'.[344]

The International Agency for Research on Cancer has concluded that this substance is unclassifiable as to carcinogenicity in humans. No data are available in humans. Limited evidence of carcinogenicity in animals.[345]

Hydrotalcite
MEDICINAL SUBSTANCE: ANTACID

What It Is: Hydrotalcite is an antacid containing a mixture of magnesium and aluminium salts. It is insoluble in water, and is thought not to be absorbed into the bloodstream.

Hydroxy propyl distarch phosphate (E1442)
FOOD ADDITIVE: STABILIZER; THICKENING AGENT; BINDER; CARRIER

Regulations: EC permitted for all foodstuffs following the *quantum satis* principle (except those specified in Table 2 on pp. 15–16 and in Appendix B on pp. 469ff).
EC permitted as carrier. Restricted use: none. Directive 95/2/EC.
Acceptable Daily Intake: Not specified.
What It Is: A chemically modified starch.

Hydroxy propyl starch (E1440)

FOOD ADDITIVE: EMULSIFIER; THICKENING AGENT; BINDER; CARRIER

Regulations: EC permitted for all foodstuffs following the *quantum satis* principle (except those specified in Table 2 on pp. 15–16 and in Appendix B on pp. 469ff).

EC permitted as carrier. Restricted use: none. Directive 95/2/EC.

Acceptable Daily Intake: Not specified.

What It Is: Another chemically modified starch, made by reacting a strongly alkaline water suspension of starch with propylene oxide.

What You Need To Know: Great care must be exercised during the manufacturing process to minimize the formation of chloride ions, since these can react with propylene oxide to form propylene chlorohydrins, which are potentially mutagenic and must be largely removed.[346] A limit of 1 mg/kg max propylene chlorohydrin residuals has been set by the Food and Agriculture Organization of the United Nations.[347] No long-term studies were available when this substance was reviewed by the World Health Organization in 1982.[348]

Hydroxypropyl cellulose (E463)

FOOD ADDITIVE: EMULSIFIER; THICKENING AGENT; STABILIZER; BINDER; FILM COATING; SUSPENSION AGENT; CARRIER

Regulations: EC permitted for all foodstuffs following the *quantum satis* principle (except those specified in Table 2 on pp. 15–16 and in Appendix B on pp. 469ff).

EC permitted as carrier. Restricted use: none. Directive 95/2/EC.

Acceptable Daily Intake: Not specified.

What It Is: A gum which is made by reacting alkali cellulose (from cotton or wood pulp) with propylene oxide, and used in whipped toppings, salad dressings, and edible films.

Hydroxypropyl methyl cellulose (E464)

FOOD ADDITIVE: THICKENING AGENT; EMULSIFIER; STABILIZER; CARRIER

Regulations: EC permitted for all foodstuffs following the *quantum satis* principle (except those specified in Table 2 on pp. 15–16 and in Appendix B on pp. 469ff).

EC permitted as carrier. Restricted use: none. Directive 95/2/EC.

Acceptable Daily Intake: Not specified.

What It Is: See Methyl cellulose.

Hyoscine hydrobromide

MEDICINAL SUBSTANCE: ANTI-EMETIC, ANTISECRETORY, ANTISPASMODIC

What It Is: Categorized as an antimuscarinic drug. Also known as scopolamine, it has similar effects to atropine (see p. 144). It has been used to relieve motion sickness, and can also be used for premedication before an operation to dry up saliva and bronchial secretions. It has also been used in products intended to relieve period pain.

What You Need To Know: See the general note about antimuscarinic drugs under the entry for homatropine methylbromide.

Hyoscyamine sulphate

MEDICINAL SUBSTANCE: ANTISECRETORY

What It Is: Categorized as an antimuscarinic drug. It is present in cold and 'flu remedies for its ability to dry up secretions.

What You Need To Know: See the general note about antimuscarinic drugs under the entry for homatropine methylbromide.

Ibuprofen

MEDICINAL SUBSTANCE: ANALGESIC

What It Is: Ibuprofen is a nonsteroidal anti-inflammatory agent (NSAIA), the class of drugs to which aspirin also belongs. It was developed in Great Britain in 1964, and was at first only available on prescription. Used in much the same way as aspirin, to reduce inflammation, lower fever and to relieve the pain of rheumatism and arthritis.

What You Need To Know: Although the exact way the drug works is not known, ibuprofen appears to function by inhibiting the production of prostaglandins, hormone-like chemicals involved in causing pain and inflammation. This is of considerable use to people who suffer from period pains (dysmenorrhoea), which appears to be caused by the elevated prostaglandin levels that the uterus produces at the time of menstruation. Ibuprofen can decrease these levels and relieve pain for many sufferers. Like aspirin, ibuprofen can cause abnormalities in the mucous membranes in the stomach, although probably to a lesser extent than aspirin. Gastrointestinal side-effects are experienced by 5 to 15 per cent of patients taking ibuprofen; epigastric pain, nausea, heartburn and sensations of 'fullness' in the gastrointestinal tract are the usual difficulties.[349] Adverse gastrointestinal effects may be minimized by taking ibuprofen with meals.

Serious adverse gastrointestinal effects (e.g. bleeding, ulceration, perforation) can occur at any time in patients receiving long-term NSAIA therapy, and such effects may not be preceded by warning signs or symptoms.[350][351] People who may be at increased risk of potentially serious adverse gastrointestinal effects (e.g. the elderly, those with a history of peptic ulcer disease, those receiving anticoagulants or corticosteroids) should be monitored closely for signs and symptoms of ulcer, perforation or severe gastrointestinal bleeding.[352] Since drinking alcohol while taking ibuprofen might cause stomach problems, it would be wise to avoid products containing it. Other reported side-effects of ibuprofen include dizziness, headache and nervousness; tinnitus (ringing in the ears) and blurred vision. Before taking ibuprofen, read thoroughly the cautions on all accompanying product literature and packaging, and consult your doctor before taking it if necessary.

Indigotine, Indigo carmine (E132)

FOOD ADDITIVE: FOOD COLOUR

Regulations: EC permitted to be used singly or in combination with other colours in the following foods up to the total maximum level specified.

- Non-alcoholic flavoured drinks, maximum level: 100 mg/l
- Candied fruits and vegetables, Mostarda di frutta, maximum level: 200 mg/kg
- Preserves of red fruits, maximum level: 200 mg/kg
- Confectionery, maximum level: 300 mg/kg
- Decorations and coatings, maximum level: 500 mg/kg
- Fine bakery wares (e.g. viennoiserie, biscuits, cakes and wafers), maximum level: 200 mg/kg
- Edible ices, maximum level: 150 mg/kg
- Flavoured processed cheese, maximum level: 100 mg/kg
- Desserts including flavoured milk products, maximum level: 150 mg/kg
- Sauces, seasonings (for example, curry powder, tandoori), pickles, relishes, chutney and piccalilli, maximum level: 500 mg/kg
- Mustard, maximum level: 300 mg/kg
- Fish paste and crustacean paste, maximum level: 100 mg/kg; Pre-cooked crustaceans, maximum level: 250 mg/kg; Salmon substitutes, maximum level: 500 mg/kg; Surimi, maximum level: 500 mg/kg; Fish roe, maximum level: 300 mg/kg; Smoked fish, maximum level: 100 mg/kg
- Snacks: dry, savoury potato, cereal or starch-based snack products: Extruded or expanded savoury snack products, maximum level: 200 mg/kg
- Other savoury snack products and savoury coated nuts, maximum level: 100 mg/kg
- Edible cheese rind and edible casings, maximum level: *quantum satis*
- Complete formulae for weight control intended to replace total daily food intake or an individual meal, maximum level: 50 mg/kg
- Complete formulae and nutritional supplements for use under medical supervision, maximum level: 50 mg/kg
- Liquid food supplements/dietary integrators, maximum level: 100 mg/l

- Solid food supplements/dietary integrators, maximum level: 300 mg/kg
- Soups, maximum level: 50 mg/kg
- Meat and fish analogues based on vegetable proteins, maximum level: 100 mg/kg
- Spirituous beverages (including products less than 15 % alcohol by volume), except those mentioned in Annex II or III, maximum level: 200 mg/l
- Aromatized wines, aromatized wine-based drinks and aromatized wine-product cocktails as mentioned in Regulation (EEC) No 1601/91, except those mentioned in Annex II or III, maximum level: 200 mg/l
- Fruit wines (still or sparkling) cider (except cidre bouche) and perry, aromatized fruit wines, cider and perry, maximum level: 200 mg/l. Directive 94/36/EC.

Acceptable Daily Intake: 0 – 5.

What It Is: A synthetic blue indigoid dye.

What You Need To Know: Scientific studies do not raise carcinogenic concerns.

Inosinic acid (E630)

FOOD ADDITIVE: FLAVOUR ENHANCER

Regulations: EC permitted to be used similarly to guanylic acid (E626). Directive 95/2/EC.

Acceptable Daily Intake: Not specified.

What It Is: See the description of flavour enhancers under monosodium glutamate (see pp. 317–8).

Iodine

FOOD ADDITIVE: CONTAMINANT

Acceptable Daily Intake: Provisional maximum tolerable daily intake: 0.017.

What It Is: Obtained from natural brine by acidification with sulphuric acid and treatment with chlorine, or from Chilean nitrate deposits. Essential to plant and animal growth, it is concentrated in the thyroid gland and involved in the synthesis of the hormone thyroxine, secreted by the thyroid gland and responsible for regulating metabolic rates. Besides affecting growth, iodine deficiency can also cause goitre, so iodine salts are added to table salts in regions where iodine levels are low. It is a potent antiseptic and is active against a wide range of bacteria, viruses and fungi.

What You Need To Know: When used to disinfect the skin there may, very occasionally, be an allergic reaction and it has been known to make conditions such as acne worse. A mild toxic syndrome called iodism can develop after repeated intake of small amounts of iodine. Symptoms include salivation, sneezing, conjunctivitis, headache, laryngitis, bronchitis, and skin rashes.[353] Since iodine is concentrated in the thyroid gland, metabolic disturbances are likely to result from excessive intake.[354] There is considerable variance in the reported lethal doses of iodine in adults, ranging from a few tenths of a gram to more than 20 grams. The mean lethal dose probably lies between 2 and 4 grams of free iodine.[355]

Ipecacuanha
MEDICINAL SUBSTANCE: EMETIC; EXPECTORANT

What It Is: Ipecacuanha is made from the dried and powdered root of a South American shrub, originally called *i-pe-kaa-guéne*, which literally means 'road-side sick-making plant' – a pretty accurate description of its function. It contains alkaloids which act as emetics, and it is therefore found in products which aim to make you vomit (emetics) and at a lower strength in some cough medicines which try to make you cough up sputum (expectorants).

What You Need To Know: In small doses it probably does little harm, but in larger doses it may cause irregular heartbeats, erosion of the gastro-intestinal tract, protein in the urine and circulatory collapse. Ipecacuanha liquid extract BP is ten times as concentrated as Ipecacuanha tincture BP, and hence is potentially more toxic. Do not use as an emetic in cases of corrosive poisoning, or where there is shock or coma.

Irish moss
See Chondrus.

Iron oxides and hydroxides (E172)
FOOD ADDITIVE: FOOD COLOUR

Regulations: EC permitted at *quantum satis* in all foods except those to which the EC only permits certain colours to be added (Appendix C, pp. 476ff) and those to which the EC forbids the adding of colours (Appendix D, pp. 482ff). Directive 94/36/EC.
Acceptable Daily Intake: $0 - 0.5$.
What It Is: Manufactured by treating a solution of ferrous sulphate or chloride with an alkali and oxidizing the precipitate in hot air for 12 hours. See ferric oxide.

Isomalt (E953)
FOOD ADDITIVE: SWEETENER; CARRIER

Regulations: EC permitted for the following foods up to the total maximum usable dose specified.

- Desserts and similar products, maximum usable dose: *quantum satis.*
- Water-based flavoured desserts, energy-reduced or with no added sugar, maximum usable dose: *quantum satis*; Milk- and milk-derivative-based preparations, energy-reduced or with no added sugar, maximum usable dose: *quantum satis*; Fruit- and vegetable-based desserts, energy-reduced or with no added sugar, maximum usable dose: *quantum satis*; Egg-based desserts, energy-reduced or with no added sugar, maximum usable dose: *quantum satis*; Cereal-based desserts, energy-reduced or with no added sugar, maximum usable dose: *quantum satis*; Fat-based desserts, energy-reduced or with no added sugar, maximum usable dose: *quantum satis*
- Breakfast cereals or cereal-based products, energy reduced or with no added sugar, maximum usable dose: *quantum satis*

- Edible ices, energy-reduced or with no added sugar, maximum usable dose: *quantum satis*
- Jams, jellies, marmalades and crystallized fruit, energy-reduced or with no added sugar, maximum usable dose: *quantum satis*
- Fruit preparations, energy-reduced or with no added sugar, with the exception of those intended for the manufacture of fruit-juice-based drinks, maximum usable dose: *quantum satis*
- Confectionery, maximum usable dose: *quantum satis*; Confectionery with no added sugar, maximum usable dose: *quantum satis*
- Dried-fruit-based confectionery, energy-reduced or with no added sugar, maximum usable dose: *quantum satis*; Starch-based confectionery, energy-reduced or with no added sugar, maximum usable dose: *quantum satis*
- Cocoa-based products, energy-reduced or with no added sugar, maximum usable dose: *quantum satis*
- Cocoa-, milk-, dried-fruit- or fat-based sandwich spreads, energy-reduced or with no added sugar, maximum usable dose: *quantum satis*
- Chewing gum with no added sugar, maximum usable dose: *quantum satis*
- Sauces, maximum usable dose: *quantum satis*
- Mustard, maximum usable dose: *quantum satis*
- Fine bakery products, energy-reduced or with no added sugar, maximum usable dose: *quantum satis*
- For purposes other than sweetening, EC permitted for foodstuffs in general (including frozen and deep-frozen unprocessed fish, crustaceans, molluscs and cephalopods, and liqueurs; excluding those foodstuffs referred to in Article 2(3)) Maximum level: *quantum satis*
- EC permitted as carrier. Restricted use: none. Directive 94/35/EC.

Acceptable Daily Intake: Not specified.

What It Is: A mixture of glucopyranosyl-sorbitol and glucopyranosyl-mannitol. About half as sweet as table sugar. See Propylene glycol (pp. 366–7).

What You Need To Know: Scientific studies do not raise carcinogenic or reproductive concerns.[356]

Isopropyl alcohol

MEDICINAL SUBSTANCE: SOLVENT; ANTIMICROBIAL

What It Is: Similar to ordinary alcohol (ethyl alcohol), but twice as toxic when absorbed. Isopropyl alcohol (also known as isopropanol) is obtained principally from petroleum. It can be used to clean the skin and remove grease, and is effective against some bacteria, but not as effective against viruses or fungi.

What You Need To Know: Dissolves fat more effectively than ethyl alcohol, therefore repeated use has a drying effect on the skin.[357] The likely lethal oral dose for an adult is 8 oz (240 ml), but as little as 20 ml in water can produce symptoms of toxicity.[358] In air, 400 parts per million is considered to be low enough not to cause central nervous system depression, although some irritation may occur.[359]

The International Agency for Research on Cancer has concluded that this substance is unclassifiable as to carcinogenicity in humans.[360]

Juniper

MEDICINAL SUBSTANCE: FLAVOURING

What It Is: The juniper is a small shrub whose berries produce juniper berry oil, used in the production of gin and the source of cade oil (see p. 169). Medicinally it has been used to treat wind and indigestion, and also as a diuretic, but should be avoided where there is kidney disease.

Kaolin

MEDICINAL SUBSTANCE: ADSORBENT

What It Is: Otherwise known as china clay, kaolin is used both externally and internally. Outside the body, it may be found in toilet powders and foot powders, where its adsorbent properties help to reduce odour and moisture. Internally, it absorbs toxic and other substances from the digestive organs and helps to increase stool bulk, and so is used to treat diarrhoea.

What You Need To Know: Kaolin and pectin (see p. 335) preparations have essentially no adverse effects, although constipation may occur.[361]

Karaya gum (gum sterculia) (E416)

FOOD ADDITIVE: EMULSIFIER; STABILIZER; THICKENING AGENT

Regulations: EC permitted for the following foods:

- Cereal- and potato-based snacks, maximum level: 5 g/kg
- Nut coatings, maximum level: 10 g/kg
- Fillings, toppings and coatings for fine bakery wares, maximum level: 5 g/kg
- Desserts, maximum level: 6 g/kg
- Emulsified sauces, maximum level: 10 g/kg
- Egg-based liqueurs, maximum level: 10 g/l
- Dietary food supplements, maximum level: *quantum satis*
- Chewing gum, maximum level: 5 g/kg
- Directive 95/2/EC.

Acceptable Daily Intake: Not specified.

What It Is: The dried exudate of the tree *Sterculia urens*, native to India, which is tapped or drilled for the gum. It is used in products such as salad dressings as an emulsifier, in ices to prevent large water crystals forming, in cheeses to stop water separating out and as a binder in meat products; also as a denture adhesive and in hair wave lotions.

What You Need To Know: Karaya gum passes through the alimentary tract without being digested, decomposed or fermented by bacteria. It absorbs a large quantity of water and therefore acts as a mechanical laxative, which, when consumed, can sometimes produce abdominal discomfort. It seems to have little effect on glucose metabolism. Occasional allergic reactions, characterized by urticaria, rhinitis, dermatitis, and asthma, have been attributed to powdered karaya gum.[362]

Lactic acid (E270)

FOOD ADDITIVE: ACIDITY REGULATOR

Regulations: EC permitted for all foodstuffs following the *quantum satis* principle (except those specified in Table 2 on pp. 15–16 and in Appendix B on pp. 469ff). Directive 95/2/EC.

Acceptable Daily Intake: Not specified.

What It Is: Obtained by fermenting sucrose, potato starch, molasses and other carbohydrates; or synthetically by hydrolysis of lactonitrile (a by-product of acrylonitrile manufacture). Lactic acid occurs naturally in the human body where it is produced in muscles during periods of exertion. When applied to the surface of the skin it may act in a similar way to salicylic acid and gently loosen its surface (i.e. as a keratolyte). Consequently, it is sometimes found in products used to treat warts, callouses and corns – where it is usually combined with another keratolyte such as salicylic acid (see pp. 379–80)

What You Need To Know: When consumed in food, no cumulative adverse effects are known or expected because of its normal occurrence in the diet and in human metabolic processes.[363]

Lactic acid esters of mono- and diglycerides of fatty acids (E472b)

FOOD ADDITIVE: EMULSIFIER

Regulations: EC permitted for all foodstuffs following the *quantum satis* principle (except those specified in Table 2 on pp. 15–16 and in Appendix B on pp. 469ff). Directive 95/2/EC.

Acceptable Daily Intake: Not specified.

What It Is: Consists of esters of glycerol with lactic acid (see above) and fatty acids occurring in food oils and fats. Used in shortening and cake improvers, to improve volume and texture of baked goods, and to provide foam stability in whipped toppings.

What You Need To Know: In 1992 the British government's

Food Advisory Committee recommended that this substance continued to be permitted for use in food subject to the provision of chronic toxicity/carcinogenicity and teratology/fertility studies, or unless clear evidence could be provided that these products could be metabolized to normal dietary components; such data to be provided within three years.[364]

Lactitol (E966)
FOOD ADDITIVE: SWEETENER; TEXTURIZER; CARRIER
Regulations: EC permitted for the following foods up to the total maximum usable dose specified.

- Desserts and similar products, maximum usable dose: *quantum satis*; Water-based flavoured desserts, energy-reduced or with no added sugar, maximum usable dose: *quantum satis*; Milk- and milk-derivative-based preparations, energy-reduced or with no added sugar, maximum usable dose: *quantum satis*
- Fruit- and vegetable-based desserts, energy-reduced or with no added sugar, maximum usable dose: *quantum satis;* Egg-based desserts, energy-reduced or with no added sugar, maximum usable dose: *quantum satis*; Cereal-based desserts, energy-reduced or with no added sugar, maximum usable dose: *quantum satis*; Fat-based desserts, energy-reduced or with no added sugar, maximum usable dose: *quantum satis*
- Breakfast cereals or cereal-based products, energy reduced or with no added sugar, maximum usable dose: *quantum satis*
- Edible ices, energy-reduced or with no added sugar, maximum usable dose: *quantum satis*
- Jams, jellies, marmalades and crystallized fruit, energy-reduced or with no added sugar, maximum usable dose: *quantum satis*
- Fruit preparations, energy-reduced or with no added sugar, with the exception of those intended for the manufacture of fruit-juice-based drinks, maximum usable dose: *quantum satis*
- Confectionery, maximum usable dose: *quantum satis;* Confectionery with no added sugar, maximum usable dose: *quantum satis*; Dried-fruit-based confectionery, energy-reduced or with no added sugar, maximum usable dose: *quantum satis*; Starch-based

confectionery, energy-reduced or with no added sugar, maximum usable dose: *quantum satis*
- Cocoa-based products, energy-reduced or with no added sugar, maximum usable dose: *quantum satis*
- Cocoa-, milk-, dried-fruit- or fat-based sandwich spreads, energy-reduced or with no added sugar, maximum usable dose: *quantum satis*
- Chewing gum with no added sugar, maximum usable dose: *quantum satis*
- Sauces, maximum usable dose: *quantum satis*
- Mustard, maximum usable dose: *quantum satis*
- Fine bakery products, energy-reduced or with no added sugar, maximum usable dose: *quantum satis*
- For purposes other than sweetening, EC permitted for foodstuffs in general (including frozen and deep-frozen unprocessed fish, crustaceans, molluscs and cephalopods, and liqueurs; excluding those foodstuffs referred to in Article 2(3)) Maximum level: *quantum satis*
- EC permitted as carrier. Restricted use: none. Directive 94/35/EC.

Acceptable Daily Intake: Not specified.

What It Is: Lactitol is a sweet-tasting polyol, or polyhydric alcohol, which is said to be a suitable sugar substitute for diabetics. It is produced by the hydrogenation of lactose (also see propane-1,2-diol (pp. 366–7).

What You Need To Know: Not metabolized in humans since it is not absorbed in the small intestines. It is well-tolerated in humans (up to 24 g per day) and does not influence blood glucose and blood insulin levels. May cause diarrhoea in doses of 50 g or more. Scientific studies do not raise mutagenic concerns, although in rats, some embryotoxicity or foetotoxicity has been demonstrated in diets composed of 5 per cent or more lactitol.[365]

Lactose

MEDICINAL SUBSTANCE: ANTACID; LAXATIVE

What It Is: Also known as milk sugar, lactose may be found in some antacid preparations. Many people become lactose-intolerant as they get older because of a natural decrease of the enzyme lactase in the gut after weaning. Lactose intolerance may be a factor in a number of diseases, including asthma and migraine; it has been shown that symptoms can sometimes be significantly improved by eliminating dietary lactose.[366]

Lactulose
MEDICINAL SUBSTANCE: LAXATIVE

What It Is: Lactulose is an ingredient of some laxative products. It is a synthetic substance which can be decomposed in the small intestine into galactose and fructose. This fermentation also produces acids, which in turn stimulate bowel movement and cause stools to become bulkier due to their uptake of fluids – a simple effect with few adverse reactions, possibly excepting flatulence; occasionally nausea and diarrhoea.

Lanolin
MEDICINAL SUBSTANCE: EMOLLIENT

What It Is: Also known as wool fat or wool grease, it is naturally present in the wool of sheep and is purified into a sticky, fatty substance used as a base in water-in-oil emulsions. It has an emollient (softening) effect on the skin.

What You Need To Know: Not considered to be an active ingredient of many products, and may therefore not be listed on the packaging. Nevertheless, some people can become allergic to it, and it may be difficult to locate lanolin-free products, other than by trial and error. In the past, lanolin has not been regarded as a significant cause of dermatitis. However, reports indicate that lanolin allergy is often overlooked because patients with a demonstrable lanolin allergy can have negative results to it when patch-tested. In one study of 100 allergy sufferers, lanolin was found to be a more common sensitizer than parabens.[367] There is a high incidence of lanolin allergy among eczema patients.[368]

Sheep are exposed to a variety of pesticides (often intentionally, for example, when they are dipped into various chemicals for pest control) and in 1988 researchers found residues of several pesticides in samples of lanolin.[369] Some of the pesticides found have been linked to cancer, and concern has been expressed that lanolin-based ointments could be used by breast-feeding mothers to treat sore or cracked nipples – thus exposing a young infant to potential carcinogens. Since lanolin has been found to be ineffective in studies on preventing nipple soreness, it would make sense to avoid ointments containing lanolin for this purpose.[370] [371]

Lavender

MEDICINAL SUBSTANCE: PERFUME

What It Is: Also used to add colour to products, and sometimes used in plant or oil form to keep insects away. Recently found to contain small amounts of perillyl alcohol, found experimentally to have both cancer preventive and regressive effects.[372]

Lead

FOOD ADDITIVE: CONTAMINANT

Acceptable Daily Intake: Provisional tolerable weekly intake: 0.025.

What It Is: Lead is a highly toxic element for which there is no safe level of exposure. In the first century BC, the Roman civil engineer Vitruvius wrote: 'Water ought by no means to be conducted in lead pipes, if we want to have it wholesome.' Some believe that lead poisoning was at the root of the fall of the Roman Empire. In Roman times water was collected from lead-covered roofs by lead gutters which ran into lead-lined storage containers. Grapes were boiled in lead pots to make wine. Many cosmetics, ointments and medicines contained significant amounts of lead. All this exposure would have lowered mental abilities and caused falling birth rates among the Roman ruling classes.

What You Need To Know: Children are particularly vulnerable

to the adverse effects of lead in their environment; their imma-
ture kidneys, liver, nervous and immune systems and the rapid
growth and development of organs and tissues such as bone
and brain means that we should take especial care to ensure
that their exposure to this poisonous substances is minimized
in every possible way.

Lead can enter the food chain by being absorbed by plants
growing near main roads or industrial plants with lead emissions; old-fashioned lead pipes may still be used in some areas
and are a major health hazard for infants; canned foods may
leach lead from their solders into the cans' contents; and
ceramic glazed storage vessels (clay or glass) can sometimes
pass a toxic dose of lead into the liquids of foods they contain.
As a result of our vastly-increased environmental exposure to
it, today's human skeletons contain about 100 times as much
lead as those of prehistoric humans.[373]

What makes lead so dangerous for humans is its ability to
bind with the most biologically important molecules, and
thereby interfere with their essential life-support functions. For
example, at very low levels of exposure, lead can disrupt the
synthesis of haemoglobin in children, causing anaemia.
Similarly low levels of exposure can impair the metabolism of
Vitamin D. Lead particularly targets certain organs and bodily
systems: the haematopoietic system (producing anaemia); the
nervous system, where it can produce mental retardation; and
the kidneys, which it progressively destroys with increasing
exposure.

Since there is absolutely no biological requirement for this
poison, it may be considered strange to see that the JECFA has
proposed a 'tolerable' weekly intake. This number is based
upon research which shows that an average daily intake of 3 –
4 mcg of lead by infants and children does not produce accumulating levels of lead in their blood. However, many people
would disagree that any intake of this toxin should be considerable 'tolerable', especially by the youngest and most

vulnerable. In adults, about 10 to 15 per cent of lead that reaches the digestive tract is absorbed. But children can absorb as much as 50 per cent.

SECRET INGREDIENTS FACT FILE
HOW TO REDUCE YOUR LEAD EXPOSURE

- Check and replace any lead pipes. Run the tap for a few minutes at the start of the day to flush out the water that has stood in the pipes overnight. Don't use water from the hot tap for anything that you're going to consume – particularly things that babies might eat – because lead dissolves more easily in hot water.
- Replace older paintwork.
- Sweep home for dust, always wash hands before meals, don't eat off the floor.
- Switch to unleaded petrol.
- Only buy seamless cans.
- Don't use ceramic glazed pots, crystal glass. You may assume that shortening the length of time your drink is in contact with the container will significantly reduce the amount of lead you're exposed to, but experiments have shown that this isn't the case. An appreciable amount of lead can be absorbed by wine held in a crystal decanter for 30 minutes or so – and rather surprisingly, 50 per cent of the total amount of lead contamination occurs in the first minute.[374]
- If you are pregnant, avoid the daily use of ceramic mugs when drinking hot beverages such as coffee or tea, and avoid the use of lead crystal ware.
- Do not store acidic foods such as fruit juices in ceramic containers.
- Use antique or collectible housewares for decoration – not to eat or drink from.
- Stop using items that show a dusty or chalky grey residue on the glaze after they are washed.

- If your wine is sealed with a foil capsule, wipe the rim of the bottle with a cloth dampened with water or lemon juice before removing the cork.

Research carried out by the Association of London Chief Environmental Health Officers has revealed that you may be at risk from lead poisoning if you grow your own vegetables within a six mile radius of Marble Arch in central London.[375] When analysed, the lead contamination of vegetation and dust along the M25 was 'near a level that mining companies would consider a worthwhile deposit for recovering metal'.[376] This research would presumably apply to other urban areas with very heavy traffic. If you can, avoid eating vegetables grown near these areas.

Lecithins (E322)

FOOD ADDITIVE: ANTIOXIDANT; EMULSIFIER; CARRIER

Regulations: EC permitted for all foodstuffs following the *quantum satis* principle (except those specified in Table 2 on pp. 15–16 and in Appendix B on pp. 469ff).
EC permitted as carrier. Restricted use: colours and fat-soluble antioxidants. Directive 95/2/EC.
Acceptable Daily Intake: Not specified.
What It Is: Lecithin is one of those 'secret' ingredients in foodstuffs which crop up in a surprisingly wide range of products, and yet few consumers seem to know why it is present, or what its function is. One of its roles is to act as a synergist (i.e. it helps another substance perform its job) to antioxidants in oils and fats – hence it is frequently found combined in products with vitamin E (see alpha-tocopherol). Its main function, however, is as an emulsifier. Lecithin itself is the most important natural emulsifier, originally obtained from egg yolk but now made from soya bean oil. Its most important use in the food industry is in bakery goods (to aid fat dispersion and as an anti-staling

agent), in chocolate products (to reduce viscosity and prevent crystals forming), in instant powdered products (to help the powder quickly mix in milk or water) and in margarine (to stabilize its water content and reduce spatter when frying). Soya lecithin has the same binding ability as the lecithin present in egg yolks, and can be used in place of eggs in many recipes. It is sometimes included in skin products for its reputed healing properties.

What You Need To Know: Can lecithin supplements improve memory? In the late 1970s it was discovered that people with Alzheimer's disease had abnormally low brain levels of the neurotransmitter acetylcholine. Acetylcholine is made from choline – a substance produced by the liver that also occurs naturally in many foods (eggs, offal, nuts) as lecithin. Scientists therefore experimentally attempted to increase acetylcholine levels by giving large amounts of choline to Alzheimer patients. Not only did it fail to improve memory, it caused a chemical reaction in the gut that made people smell of rotting fish. Some researchers then tested lecithin. While most studies failed to show that lecithin improved any aspect of Alzheimer's dementia in humans, one animal study did seem to show an improvement in memory function in mice suffering from dementia.[377] It has also been claimed that lecithin supplements can 'dissolve cholesterol deposits and reduce cholesterol levels in the blood'.

While there are certainly very effective dietary (i.e. non-drug) means of lowering cholesterol levels, an examination by university researchers in Wageningen, the Netherlands, of the results of 24 studies on lecithin and cholesterol dating all the way back to 1943, found that only poorly designed research or research in which the data were misinterpreted suggested a connection between lowered blood cholesterol and lecithin.[378] Research does show, however, that lecithin can have some preventive effect on alcohol-induced cirrhosis of the liver.[379]

Lignocaine

MEDICINAL SUBSTANCE: LOCAL ANAESTHETIC

What It Is: Lignocaine (also known as lidocaine) is widely used as a local anaesthetic, giving topical pain relief (i.e. on the surface of the skin).

Linseed

MEDICINAL SUBSTANCE: DEMULCENT

What It Is: Linseed oil is made from the seed of the flax plant, and can be found in some cough syrups, presumably present for its demulcent (i.e. soothing) properties. It has also been used as an emollient on the skin and in rubs intended to relieve deep-seated inflammation.

What You Need To Know: The two classes of essential fatty acids (EFAs) are named omega-6 and omega-3. Both are necessary for good health and, through a complicated transformation process, they become biologically active in many of the body's metabolic systems. They are called essential because the body cannot make them, and therefore they must be obtained from food sources. Omega-6 fatty acids (e.g. linoleic acid) are found in vegetable seeds and the oils produced from them. Omega-3 fatty acids (e.g. alpha linolenic acid) have received much public attention in recent years, and it is probably generally believed that they can only be obtained from deep-water fish oils. Linseed oil, however, is a good source of omega-3s.

Omega-3 fatty oils turn rancid and spoil easily. They have therefore been largely removed from our diets in recent decades, in the eternal quest to continually extend foods' shelf-life: the process of hydrogenation is one such way that easily spoiled oils such as omega-3s may be transformed into more stable products with longer shelf-lives.

If you supplement your diet with linseed oil, note that exposure to sunlight, oxygen and heat can quickly turn it rancid. Purchase it from a reputable health food shop where it is stored in opaque glass bottles under refrigeration, and keep it at home in similar conditions.

Liquorice

MEDICINAL SUBSTANCE: FLAVOURING

What It Is: Obtained from the roots and stems of *Glycyrrhiza glabra*, native to Southern and Eastern Europe. Found in some cough syrups, either to disguise the unpleasant taste of certain ingredients, or for its demulcent (i.e. soothing) and presumed expectorant properties. Liquorice has long been used for chest complaints ranging from dry coughs and asthma to bronchitis, and extracts of liquorice have been used to treat gastric and duodenal ulcers.

What You Need To Know: Liquorice sweets rarely, if ever, contain more than 2 per cent liquorice extract. Liquorice is, however, pharmacologically active – in one study, people receiving a gradually-increased dose of ammonium glycyrrhizate (the substance responsible for liquorice's taste and smell, and constituting about 15 per cent of it by weight) experienced raised blood pressure, weight gain, and increased sodium levels in blood.[380] Its active ingredients are believed to function similarly to corticosteroids (e.g. see hydrocortisone pp. 259–60).

Litholrubine BK (E180)

FOOD ADDITIVE: FOOD COLOUR

Regulations: EC permitted for edible cheese rind, maximum level: *quantum satis.* Directive 94/36/EC.

Acceptable Daily Intake: No acceptable daily intake allocated.

What It Is: A synthetic red monoazo dye.

What You Need To Know: People who suffer from asthma, rhinitis or urticaria may find their symptoms become worse following consumption of foods or beverages containing azo dyes. Such people may be mistakenly thought to be suffering from specific food allergies.[381]

Lobelia

MEDICINAL SUBSTANCE: EXPECTORANT

What It Is: Also called pukeweed or vomitwort, which graphically conveys its potential to induce vomiting. Contains an alkaloid (lobeline) whose effects are similar to nicotine, and consequently lobelia has been used in anti-smoking products. It is sometimes found in cough medicines to promote expectoration.

What You Need To Know: Lobelia closely resembles nicotine in its effects: as with nicotine overdose, central nervous stimulation is followed by severe depression and sometimes death from respiratory paralysis.[382]

Locust bean gum (E410)

FOOD ADDITIVE: CARRIER; THICKENING AGENT; STABILIZER

Regulations: EC permitted as carrier. Restricted use: none.

EC permitted for all foodstuffs following the *quantum satis* principle (except those specified in Table 2 on pp. 15–16 and in Appendix B on pp. 469ff). May not be used to produce dehydrated foodstuffs intended to rehydrate on ingestion. Directive 95/2/EC.

What It Is: Another ancient food ingredient, certainly used by the Egyptians as an adhesive in mummy binding, and probably the biblical 'locust' (it comes from the locust bean or carob tree) which sustained John the Baptist in the wilderness when all he could find for nourishment were 'locusts and wild honey'. The tree grows up to 15 metres high, may produce up to a ton of fruit every year, and the gum is made from the pod only (not the seed, which is used as a nutritious flavouring and chocolate substitute). Ground into fine flour, the gum is purified by boiling and filtering, but otherwise relatively unprocessed. Locust bean gum can be used in combination with carrageenan or agar to produce a very elastic gel, and will prevent fluid droplets forming on the gel's surface. It is therefore used as an ice-cream stabilizer, to make soft yet resilient baker's doughs, as a texture modifier in soft cheese and a lubricating agent in sausages.

What You Need To Know: May contain tannins, which inhibit appetite and growth, and trypsin inhibitors, which may depress growth. Scientific studies do not raise carcinogenic or mutagenic concerns.[383]

Loperamide

MEDICINAL SUBSTANCE: ANTI-DIARRHOEA

What It Is: Loperamide is a drug which acts to slow down the contractions of the muscles of the gut, and consequently is used to treat the symptoms of acute diarrhoea. Unlike morphine or codeine, it is not an opiate and so is unlikely to cause dependence. It may cause occasional rashes.

Lutein (E161b)

FOOD ADDITIVE: FOOD COLOUR

Regulations: EC permitted to be used singly or in combination with other colours in the following foods up to the total maximum level specified.

- Non-alcoholic flavoured drinks, maximum level: 100 mg/l
- Candied fruits and vegetables, Mostarda di frutta, maximum level: 200 mg/kg
- Preserves of red fruits, maximum level: 200 mg/kg
- Confectionery, maximum level: 300 mg/kg
- Decorations and coatings, maximum level: 500 mg/kg
- Fine bakery wares (e.g. viennoiserie, biscuits, cakes and wafers), maximum level: 200 mg/kg
- Edible ices, maximum level: 150 mg/kg
- Flavoured processed cheese, maximum level: 100 mg/kg
- Desserts including flavoured milk products, maximum level: 150 mg/kg
- Sauces, seasonings (for example, curry powder, tandoori), pickles, relishes, chutney and piccalilli, maximum level: 500 mg/kg
- Mustard, maximum level: 300 mg/kg
- Fish paste and crustacean paste, maximum level: 100 mg/kg; Pre-cooked crustaceans, maximum level: 250 mg/kg; Salmon

substitutes, maximum level: 500 mg/kg; Surimi, maximum level: 500 mg/kg; Fish roe, maximum level: 300 mg/kg; Smoked fish, maximum level: 100 mg/kg
- Snacks: dry, savoury potato, cereal or starch-based snack products: Extruded or expanded savoury snack products, maximum level: 200 mg/kg
- Other savoury snack products and savoury coated nuts, maximum level: 100 mg/kg
- Edible cheese rind and edible casings, maximum level: *quantum satis*
- Complete formulae for weight control intended to replace total daily food intake or an individual meal, maximum level: 50 mg/kg
- Complete formulae and nutritional supplements for use under medical supervision, maximum level: 50 mg/kg
- Liquid food supplements/dietary integrators, maximum level: 100 mg/l
- Solid food supplements/dietary integrators, maximum level: 300 mg/kg
- Soups, maximum level: 50 mg/kg
- Meat and fish analogues based on vegetable proteins, maximum level: 100 mg/kg
- Spirituous beverages (including products less than 15 % alcohol by volume), except those mentioned in Annex II or III, maximum level: 200 mg/l
- Aromatized wines, aromatized wine-based drinks and aromatized wine-product cocktails as mentioned in Regulation (EEC) No 1601/91, except those mentioned in Annex II or III, maximum level: 200 mg/l
- Fruit wines (still or sparkling) cider (except cidre bouche) and perry, aromatized fruit wines, cider and perry, maximum level: 200 mg/l. Directive 94/36/EC.

What It Is: An xanthophyll (oxygen-containing carotene compound) found in all green leaves, green vegetables, eggs and some flowers. The Aztec Marigold yields an oily yellow extract which is mainly lutein.

Lycopene (E160d)
FOOD ADDITIVE: FOOD COLOUR

Regulations: EC permitted to be used singly or in combination with other colours in the following foods up to the total maximum level specified.

- Non-alcoholic flavoured drinks, maximum level: 100 mg/l
- Candied fruits and vegetables, Mostarda di frutta, maximum level: 200 mg/kg
- Preserves of red fruits, maximum level: 200 mg/kg
- Confectionery, maximum level: 300 mg/kg
- Decorations and coatings, maximum level: 500 mg/kg
- Fine bakery wares (e.g. viennoiserie, biscuits, cakes and wafers), maximum level: 200 mg/kg
- Edible ices, maximum level: 150 mg/kg
- Flavoured processed cheese, maximum level: 100 mg/kg
- Desserts including flavoured milk products, maximum level: 150 mg/kg
- Sauces, seasonings (for example, curry powder, tandoori), pickles, relishes, chutney and piccalilli, maximum level: 500 mg/kg
- Mustard, maximum level: 300 mg/kg
- Fish paste and crustacean paste, maximum level: 100 mg/kg; Pre-cooked crustaceans, maximum level: 250 mg/kg; Salmon substitutes, maximum level: 500 mg/kg; Surimi, maximum level: 500 mg/kg; Fish roe, maximum level: 300 mg/kg; Smoked fish, maximum level: 100 mg/kg
- Snacks: dry, savoury potato, cereal or starch-based snack products: Extruded or expanded savoury snack products, maximum level: 200 mg/kg
- Other savoury snack products and savoury coated nuts, maximum level: 100 mg/kg
- Edible cheese rind and edible casings, maximum level: *quantum satis*
- Complete formulae for weight control intended to replace total daily food intake or an individual meal, maximum level: 50 mg/kg
- Complete formulae and nutritional supplements for use under medical supervision, maximum level: 50 mg/kg
- Liquid food supplements/dietary integrators, maximum level: 100 mg/l

- Solid food supplements/dietary integrators, maximum level: 300 mg/kg
- Soups, maximum level: 50 mg/kg
- Meat and fish analogues based on vegetable proteins, maximum level: 100 mg/kg
- Spirituous beverages (including products less than 15 % alcohol by volume), except those mentioned in Annex II or III, maximum level: 200 mg/l
- Aromatized wines, aromatized wine-based drinks and aromatized wine-product cocktails as mentioned in Regulation (EEC) No 1601/91, except those mentioned in Annex II or III, maximum level: 200 mg/l
- Fruit wines (still or sparkling) cider (except cidre bouche) and perry, aromatized fruit wines, cider and perry, maximum level: 200 mg/l. Directive 94/36/EC.

Acceptable Daily Intake: Decision postponed.

What It Is: A carotene compound which, unlike beta-carotene, is not converted in the body to vitamin A. It gives tomatoes, watermelon, pink grapefruit and palm oil their distinctive colour.

Lysozyme (E1105)

FOOD ADDITIVE: PRESERVATIVE

Regulations: EC permitted for ripened cheese, at *quantum satis.* Directive 95/2/EC.

Acceptable Daily Intake: Acceptable.

What It Is: An enzyme present in tears, saliva, and many tissues, whose enzymatic properties include the ability to decompose (hydrolyze) cell wall components of bacteria (e.g. streptococcus), which gives it antibacterial uses.

Magnesium carbonates (i) magnesium carbonate (ii) magnesium hydroxide carbonate (syn.: magnesium hydrogen carbonate) (E504)

FOOD ADDITIVE: ANTICAKING AND ANTIBLEACHING AGENT; CARRIER

Regulations: EC permitted for all foodstuffs following the *quantum satis* principle (except those specified in Table 2 on pp. 15–16 and in Appendix B on pp. 469ff).

EC permitted as carrier. Restricted use: none. Directive 95/2/EC.

Acceptable Daily Intake: Not specified – intake limited by laxative action.

What It Is: Made from magnesium sulphate and sodium carbonate.

What You Need To Know: Even the more soluble magnesium salts are generally so slowly absorbed that oral administration causes nothing more than purging.[384] Sometimes used as an antacid, it possesses a laxative effect (hence it is sometimes found in antacid products combined with substances that tend to produce constipation).

Magnesium chloride (E511)

FOOD ADDITIVE: FIRMING AGENT; COLOUR RETENTION AGENT; CARRIER

Regulations: EC permitted for all foodstuffs following the *quantum satis* principle (except those specified in Table 2 on pp. 15–16 and in Appendix B on pp. 469ff).

EC permitted as carrier. Restricted use: none. Directive 95/2/EC.

Acceptable Daily Intake: Not specified – intake limited by laxative action.

What It Is: Made by reacting hydrochloric acid with magnesium oxide or hydroxide.

Magnesium diglutamate (E625)

FOOD ADDITIVE: FLAVOUR ENHANCER; SALT SUBSTITUTE

Regulations: EC permitted to be used similarly to glutamic acid (E620). Directive 95/2/EC.

Acceptable Daily Intake: Not specified – intake limited by laxative action.

What It Is: Obtained from glutamic acid (see pp. 244–5), lacking the flavour potentiating properties of monosodium glutamate (see pp. 317–8)[385]

Magnesium hydroxide (E528)

FOOD ADDITIVE: ALKALI; COLOUR ADJUNCT

Regulations: EC permitted for all foodstuffs following the *quantum satis* principle (except those specified in Table 2 on pp. 15–16 and in Appendix B on pp. 469ff). Directive 95/2/EC.

Acceptable Daily Intake: Not specified.

What It Is: Made from magnesium chloride or sulphate and sodium hydroxide, or by precipitation from sea water with lime. Milk of magnesia is magnesium hydroxide suspended in water.

What You Need To Know: Prolonged use may rarely cause rectal stones.[386]

Magnesium oxide (E530)

FOOD ADDITIVE: ANTICAKING AGENT; NEUTRALIZING AGENT

Regulations: EC permitted for all foodstuffs following the *quantum satis* principle (except those specified in Table 2 on pp. 15–16 and in Appendix B on pp. 469ff). Directive 95/2/EC.

Acceptable Daily Intake: Not specified.

What It Is: See Magnesium hydroxide.

Magnesium salts of fatty acids (E470b)

FOOD ADDITIVE: ANTICAKING AGENT; EMULSIFIER; CARRIER

Regulations: EC permitted for all foodstuffs following the

quantum satis principle (except those specified in Table 2 on pp. 15–16 and in Appendix B on pp. 469ff).
EC permitted as carrier. Restricted use: colours and fat-soluble antioxidants. Directive 95/2/EC.
Acceptable Daily Intake: Not specified.

Magnesium silicate (i), magnesium trisilicate (ii) (asbestos-free) (E553a)

FOOD ADDITIVE: ANTICAKING AGENT

Regulations: EC permitted to be used similarly to silicon dioxide (E551). Directive 95/2/EC.

Acceptable Daily Intake: No acceptable daily intake specified – these salts are insoluble in water and so not expected to provide a significant level of available silicate to the diet.

What It Is: Magnesium silicate is made by reacting a magnesium salt and a soluble silicate. Magnesium trisilicate is prepared from sodium silicate and magnesium sulphate. Talc (talcum powder) is hydrous magnesium silicate, and obtained by open pit or underground mining and processed by crushing, washing, drying, and milling. Soapstone is an impure variety of natural talc.

What You Need To Know: Magnesium silicate and magnesium trisilicate are practically non-toxic.[387]

The International Agency for Research on Cancer has concluded that there is inadequate evidence that asbestos-free talc is carcinogenic in humans, but that there is sufficient evidence that talc containing asbestos fibres is carcinogenic to humans.[388] The US Food and Drink Administration has taken no action to date with regard to asbestos in food because 'there is no evidence that the ingestion of small amounts of asbestos found in food poses any human health risk'.[389]

Magnesium sulphate
MEDICINAL SUBSTANCE: LAXATIVE

What It Is: Sometimes known as Epsom salts, magnesium sulphate is generally used as a fast-acting laxative. Although magnesium salts are not easily absorbed by a healthy body, a person with kidney failure could accumulate a dangerous amount, leading to hypermagnesaemia (too much magnesium in the bloodstream).

Magnesium trisilicate
MEDICINAL SUBSTANCE: ANTACID

What It Is: Magnesium trisilicate is similar in use and effects to magnesium carbonate (see p. 288). It is possible that, if magnesium trisilicate is used for prolonged periods, stones in the urinary tract and kidneys could be formed from its silica content.

Malic acid (E296)
FOOD ADDITIVE: ACIDIFIER; FLAVOURING AGENT

Regulations: EC permitted for all foodstuffs following the *quantum satis* principle (except those specified in Table 2 on pp. 15–16 and in Appendix B on pp. 469ff). Directive 95/2/EC.
Acceptable Daily Intake: Not specified.
What It Is: Made by fermentation from sugars, or made synthetically by oxidation of benzene to maleic acid, which is converted to malic by heating with steam under pressure. Present in many natural food products, especially fruit and vegetables. The main acid in apples, apricots, bananas, cherries, grapes, plums, broccoli and carrots. It has a pleasingly tart yet smooth flavour and is used to give foods such as sweets, non-alcoholic drinks, canned tomatoes and fruit pie fillings a 'natural' taste.
What You Need To Know: A strong acid, able to produce some irritation of skin and mucous membranes if applied in concentrated form. No cumulative effects are known.[390]

Maltitol (E965)

FOOD ADDITIVE: SWEETENER; HUMECTANT; STABILIZER; CARRIER

Regulations: EC permitted for the following foods up to the total maximum usable dose specified.

* Desserts and similar products, maximum usable dose: *quantum satis*; Water-based flavoured desserts, energy-reduced or with no added sugar, maximum usable dose: *quantum satis*; Milk- and milk-derivative-based preparations, energy-reduced or with no added sugar, maximum usable dose: *quantum satis*; Fruit- and vegetable-based desserts, energy-reduced or with no added sugar, maximum usable dose: *quantum satis*; Egg-based desserts, energy-reduced or with no added sugar, maximum usable dose: *quantum satis*; Cereal-based desserts, energy-reduced or with no added sugar, maximum usable dose: *quantum satis*; Fat-based desserts, energy-reduced or with no added sugar, maximum usable dose: *quantum satis;* Breakfast cereals or cereal-based products, energy reduced or with no added sugar, maximum usable dose: *quantum satis*
* Edible ices, energy-reduced or with no added sugar, maximum usable dose: *quantum satis*
* Jams, jellies, marmalades and crystallized fruit, energy-reduced, maximum usable dose: *quantum satis* reduced or with no added sugar, maximum usable dose: *quantum satis*
* Fruit preparations, energy-reduced or with no added sugar, with the exception of those intended for the manufacture of fruit-juice-based drinks, maximum usable dose: *quantum satis*
* Confectionery, maximum usable dose: *quantum satis*; Confectionery with no added sugar, maximum usable dose: *quantum satis*; Dried-fruit-based confectionery, energy-reduced or with no added sugar, maximum usable dose: *quantum satis*; Starch-based confectionery, energy-reduced or with no added sugar, maximum usable dose: *quantum satis*
* Cocoa-based products, energy-reduced or with no added sugar, maximum usable dose: *quantum satis*; Cocoa-, milk-, dried-fruit- or fat-based sandwich spreads, energy-reduced or with no added sugar, maximum usable dose: *quantum satis*
* Chewing gum with no added sugar, maximum usable dose: *quantum satis*
* Sauces, maximum usable dose: *quantum satis*
* Mustard, maximum usable dose: *quantum satis*

- Fine bakery products, energy-reduced or with no added sugar, maximum usable dose: *quantum satis*
- For purposes other than sweetening, EC permitted for foodstuffs in general (including frozen and deep-frozen unprocessed fish, crustaceans, molluscs and cephalopods, and liqueurs; excluding those foodstuffs referred to in Article 2(3)) Maximum level: *quantum satis*
- EC permitted as carrier. Restricted use: none. Directive 94/35/EC.

Acceptable Daily Intake: Not specified.

What It Is: A polyol, or polyhydric alcohol, produced by hydrogenation of maltose. See Propylene glycol (pp. 366–7).

Mannitol (E421)

FOOD ADDITIVE: SWEETENER; HUMECTANT; STABILIZER; CARRIER

Regulations: EC permitted for the following foods up to the total maximum usable dose specified.

- Desserts and similar products, maximum usable dose: *quantum satis;* Water-based flavoured desserts, energy-reduced or with no added sugar, maximum usable dose: *quantum satis*; Milk- and milk-derivative-based preparations, energy-reduced or with no added sugar, maximum usable dose: *quantum satis*; Fruit- and vegetable-based desserts, energy-reduced or with no added sugar, maximum usable dose: *quantum satis*; Egg-based desserts, energy-reduced or with no added sugar, maximum usable dose: *quantum satis;* Cereal-based desserts, energy-reduced or with no added sugar, maximum usable dose: *quantum satis*; Fat-based desserts, energy-reduced or with no added sugar, maximum usable dose: *quantum satis;* Breakfast cereals or cereal-based products, energy reduced or with no added sugar, maximum usable dose: *quantum satis*
- Edible ices, energy-reduced or with no added sugar, maximum usable dose: *quantum satis*
- Jams, jellies, marmalades and crystallized fruit, energy-reduced, maximum usable dose: *quantum satis* reduced or with no added sugar, maximum usable dose: *quantum satis*
- Fruit preparations, energy-reduced or with no added sugar, with the exception of those intended for the manufacture of fruit-juice-based drinks, maximum usable dose: *quantum satis*
- Confectionery, maximum usable dose: *quantum satis*;

Confectionery with no added sugar, maximum usable dose: *quantum satis*; Dried-fruit-based confectionery, energy-reduced or with no added sugar, maximum usable dose: *quantum satis*; Starch-based confectionery, energy-reduced or with no added sugar, maximum usable dose: *quantum satis*

- Cocoa-based products, energy-reduced or with no added sugar, maximum usable dose: *quantum satis*; Cocoa-, milk-, dried-fruit- or fat-based sandwich spreads, energy-reduced or with no added sugar, maximum usable dose: *quantum satis*
- Chewing gum with no added sugar, maximum usable dose: *quantum satis*
- Sauces, maximum usable dose: *quantum satis*
- Mustard, maximum usable dose: *quantum satis*
- Fine bakery products, energy-reduced or with no added sugar, maximum usable dose: *quantum satis*
- For purposes other than sweetening, EC permitted for foodstuffs in general (including frozen and deep-frozen unprocessed fish, crustaceans, molluscs and cephalopods, and liqueurs; excluding those foodstuffs referred to in Article 2(3)) Maximum level: *quantum satis*
- EC permitted as carrier. Restricted use: none. Directive 94/35/EC.

Acceptable Daily Intake: Not specified.

What It Is: A polyol, or polyhydric alcohol, produced by hydrogenation of fructose. See propylene glycol (pp.366–7). D-mannitol occurs widely in nature in a variety of plants, algae, fungi and certain bacteria. L-mannitol does not occur naturally. Used intravenously to increase urine output in poisoning cases.[391]

What You Need To Know: Slowly absorbed from the intestinal tract, it exerts a laxative effect (starts at between 10 g to 20 g per dose). Dehydrogenated to fructose then metabolized. Clinical experience with mannitol as a thereapeutic agent has indicated no adverse effects.[392]

Marshmallow
MEDICINAL SUBSTANCE: DEMULCENT

What It Is: The Romans ate marshmallow as a vegetable delicacy and used it as an external application for bee-stings and other swellings. Today, the dried root can be found in products intended to soothe irritation and reduce inflammation in the lungs, throat and urinary tract.

Menthol

MEDICINAL SUBSTANCE: DECONGESTANT; FLAVOURING

What It Is: Menthol is the main active ingredient of natural peppermint oil, from which it can be obtained. It may also be synthesized from thymol or menthone. It has a host of uses in flavourings and cosmetics: medicinally, it is used as a decongestant and mild analgesic. On the skin it dilates the blood vessels, produces a feeling of coldness, and may help to relieve itching. It is inhaled or sucked in the form of sweets or pastilles to try and relieve the symptoms of sinusitis and bronchitis, and it may also help to relieve flatulence.

What You Need To Know: Moderately irritating to the mucous membranes on inhalation.[393] The application of menthol to the nostrils of an infant or young child could be dangerous, resulting in severe reaction with spasm of the breathing passage. There have been isolated reported cases of contact dermatitis and hypersensitivity.

SECRET INGREDIENTS FACT FILE
CHEST, NOSE, COUGH AND COLD MEDICATIONS

The extraordinary diversity of pills, potions, drops and sprays, powders and inhalations on offer for the treatment of our coughs, sneezes, wheezes and sniffles is perhaps as confusing as it is daunting. The complexity of product formulations is also, on occasion, baffling. If you feel bewildered by the plethora of pills and potions available, you can imagine how many doctors felt before Britain's National Health Service (NHS) introduced a 'limited list' of medicines from which they were encouraged to select appropriate medication for their patients. The limited list was introduced partly to control NHS expenditure on prescriptions, and partly to set the standards for the rational prescribing of medicines. The entire approved list for cough and cold medicine now only numbers just over two dozen items. This was clearly a good move, of which one authority commented: 'The drastic pruning of the vast array of cough medicines is welcome. Those that remain appear adequate; recourse to others by purchasing them over the counter is likely to be wasteful and may sometimes be hazardous.'[394]

EXPECTORANTS

An expectorant is a substance that is intended to help you cough up sputum and so clear the bronchial airways. Some expectorant substances are dilute emetics (i.e. substances which, in stronger doses, would produce vomiting). Ipecacuanha, for example, is used both as an expectorant and, at higher doses, as an emetic for the emergency treatment of certain types of poisoning. Although expectorants are therefore supposed to stimulate coughing and phlegm production in the human body, one respected medical authority (used by doctors for guidance on prescribing) states that 'there is no evidence that any drug whether given by mouth, injection or inhalation can specifically facilitate expectoration by stimulation or augmentation of the cough reflex ... the assumption that sub-emetic doses can also promote expectoration is a myth.'[395] Occasionally, expectorants may be found combined with cough suppressants – which seems rather strange.

DEMULCENTS

Most demulcents are inert substances, such as glycerine, honey and syrups, and are intended to soothe irritated areas. They may contain significant amounts of sugar, and are therefore undesirable from the dental point of view for regular usage. Home-made remedies such as lemon and honey are probably just as acceptable. Demulcents are unlikely to have any major therapeutic effect, since most irritated areas of the throat and chest are not bathed by cough mixtures when swallowed.

COUGH SUPPRESSANTS

So far, you may be rather discouraged to find that the first two types of medications we have considered are both less than outstanding in their efficacy. You may be pleased to learn that in this third category there are indeed some highly effective substances.

A cough is a method devised by our body to clear an obstruction in the respiratory tract – the airway. It is both a voluntary and involuntary reflex, which we can either consciously choose to initiate, or which can be switched on and off by our body while in 'auto-pilot' mode. Coughing is controlled by the cough centre of the brain, and it is here that most cough suppressant drugs go to work. It is important to realize, therefore, that most of these substances are centrally acting, in other words, they exercise an effect on the central nervous system. This means that side-effects may sometimes occur – breathing may become depressed, for example, which could be dangerous for asthmatics or those suffering from chronic bronchitis.

Coughing is not only a useful and effective way of clearing the air passages, but it can also be an indication of illness, which requires medical attention. In many cases, an acute attack of coughing will sort itself out after a day or two, without the need to resort to unnecessary medication. Remember, a cough suppressant will only suppress unpleasant symptoms, it won't actually cure any respiratory infection you may be suffering from. Sometimes, a dry, unproductive cough may be usefully treated with a suppressant, to enable you to sleep, for example. Even so, one authority considers that the drawbacks of prescribing cough suppressants are rarely outweighed by the benefits of treatment, and that the sputum retention they may cause could be harmful to those suffering from chronic bronchitis.[396] An irritating or worrying cough, or one that does not quickly resolve itself, certainly needs medical investigation.

ANTIHISTAMINES

Most people are familiar with antihistamines as valuable drugs used to suppress the symptoms of that curse of the summer months – hay fever. As the name suggests, antihistamines are substances that counter the effects of histamine in the body. Histamine itself is contained in all body tissues, and is released from cells when they are stimulated to do so. They can be stimulated to do this if the body becomes sensitive to a particular substance – this is called an allergen (such as food, dust, pollen, etc.). The effect of histamine release can be just as varied as the cause. Sometimes it may produce a skin rash, sneezing, watery eyes, asthma, swellings, or, of course, hay fever (often the result of pollen allergy). Histamine also has the general effect of producing a fall in blood pressure, an increase in stomach secretions and an increase in the heart rate. Antihistamine drugs can prevent histamine from reaching its final destination in the body, and so may moderate some of its effect.

Antihistamine drugs have other effects, too. Many of them will produce drowsiness, which may be almost unnoticeable, or may manifest itself as deep sleep. Alcohol should be avoided while taking antihistamines since its sedative effect can be magnified. The drowsiness that antihistamines can cause may be dangerous if you drive or are in other situations which demand a high degree of mental alertness for your own and other people's safety. If you are taking other depressants (tranquillizers, sleeping pills, narcotics, etc.) you should check with your doctor or pharmacist before taking antihistamines. You should also obtain medical advice before taking them if you have an enlarged prostate, heart or liver disease, epilepsy, high blood pressure, glaucoma, thyroid problems or ulcers.

Antihistamines are of little use in treating the common cold. There have been claims that antihistamine drugs are effective for this purpose, but one authority has concluded that 'extensive trials have shown these claims to be unsubstantiated'.[397]

DECONGESTANTS

'Rhinitis' is the word used by doctors to describe an inflammation of the mucous membrane of the nose. We are all familiar with 'stuffy nose', which can be a miserable symptom of a cold or an allergy such as hay fever. This congestion can be relieved – at least temporarily – by a decongestant, which can either be applied straight onto the inflamed area (topically) or by swallowing it (systemically). The effect is generally to constrict the nasal blood vessels, which causes the swelling of the tissues to reduce. Once again, the treatment is directed towards suppressing the symptom, and is not curative. The drawbacks are twofold: firstly, most of the drugs used as decongestants are quite potent, and could have undesirable side-effects, and secondly, certain forms of treatment may actually prolong the condition.

Most decongestants are 'sympathomimetic' drugs, whose general effect on the body include:

- Stimulation of the heart's force and contraction
- Stimulation of the central nervous system (increased alertness, faster breathing, reduced appetite)
- Changes (usually rises) in blood pressure and blood sugar level
- Constriction of skin and gut blood vessels
- Relaxation of other blood vessels (e.g. in the bronchial muscles)

When these substances are applied direct to the nose, very little is absorbed by the rest of the body and the above

effects are less likely to occur. There is, however, one important effect that is associated with the topical (i.e. direct
contact with the skin) use of sympathomimetics – and that is
the phenomenon known as 'rebound congestion'. As the
effect of the drug begins to wear off, the mucosal blood
vessels may swell even more than before, making your nose
feel even more stuffy than it was. This effect becomes more
likely with frequent medication, which may damage the nose
and lead to dependence on these substances.

Do not use products which contain sympathomimetic
drugs without medical advice if you are diabetic, have high
blood pressure (hypertension), have prostate or thyroid problems, suffer from glaucoma, or if you have heart or circulatory
impairments, or if you are currently taking other medicines
(especially amphetamines, medication for high blood pressure or heart problems, treatment for asthma, hay fever or
other allergies, or antidepressants).

Mepyramine maleate

MEDICINAL SUBSTANCE: ANTIHISTAMINE

What It Is: An antihistamine which is thought to possess some
local anaesthetic action. For a general description of the uses
and effect of antihistamine drugs see the entry under 'Antihistamines' above.

Mercury

FOOD ADDITIVE: CONTAMINANT

Acceptable Daily Intake: Provisional tolerable weekly intake:
0.005.

What It Is: Mercury is very heavy, weighing 13.6 times as much
as an equal volume of water. Stone, iron, and even lead can
float on its surface. Most mercury produced is consumed in the
manufacture of electrical goods such as dry-cell batteries,
fluorescent light bulbs and switches; it is also used in the
production of chlorine and caustic soda. In the ancient world,

mercury was one of the most highly prized of all trading commodities – today reflected in our modern words 'merchandise', 'merchant' and 'mercantile', which are all derived from it. Mercury's uses in ancient medicine were legion. As a treatment for syphilis it has been used from the most ancient of times right up to the present century when, in 1909, Ehrlich's famous 'magic bullet' was developed. The administration of mercury was known as 'salivation', because of the copious quantities of saliva it produced in patients. For chronic diarrhoea, typhoid, disinfection, even as a diuretic, mercury was historically the drug of choice. As quicksilver, mercury was prescribed for so many illnesses that physicians became known as 'quicks' – from which the modern word 'quack' is derived.

What You Need To Know: Chronic exposure to mercury vapour produces a wide range of symptoms. The most consistent and distinctive are on the central nervous system, and include depression, irritability, exaggerated response to stimulation, excessive shyness, insomnia, emotional instability, forgetfulness, confusion, excessive perspiration and uncontrolled blushing. A fine trembling of the fingers, eyelids, lips, and tongue (interrupted intermittently by coarse shaking movements) is also common.[398]

Children are more susceptible than adults to mercury poisoning.[399] Mothers exposed to mercury through dental fillings have been found to have significantly increased mercury content in their babies' placentae and membranes (see special feature pp. 300–11).[400] People with a history of allergies or known sensitization to mercury, chronic respiratory disease, nervous system disorders, or kidney disorders are at increased risk from exposure.[401]

The International Agency for Research on Cancer has concluded that metallic mercury and inorganic mercury compounds are unclassifiable as to carcinogenicity in humans.[402]

The US Environmental Protection Agency was unable to

classify this substance as to human carcinogenicity, based on inadequate human and animal data. Epidemiological studies failed to show a correlation between exposure to elemental mercury vapour and carcinogenicity; the findings in these studies were confounded by possible or known concurrent exposures to other chemicals, including human carcinogens, as well as lifestyle factors (e.g. smoking). Findings from genotoxicity tests are severely limited and provide equivocal evidence that mercury adversely affects the number or structure of chromosomes in human somatic cells. Human carcinogenicity data: inadequate. Animal carcinogenicity data: inadequate.[403]

Note On Methylmercury

Methylmercury is a compound that can be produced from mercury by bacteria present in water, sediments, soil, rotten fish and the gastrointestinal tract of humans.[404] Methylmercury readily passes through such physiological barriers as the blood-brain barrier, blood-testes barrier, and the placenta. Consumption of fish and shellfish is the main source of methylmercury exposure in the general population. Fish and shellfish generally contain two orders of magnitude more mercury than other food items.[405 406 407]

The International Agency for Research on Cancer has concluded that methylmercury compounds are probably carcinogenic to humans. There is sufficient evidence in experimental animals for the carcinogenicity of methylmercury chloride. In making the overall evaluation, the Working Group took into account evidence that methylmercury compounds are similar with regard to absorption, distribution, metabolism, excretion, genotoxicity and other forms of toxicity.[408]

The US Environmental Protection Agency has classified this substance as a possible human carcinogen, based on inadequate data in humans and limited evidence of carcinogenicity in animals. Human carcinogenicity data: inadequate. Animal carcinogenicity data: limited.[409]

Secret Ingredients Fact File
MERCURY – DRILLER KILLER?

If you have mercury fillings, you may well have wondered what impact they may be having on your health. Read on, and we'll tell you.

Mercury is associated with many occult and metaphysical properties. In his poetical book *The Periodic Table*, Primo Levi tells of mercury's supernatural ability to transmute everything – and everyone – it touches.[410] To the Romans, mercury was the god of eloquence, skill, trading and thieving, the conductor of lost souls to the underworld, and the messenger of the gods. In other cultures, mercury was personified as Thoth, Hermes, or Odin – slippery, dazzling, and totally uncontrollable. To the alchemists, sulphur was the male principle, and mercury the female. Ancient alchemical theory held that all metals – including gold and silver – could be obtained from these two original principles.

LICENSED TO FILL
Mercury's severe neurotoxic effects have been recognized since the end of the 17th century, first in mercury miners, then in hatters exposed to mercury-treated fur felt. Lewis Carroll accurately depicted the symptoms of mercury poisoning in the character of the mad hatter:

'Have you guessed the riddle yet?' the Hatter said, turning to Alice again.

'No, I give it up,' Alice replied: 'what's the answer?'

'I haven't the slightest idea,' said the Hatter.

Getting to the truth about mercury amalgam fillings is every bit as difficult as grasping a handful of the slippery metal itself. Everyone has an opinion about it . . . but until recently, hard scientific evidence was lacking. That situation has now changed. An accumulating body of scientific work now indicates that mercury amalgam dental fillings may be a significant source of mercury pollution for humans. The implications are considerable.

Dentists have been using mercury in fillings since the early 19th century, and it has been a topic of fierce controversy (both inside and outside the profession) for just as long. Why is mercury used in fillings? The answer lies in its unusual physical properties, such as its uniform volume expansion, its ability to alloy with other metals, its performance in exacting environments, and its ability to cause the filling to harden after placement. The first amalgam filling was produced in the early 1800s in France, and consisted of a mixture of bismuth, lead, tin and mercury which had to be heated to 100°C and was then poured directly into the tooth cavity. How many patients survived this excruciating torture is not known! Soon, however, the amount of mercury in the mixture was increased, which allowed the amalgam to be prepared and administered without additional heating (mercury is liquid at room temperature).

Adults in the UK have an average of 7.5 teeth with fillings. A scientist has recently calculated that, assuming an average throughput, this means that each crematorium chimney in Britain will emit about 11 kilograms of mercury every year into the environment.[411] Enough to pose a health hazard for those unlucky enough to be downwind . . .

Concern about the toxicity of mercury in fillings mounted during the first quarter of the 20th century. Then, in 1926, Professor Alfred Stock of the Kaiser-Wilheim Institute in Germany published a scientific paper which first identified dental fillings as a source of mercury vapour. He concluded: 'There is no doubt that many symptoms: tiredness, depression, irritability, vertigo, weak memory, mouth inflammations, diarrhoea, loss of appetite and chronic catarrhs often are caused by mercury which the body is exposed to from amalgam fillings, in small amounts, but continuously. Doctors should give this fact their serious consideration.'[412]

While researching *Secret Ingredients*, we interviewed one scientist – Dr Murray Vimy, of Calgary, Canada – who is at the forefront of research into the health effects of amalgam fillings. 'The issue really is dental opinion versus medical science,' he told us. '[Dentists] have been using the material for 150 years. Most of them are good caring people, and I think it's a shock to them to realize that science is presenting evidence that goes against everything they've believed in. Using dental amalgam is a cornerstone of dentistry; and in the United States especially, [the health hazards of amalgam fillings] raises the spectre of tremendous lawsuits.'

YOUR DAILY DOSE OF MERCURY

Research was conducted during the 1970s and 1980s showing that dentists were themselves being exposed to decidedly unhealthy amounts of mercury vapour. In the United States, at least 10 per cent of all dental offices had air levels of mercury which exceeded the established safety level; one study reported that one in three dentists with elevated body mercury levels showed signs of neuropathy.[413] Others displayed overt symptoms of mercury poisoning (called erethism) involving irritability, emotional instability, depression, shyness and fatigue – the symptoms so accurately depicted by Lewis Carroll's Mad Hatter. It is perhaps surprising that, after such first-hand experiences of the health hazards of mercury in clinical use, the world's dental associations did not take the opportunity to reconsider their staunch support for amalgam fillings. The authorities have generally claimed that for average people, amalgam fillings only contribute about 10 per cent of their daily mercury intake; the rest coming from food, air and water.

DOES IT ADD UP?

For someone with eight amalgam filling surfaces in their mouth, the authorities believe that the daily dose of mercury is 1.2 micrograms (abbreviated to mcg). Someone with 12 or more fillings would receive, it is claimed, about 1.8 mcg. But how accurate is this? Solid research indicates that the amount of mercury released by one filling may be in the region of 15 mcg a day.[414] This means that, for a person with eight fillings, the amount of mercury released into the mouth could actually be 120 mcg daily. And how much of this 120 mcg is actually absorbed? Here, we enter a very murky area, because there are many imprecise variables to consider. For example, the more you chew, the more mercury vapour is generated. When you stop chewing, it takes about 90 minutes to decline to pre-chewing levels.[415] Most mercury seems to enter the body as vapour absorbed via the lungs, but it may also be absorbed from the gastro-intestinal tract, from the oro-nasal cavity directly into the brain, upwards from the base of the tooth cavity, and through mucous membranes. These factors, and more besides, conspire to make the art of calculating the absorbed mercury dose for an individual very imprecise.

If you are wondering how the authorities can confidently claim that we only absorb between 1.2 and 1.8 mcg a day, you'll find the answer rather surprising. In 1985, Drs Murray Vimy and Fritz Lorscheider of the University of Calgary published two important research papers in the *Journal of Dental Research*.[416] [417] By using an ultra-sensitive gold film detector, it was possible to measure the mercury given off from amalgam fillings, and calculate how much would be taken into the lungs. The result, as measured amongst a randomly selected group of people, averaged 20 mcg of mercury a day. These findings were attacked by some, who, while accepting the accuracy of Vimy and Lorscheider's measurements, declared that their subsequent calculations concerning dose rates were 16 times too high. By applying a suitable correctional factor (i.e. dividing by 16), Vimy and Lorscheider's results were brought down to the 1.2 – 1.8 mcg range which is so widely quoted today. We asked Dr Vimy about this revision of his work. 'If you change the assumptions and you take someone else's data,' he said, 'you can come up with a different answer.'

In 1990, Drs Vimy and Lorscheider published a detailed paper which painstakingly answered all previously made criticisms of their calculations, and produced a very refined generic equation to compute mercury dose from amalgams.[418] It took into account such factors as air flow rate, dilution of air, oral and nasal uptake, and retention of mercury in the lungs. This is what it reveals:

- The average mercury intake for most people with fillings is 9.98 mcg a day
- People with 12 or more fillings have a higher average mercury intake of 14.68 mcg a day.

Interestingly, the two scientists went further, and checked this calculation against the actual amounts of mercury found in human brains during autopsies: the results agreed very neatly.

MERCURY RISING

So the crucial question now becomes: what effect is mercury from amalgam fillings having on our health? Mercury vapour from fillings is mainly absorbed in the lungs (particularly during and after chewing or brushing teeth), where it rapidly enters the blood stream. Mercury is transported by plasma to all cells in the body where, quicksilver-like, it has little difficulty in jumping across the membrane to enter the cell itself. Mercury also enters the brain (by foiling the blood-brain barrier) and is capable of crossing the placenta.[419] It eventually accumulates in the kidneys, and is finally excreted in urine and faeces. After one short exposure to mercury vapour, it takes about two months for the body to excrete half the quantity absorbed.[420] Estimating the precise amount of mercury your body contains is difficult (without an autopsy!) since blood levels are not thought to be an accurate guide because mercury is absorbed from the blood into cells, meaning that blood levels can be low yet cell levels may be high.[421] Some relevant facts:

- Post-mortem analyses of patients suffering from Alzheimer's disease show high levels of mercury in brain areas associated with memory function.[422]
- Having amalgam fillings inserted causes a massive increase in the amount of antibiotic-resistant bacteria present in the gut – from 9 per cent (before fillings) to 70 per cent (after fillings).[423] It seems the genes that protect bacteria from mercury lie close to those that protect against antibiotics, so bacteria that survive one tend to survive the other.
- Ongoing research in Sweden 'strongly indicates that mercury vapour is a potent neuroteratogenic agent'.[424] In other words, it is capable of causing defects in the developing brain and nervous system. Whether the amount of mercury which reaches the baby is sufficient to cause an adverse health impact is still an open question. Most doctors believe that it is sensible to reduce medical treatment to a minimum in any case during pregnancy. Note: having amalgam fillings removed can result in a substantial short-term increase in the amount of mercury in your body – this should be carefully discussed with your medical advisers before treatment, especially in the early stages of pregnancy. By the same token, Drs Lorscheider and Vimy comment: 'Experimental evidence suggests that it would be prudent to avoid placing amalgam fillings in pregnant women.'[425]

Aside from the medical and scientific journals, there is an ever-increasing body of evidence, from patients themselves, who have had their amalgam fillings removed and have felt better. We spoke to one such person – a dentist herself – about her own experience.

'I first suspected dental amalgam when, by chance, I met a lady whose filling I'd repaired. As we were talking, she started to tell me about a disease she had; I hadn't heard of it before – it was ME [Myalgic Encephalomyelitis or Chronic Fatigue Syndrome]. The description of her disease was so similar to what I would expect from mercury poisoning that I rushed to the dental bookshops to get a book out on dental mercury poisoning – and found there weren't any! So I then had to start searching around and I finally found *The Toxic Time Bomb*.[426] At the same time, I was reading another book in which appeared a chart describing cerebral allergies. I had both books open on my desk at the same time, and the more I read the more I recognized the patient's symptoms – and it came as a very sudden revelation that the symptomology actually described my own condition at the time. I was so exhausted by dentistry, to the extent I felt it was killing me. Until that point, I had assumed it was a psychological problem. However, I sometimes had the opportunity to occasionally do mornings where I wasn't exposed to amalgam, and I felt quite different – much, much better. I now know I am very, very sensitive to mercury – so much so that if I take an amalgam filling out and I am not protected, I can't think clearly or speak coherently afterwards – I mix numbers and letters almost immediately – and that evening I'll have very profound symptoms at home. Biochemically, mercury has an affinity for SH radicals. They occur anywhere where sulphur and hydrogen combine to form a rather reactive little wing or little arm on a biochemic chemical – very often in enzymes and hormones. Now an enzyme is a catalyst which allows biochemic reactions to take place. If that catalyst is rendered useless by mercury attaching itself to it, then certain reactions can't take place. And this is how it is so subtle: mercury rushes around the body damaging enzyme functions and yet can't be easily found. It's quicksilver . . . it runs all over the place. It particularly loves neurological tissue – it loves to sit in brains.

'Remember, also, that the amalgam fillings in teeth act like little batteries. I have personally measured up to 400 millivolts on individual teeth. If a tooth is creating a battery effect in the mouth, then the electrical current must interfere in some way or another with acupuncture meridians, if you believe in them, or if you don't believe in them there must be a transferring of the ions through the battery, through the saliva. If it is mercury coming off then that saliva which is constantly being swallowed will have more mercury ions in it and then these will go into the gut and are potentially capable of being methylated by the colon bacteria and can be much more lethal than ordinary metallic mercury.

'Information about mercury has not been published in dental journals. Because the subject hasn't come up, dentists don't think to question it themselves. Whatever they were taught at dental school seems satisfactory to them. If you are deciding to have amalgam fillings taken out, find somebody who believes in you and what you are trying to do, who will take your wishes into account, and who has read something of the subject and perhaps is starting to question the orthodox view themselves. If all the old amalgam is not removed from the tooth you will not be truly mercury-free. I frequently see an improvement in clarity of thought when mercury fillings are removed. Patients are sometimes initially unable to speak coherently, finding their words difficult, unable to describe things, often jumping from one idea to another. They are quicksilvery . . . running all over the place, out of control. I've seen these symptoms improve.

'Your body is detoxifying mercury all the time. If you measure the faecal mercury and the urine mercury, you will see amounts coming out all the time. Mercury will bond to certain substances, including zinc, selenium, methionine and the antioxidant glutathione (good sources include fresh parsley, avocado, asparagus, cauliflower and broccoli). Mercury combines with these substances to form a complex chemical which then can leave the body. Sulphur historically is the great detoxifier of mercury . . . in this day and age

> people don't like the taste of sulphury foods. When you ask somebody if they eat their greens, they eat lettuce, but they don't necessarily eat Brussels sprouts, curly kale, garlic, cabbage . . . all these sort of smelly-type foods which contain sulphur.'

Metatartaric acid (E353)

FOOD ADDITIVE

Regulations: Wine in accordance with Regulations (EEC) No 822/87, (EEC) No 4252/88, (EEC) No 2332/92 and (EEC) No 1873/84 and their implementing regulations.

EC permitted for made wine, maximum limit 100 mg/l. Directive 95/2/EC.

What It Is: See Tartaric acid.

Methyl cellulose (E461)

FOOD ADDITIVE: THICKENING AGENT; EMULSIFIER; STABILIZER; CARRIER

Regulations: EC permitted for all foodstuffs following the *quantum satis* principle (except those specified in Table 2 on pp. 15–16 and in Appendix B on pp. 469ff).

EC permitted as carrier. Restricted use: none. Directive 95/2/EC.

Acceptable Daily Intake: Not specified.

What It Is: Made by reacting cellulose (cotton or wood pulp) with methyl chloride, this gum has the unique quality of forming a gel when heated, which reverts to a normal solution on cooling. In food products, it can be used to increase water absorption and retention, to imitate the taste and 'mouth-feel' of fat in reduced-fat products, and prevents fried food (e.g. doughnuts) from absorbing too much oil. It is not digestible and therefore makes no calorie contribution to the diet. Hydroxypropylmethylcellulose is similarly made and used, except that the raw cellulose is also reacted with propylene oxide, with the result that the temperature at which it gels is even higher (up to 85°C).

What You Need To Know: Practically non-toxic.[427] Methylcellulose has been used both as a laxative and as a slimming aid. Once swallowed, it swells up with water, creating distension of the stomach. The body's natural reaction to this is to speed up the processes of digestion and elimination so as to get rid of the bulk as soon as possible. If you're thinking of using a product containing methylcellulose to try to help you lose weight, you should be aware that by consuming such a bulky mass, you may actually be conditioning your stomach to expect large amounts of food regularly. So when you stop using the product, you may feel just as hungry as ever. You could also experience flatulence. To prevent internal blockage, methyl cellulose should always be taken with plenty of water, and if you have bowel problems, check with your doctor first.

Methyl nicotinate

MEDICINAL SUBSTANCE: COUNTER-IRRITANT

What It Is: Methyl nicotinate is a counter-irritant used to try and relieve deep-seated pain such as arthritis. The skin is quickly irritated when it comes into contact with methyl nicotinate, its temperature rises and blood flow increases – much the same effect as putting a hot water bottle on it. Rubbing and massaging may aid the process.

Methyl p-hydroxybenzoate (E218)

FOOD ADDITIVE: PRESERVATIVE

Regulations: EC permitted to be used similarly to ethyl p-hydroxybenzoate (E214). Directive 95/2/EC.

Acceptable Daily Intake: 0 – 10 as sum of ethyl, methyl and propyl esters of p-hydroxybenzoic acid.

What It Is: Also known as methylparaben. A closely related compound to benzoic acid (see pp. 151–3), but more soluble in water, and a more effective preservative than benzoic acid in food which tends towards the alkali. An inhibitor of moulds, to a lesser extent bacteria.[428]

What You Need To Know: Not toxic in the small amount found in most food products. In antibacterial ointments, skin lotions and creams the parabens group may cause contact dermatitis.[429]

Methyl salicylate

MEDICINAL SUBSTANCE: COUNTER-IRRITANT

FOOD ADDITIVE: FLAVOURING

Acceptable Daily Intake: 0 – 0.5.

What It Is: Also called oil of wintergreen, made synthetically by esterification of salicylic acid with methanol, or distilled from the wintergreen shrub. Because it produces a powerful irritation and stimulates blood flow when applied to the skin, it is sometimes used in liniments and ointments for the relief of pain of lumbago, sciatica, rheumatic conditions and other deep-seated pains. It is also used on horses for over-exertion-related stiffness and soreness. Greatly diluted, it is sometimes used as a flavouring and perfume, and an ultraviolet absorber in sunburn lotions.

What You Need To Know: Toxic effects similar to other salicylates (see aspirin) although methyl is the most dangerous salicylate formulation by strength. One teaspoon contains 7000 mg of salicylate, equivalent to 21 aspirin tablets, and childhood fatalities may occur after ingestion of as little as 4 ml of oil of wintergreen. A 1 oz tube of external liniment (20 per cent methyl salicylate) is equivalent to the above fatal dose of oil of wintergreen. When applied to large areas of skin, topical salicylic acid may cause sufficient dermal absorption to produce toxic serum salicylate levels.[430] Ointments or liniments should not be applied to burned areas or to otherwise damaged skin. It is said to be a common paediatric (child) poison, and its use should be strongly discouraged.[431]

Methylene Blue

MEDICINAL SUBSTANCE: DYE

What It Is: Methylene blue has been used extensively as a dye (e.g. for staining microscope specimens) and, in the past, for colouring urine in kidney function tests.

What You Need To Know: In high concentrations it can cause methaemoglobinaemia (a reduction in the oxygen-carrying capacity of the blood) although in lower concentrations it has been used to treat this condition. Given by mouth it can cause nausea and vomiting, and after absorption it is excreted by the kidneys and gives the urine a blue-green colour.

Methylephedrine hydrochloride

MEDICINAL SUBSTANCE: DECONGESTANT

What It Is: A sympathomimetic substance used as a decongestant, with similar properties and side-effects to ephedrine (see pp. 229–30).

Miconazole

MEDICINAL SUBSTANCE: ANTIMICROBIAL

What It Is: Miconazole is used on the skin to treat fungal infections including candida, ringworm, and athlete's foot, and it is active against some bacteria.

What You Need To Know: It may occasionally irritate or sensitize the skin, and should not be used on young children. Stop using it if there are signs of dermatitis.

Mixed acetic and tartaric acid esters of mono- and diglycerides of fatty acids (E472f)

FOOD ADDITIVE: EMULSIFIER

Regulations: EC permitted for all foodstuffs following the *quantum satis* principle (except those specified in Table 2 on pp. 15–16 and in Appendix B on pp. 469ff). Directive 95/2/EC.

Acceptable Daily Intake: Not specified.
What It Is: Made from esters of glycerol with acetic and tartaric acids, and fatty acids occurring in food fats.
What You Need To Know: In 1992 the British government's Food Advisory Committee recommended that this substance be provisionally acceptable for use in food, pending receipt of toxicity studies on DATEM (see following).[432]

Mono- and diacetyl tartaric acid esters of mono- and diglycerides of fatty acids (DATEM) (E472e)

FOOD ADDITIVE: EMULSIFIER

Regulations: EC permitted for all foodstuffs following the *quantum satis* principle (except those specified in Table 2 on pp. 15–16 and in Appendix B on pp. 469ff). Directive 95/2/EC.
Acceptable Daily Intake: Not specified.
What It Is: Made by reacting tartaric acid (see pp. 469ff) with acetic acid (see pp. 106–7) anhydride; the diacetylated tartaric acid is then reacted with monoglycerides. Depending on the type of monoglyceride (fat) used, the end result can either be crystallized in block, flake or powder form, or it can be semi-liquid. Its main application is as a dough conditioner in yeast-raised bakery products.
What You Need To Know: In 1992 the British government's Food Advisory Committee concluded that the major components of DATEM do not fully break down in the human intestine to normal dietary constituents. It therefore recommended that DATEM remained provisionally acceptable for use in food, but required the results of a satisfactory long-term study in at least one species, of a reproduction study in one species and of teratology studies in two species; such data to be provided within three years.[433]

Mono- and diglycerides of fatty acids (E471)

FOOD ADDITIVE: EMULSIFIER; STABILIZER; CARRIER

Regulations: EC permitted for all foodstuffs following the *quantum satis* principle (except those specified in Table 2 on pp. 15–16 and in Appendix B on pp. 469ff).

EC permitted as carrier Restricted use: colours and fat-soluble antioxidants. Directive 95/2/EC.

Acceptable Daily Intake: Not specified.

What It Is: Produced by heating triglyceride fats with an excess of glycerol (see pp. 245–7). The most commonly used emulsifiers in the food industry. They produce and stabilize water-in-oil emulsions and, as starch complexing agents, retard staling in baked goods.

Monoammonium glutamate (E624)

FOOD ADDITIVE: FLAVOUR ENHANCER; SALT SUBSTITUTE

Regulations: EC permitted to be used similarly to glutamic acid (E620). Directive 95/2/EC.

Acceptable Daily Intake: Not specified.

What It Is: Obtained from glutamic acid (see pp. 244–5), but apparently lacking the strong flavour-potentiating properties of monosodium glutamate (see pp. 317–8).[434]

Monopotassium glutamate (E622)

FOOD ADDITIVE: FLAVOUR ENHANCER; SALT SUBSTITUTE

Regulations: EC permitted to be used similarly to glutamic acid (E620). Directive 95/2/EC.

Acceptable Daily Intake: Not specified.

What It Is: Obtained from glutamic acid (see p. 244), but apparently lacking the strong flavour potentiating properties of monosodium glutamate (see pp. 317–8).[435]

Monosodium glutamate (E621) ⚠

FOOD ADDITIVE: FLAVOUR ENHANCER

Regulations: EC permitted to be used similarly to glutamic acid (E620). Directive 95/2/EC.

Acceptable Daily Intake: Not specified.

What It Is: Kombu (a seaweed) has been used in Japan for centuries as the somewhat magical basis for the preparation of the most exquisite soups, for while most ingredients in a recipe have their own flavour, kombu has none – it simply makes the other ingredients taste better. In 1908, Professor Kikunae Ikeda of Japan succeeded in isolating glutamic acid from kombu, and named the unique glutamate quality 'umami', or 'delicious'. He suggested that umami should be a basic taste independent of the four traditional ones: sweet, sour, bitter and salty. In 1913, Ikeda's protégé Shintaro Kodama discovered that inosinic acid (from dried bonito tuna) was another important umami substance. The full configuration of umami was not, however, discovered until 1960, when another Japanese researcher, Akira Kuninaka, discovered that 5'-guanylate (from guanylic acid) was another key component (obtained from another important flavouring ingredient of Japanese cookery, the Shiitake mushroom). From these three basic substances, a huge worldwide industry of 'flavour potentiators' has been created. How do they actually work? There are two main theories. First, they may operate on taste-receptor cells (sensitive to the four basic flavours) to enhance their perception – rather like turning up the volume on a hi-fi. Alternatively, umami may have its very own receptor cells – meaning that umami is, as Professor Ikeda predicted, a separate and distinct taste in its own right. There is evidence to support both conclusions. It is manufactured by fermentation of glucose preparations. Mostly used in dry and wet soup products and general convenience foods; one fifth of overall production is used in restaurants, hotels, and other catering outlets. Apart from human use, it has been added to animal feed in order to induce the early weaning of baby piglets.

What You Need To Know: See glutamic acid (pp. 244–5) for information about excitotoxicity. Adverse effects in those sensitive to this substance have included feeling of pressure in the head, tightness of face, and seizures.[436] Burning sensations, facial pressure and chest pains have been experimentally induced in people given 4 grams or less.[437] The toxic dose of MSG that frequently provokes an attack is at least 1 gram orally. The serious headache/nausea side-effect may not begin for some hours (often 6) after ingestion, but can last for half a day to 2 days.[438] It has been suggested that deficiency of vitamin B6 may cause or exacerbate MSG symptoms.[439]

In 1969 Washington University neurophysiologist John Olney demonstrated that that one dose of MSG could raise blood glutamate levels in rats and monkeys, and affect the hypothalamus (a region of the brain that is not well protected by the blood-brain barrier). Olney's discovery introduced the concept of excitotoxicity (the ability of amino acids such as glutamate to literally excite nerve cells to death – see pp. 244–5). Olney believed that food additives such as MSG could harm children, who are more susceptible to excitotoxic damage than adults. Today, many baby food manufacturers have voluntarily stopped adding MSG to their products.

Monostarch phosphate (E1410)
FOOD ADDITIVE: STABILIZER; THICKENING AGENT; BINDER; CARRIER

Regulations: EC permitted for all foodstuffs following the *quantum satis* principle (except those specified in Table 2 on pp. 15–16 and in Appendix B on pp. 469ff).

EC permitted as carrier. Restricted use: none. Directive 95/2/EC.

Acceptable Daily Intake: Not specified.

What It Is: A chemically modified starch, made by reacting dry starch (from wheat, potato, etc.) with sodium orthophosphate / tripolyphosphate in the presence of heat. The resulting starch is thicker and dissolves more readily than unmodified (i.e. natural) starch.

Morphine

MEDICINAL SUBSTANCE: ANALGESIC

What It Is: The most important alkaloid present in the opium poppy, *Papaver somniferum*, indigenous to Asia Minor (opium contains between 9 and 14 per cent of morphine; heroin is prepared from morphine and acetyl chloride). A powerful narcotic and pain-killer – therapeutic uses include treatment of the most severe types of pain as found in patients suffering from terminal illnesses. It has been used, in small quantities, in some preparations sold to treat diarrhoea, because it tends to produce constipation, although whether it is effective in such small doses is questionable.

What You Need To Know: Capable of quickly producing drug dependence. Its side-effects may include skin rashes, nausea, mental confusion, dry mouth, difficulty in passing water, palpitations, and decrease in the rate and volume of respiration.

Random drugs testing is increasingly practised both in the sports world and at work, so it is worth noting that a positive finding of codeine or morphine in the urine of an individual does not necessarily indicate heroin, morphine, or codeine use. Detectable levels of these drugs can be found in the urine up to 22 hours after poppy-seed bagels have been consumed.[440]

Myrrh

MEDICINAL SUBSTANCE: ASTRINGENT; ANTIMICROBIAL; FLAVOURING

What It Is: Used by the Egyptians to embalm the dead, myrrh is made from the resin of the *Commiphora myrrha* shrub, and has an astringent and antiseptic action in oral applications.

Naphazoline

MEDICINAL SUBSTANCE: DECONGESTANT

What It Is: Naphazoline is a sympathomimetic drug with similar uses and cautions to ephedrine (see pp. 229–30), used to constrict the blood vessels in the nose, thus producing relief from swelling and inflammation. It is thought that rebound congestion may occur more easily than with ephedrine preparations, and it is quite likely to occur with prolonged use.

What You Need To Know: See ephedrine. Additionally, it will cause drowsiness if it is accidentally swallowed (unlike other sympathomimetics, it depresses instead of stimulating the central nervous system).[441] Should be used with particular caution in patients with cardiovascular disease.[442] May occasionally cause headache, nervousness, nausea, dizziness, weakness. Overdosage may produce a decrease in body temperature, low blood pressure, and coma.[443]

Natamycin (pimaricin) (E235)

FOOD ADDITIVE: PRESERVATIVE

Regulations: EC permitted for surface treatment of hard, semi-hard and semi-soft cheese; dried, cured sausages, maximum level: 1 mg/dm2 surface (not present at a depth of 5 mm). Directive 95/2/EC.

Acceptable Daily Intake: 0 – 0.3.

What It Is: Similar to Nisin (see pp. 323–4).

Neohesperidine DC (E959)

FOOD ADDITIVE: SWEETENER

Regulations: EC permitted for the following foods up to the total maximum usable dose specified.

- Water-based flavoured drinks, energy-reduced or with no added sugar, maximum usable dose: 30 mg/l
- Milk- and milk-derivative-based drinks, energy-reduced or with no added sugar, maximum usable dose: 50 mg/l

- Fruit-juice-based drinks, energy-reduced or with no added sugar, maximum usable dose: 30 mg/l
- Water-based flavoured desserts, energy-reduced or with no added sugar, maximum usable dose: 50 mg/kg; Milk- and milk-derivative-based preparations, energy-reduced or with no added sugar, maximum usable dose: 50 mg/kg; Fruit- and vegetable-based desserts; energy-reduced or with no added sugar, maximum usable dose: 50 mg/kg; Egg-based desserts, energy-reduced or with no added sugar, maximum usable dose: 50 mg/kg; Cereal-based desserts, energy-reduced or with no added sugar, maximum usable dose: 50 mg/kg; Fat-based desserts, energy-reduced or with no added sugar, maximum usable dose: 50 mg/kg
- Confectionery with no added sugar, maximum usable dose: 100 mg/kg; Cocoa- or dried-fruit-based confectionery, energy-reduced or with no added sugar, maximum usable dose: 100 mg/kg; Starch-based confectionery, energy-reduced or with no added sugar, maximum usable dose: 150 mg/kg
- Cocoa-, milk-, dried-fruit- or fat-based sandwich spreads, energy-reduced or with no added sugar, maximum usable dose: 50 mg/kg
- Chewing gum with no added sugar, maximum usable dose: 400 mg/kg
- Cider and perry, maximum usable dose: 20 mg/l
- Alcohol-free beer or with an alcohol content not exceeding 1,2% vol, maximum usable dose: 10 mg/l
- 'Biere de table/Tafelbier/Table beer' (original wort content less than 6 %) except 'Obergariges Einfachbier', maximum usable dose: 10 mg/l
- Beers with a minimum acidity of 30 milli-equivalents expressed as NaOH, maximum usable dose: 10 mg/l
- Brown beers of the 'oud bruin' type, maximum usable dose: 10 mg/l
- Edible ices, energy-reduced or with no added sugar, maximum usable dose: 50 mg/kg
- Canned or bottled fruit, energy-reduced or with no added sugar, maximum usable dose: 50 mg/kg
- Energy-reduced jams, jellies and marmalades, maximum usable dose: 50 mg/kg
- Sweet-sour preserves of fruit and vegetables, maximum usable dose: 100 mg/kg

- Energy-reduced fruit and vegetable preparations, maximum usable dose: 50 mg/kg
- Sweet-sour preserves and semi-preserves of fish and marinades of fish, crustaceans and molluscs, maximum usable dose: 30 mg/kg
- Sauces, maximum usable dose: 50 mg/kg
- Mustard, maximum usable dose: 50 mg/kg
- Fine bakery products for special nutritional uses, maximum usable dose: 150 mg/kg
- Complete formulae for weight control intended to replace total daily food intake or an individual meal, maximum usable dose: 100 mg/kg
- Liquid food supplements/dietary integrators, maximum usable dose: 50 mg/kg
- Solid food supplements/dietary integrators, maximum usable dose: 100 mg/kg
- EC permitted for the following foods:
- Chewing gum with added sugars, maximum level: 150 mg/kg
- Margarine, Minarine, Meat products, Fruit jellies, Vegetable proteins, maximum level: 5 mg/kg (as flavour enhancer only)
- Directive 94/35/EC.

What It Is: Like many artificial sweeteners, neohesperidine dihydrochalcone was discovered by accident – scientists at the US Department of Agriculture's Western Regional Research Labs were originally examining the structure-taste relationship of naringin (obtained from grapefruit seeds) and the sweet taste of the dihydrochalcone was totally unexpected. In subsequent work it was found that Seville oranges yielded a more potent substance (weight for weight, it is 340 times sweeter than sugar). Its taste profile is characterized by a lingering cooling aftertaste, which might restrict its commercial application. It is, however, now used in speciality beers in Belgium.

Nickel

CONTAMINANT

What It Is: A metallic element obtained from nickel ore. Used to make stainless steel (which may contain up to 35 per cent nickel), also in nickel plating, coinage, spark plugs, and as a catalyst in the hydrogenation of fats and oils.

What You Need To Know: Nickel metal can cause contact dermatitis. Instances of dermatitis around the eyes has resulted from contact with nickel spectacle frames.[444] It has been estimated that 5 per cent of all eczema can be linked to contact with nickel-containing compounds.[445]

The toxicity to humans of nickel or nickel salts through oral intake is low.[446] Nickel compounds are poorly absorbed from the gastrointestinal tract, making them essentially non-toxic by mouth. However, certain nickel compounds are extremely potent carcinogens if breathed in.[447]

The International Agency for Research on Cancer has concluded that nickel compounds, evaluated as a group, are carcinogenic to humans. Metallic nickel is possibly carcinogenic to humans.[448]

The US Environmental Protection Agency has classified nickel as a human carcinogen. Human data in which exposure to nickel refinery dust caused lung and nasal tumors in sulphide nickel matte refinery workers in several epidemiological studies in different countries and on animal data in which carcinomas were produced in rats by inhalation and injection. Human carcinogenicity data: sufficient.[449]

Food processing methods may apparently add to the nickel levels already present in foodstuffs via (1) leaching from nickel-containing alloys in food processing equipment made from stainless steel, (2) the milling of flour, and (3) catalytic hydrogenation of fats and oils by use of nickel catalysts.[450]

Nisin (E234)
FOOD ADDITIVE: PRESERVATIVE
Regulations: EC permitted for semolina and tapioca puddings and similar products, maximum level: 3mg/kg; ripened cheese and processed cheese, maximum level: 12.5 mg/kg; clotted cream, maximum level: 10 mg/kg. Directive 95/2/EC.

Acceptable Daily Intake: 0 – 33,000 unconditional acceptable daily intake given in units/kg of body weight.

What It Is: Nisin is a 'bacteriocin' – a protein produced by one type of bacteria with the effect of killing off bacteria of a similar species – perhaps as a kind of chemical warfare agent intended to give the producing bacterium a competitive advantage. Nisin is produced by the lactococci bacteria when fermented in milk.

Nitric acid

MEDICINAL SUBSTANCE: FLAVOURING

What It Is: Nitric acid is highly corrosive, but is found at great dilutions in a few products as a sharp flavouring. It may also be found in products sold for the destruction of warts.

What You Need To Know: Skin contact with concentrated nitric acid will produce burns at the site of contact.

Nitrogen (E941)

FOOD ADDITIVE: PACKING GAS; CRYOGENIC FREEZANT

Regulations: EC permitted for all foodstuffs following the *quantum satis* principle. Directive 95/2/EC.

Acceptable Daily Intake: No acceptable daily intake necessary.

What It Is: Constitutes about 75 per cent of the atmosphere. Separated from the air by cryogenic distillation or fixation, or by combustion of natural gas or propane and air.

What You Need To Know: It is generally considered that the only physiological effects due to the inhalation of nitrogen result from oxygen dilution.[451] However, in deep-sea diving it is well known that nitrogen-induced CNS depression occurs despite the fact that nitrogen is a so-called inert gas.[452]

Nitrous oxide (E942)

FOOD ADDITIVE: PROPELLANT

Regulations: EC permitted for all foodstuffs following the *quantum satis* principle. Directive 95/2/EC.

Acceptable Daily Intake: Acceptable.

What It Is: Also known as laughing gas, made by thermal decomposition of ammonium nitrate. Mostly used in combination with oxygen as a general medical anaesthetic, also used as a propellant for food aerosols, and in rocket fuel. One of the greenhouse gases (the others are carbon dioxide, methane, ozone and chlorofluorocarbons) responsible for global warming. Sources of 'greenhouse' nitrous oxide are not well understood but may include production of nylon, catalytic converters on cars, the decomposition of organic matter and emissions from nitrogen-based fertilizers.[453]

What You Need To Know: When used as a general anaesthetic, it has been reported that nitrous oxide can inactivate vitamin B12 and impair DNA synthesis on bone marrow cells. Folate deficiency may also develop, which can prolong recovery from these abnormalities in some seriously ill patients. Treatment with folic acid accelerates the recovery of the bone marrow abnormalities.[454] Many anaesthesiologists feel that use of nitrous oxide should be restricted during the first two trimesters of pregnancy because of its effects on DNA production, and the experimental and epidemiological evidences that nitrous oxide causes undesirable reproductive outcomes. Since nitrous oxide affects white blood cell production and function, it has been recommended that it not be given to immuno-suppressed patients or to patients requiring multiple general anaesthetics.[455] Epidemiological and experimental evidence indicates that long-term exposure to trace concentrations of nitrous oxide may produce abortion. Similar but less complete evidence suggests that prolonged exposure may cause neurologic injury and congenital anomalies.[456] One medical authority warns that dentists and assistants chronically exposed to nitrous oxide may suffer increased rates of neurologic disease, kidney disease, liver disease, cancer and spontaneous abortion.[457]

Noscapine
MEDICINAL SUBSTANCE: COUGH SUPPRESSANT

What It Is: Like codeine (see pp. 210–11), noscapine is an alkaloid derived from opium, although it has no morphine-like effects.[458] It has no analgesic properties.[459] Studies are divided on its ability to suppress coughing – one finding no antitussive effect, another rating it about equal to codeine.[460] [461]

What You Need To Know: Adverse reactions occur infrequently but may include drowsiness, headache, nausea, allergic rhinitis, and conjunctivitis.[462]

Nutmeg oil
MEDICINAL SUBSTANCE: FLAVOURING

What It Is: Extracted from the kernel of the nutmeg seed (*Myristica*), nutmeg oil is said to have stimulant properties to both the mood and the digestion. It is sometimes used to mask the flavour or odour of less pleasant ingredients in a product.

What You Need To Know: Nutmeg poisoning case report: 'patient exhibited appearance of snarling dog. Upon being questioned, retracted head back into his neck, tightened up neck muscles, retracted tongue and bared his teeth. Semicomatose state, would not respond to questioning.'[463]

Some people take toxic doses of nutmeg in the hope that it may produce pleasantly hallucinogenic effects. As you can see from the above case report, they are in for a rough trip. Typically, excessive ingestion of nutmeg results in extended periods of delirium and stupor (usually resolved by heavy sleep) with feelings of acute terror and fears of impending death or doom.[464]

Ochratoxin A

FOOD ADDITIVE: CONTAMINANT

Acceptable Daily Intake: Provisional tolerable weekly intake: 0.000112.

What It Is: A mycotoxin produced by *Aspergillus* and *Penicillium* type bacteria. Found mainly in cereal and cereal type products, some pulses, coffee, cocoa, figs, nuts and coconut products; can also occur in meat and dairy products derived from animals exposed to contaminated feedstuffs.

What You Need To Know: Produces nephropathy (kidney disease) in humans, kidneys become small with impaired function. Causes kidney and other tumours, genetic damage, malformations in foetus (teratogen) and inhibits testosterone secretion.

The International Agency for Research on Cancer has concluded that this substance is possibly carcinogenic to humans. There is inadequate evidence in humans for the carcinogenicity of ochratoxin A. There is sufficient evidence in experimental animals for the carcinogenicity of ochratoxin A.[465]

Octaphomium chloride

MEDICINAL SUBSTANCE: ANTIMICROBIAL

What It Is: Octaphomium chloride is a disinfectant with antibacterial and antifungal properties, similar in its usage and effect to cetrimide (see p. 197)

Octyl gallate (E311)

FOOD ADDITIVE: ANTIOXIDANT

Regulations: EC permitted to be used similarly to propyl gallate (E310). Directive 95/2/EC.

Acceptable Daily Intake: 0 – 0.1, temporary.

What It Is: See Propyl gallate.

Oleyl alcohol
MEDICINAL SUBSTANCE: EMOLLIENT
What It Is: Naturally present in fish and marine mammal oils, used as a softening and soothing agent on the skin and as a stabilizer in pharmaceutical products.

Orthophenyl phenol (2-hydroxybiphenyl) (E231)
FOOD ADDITIVE: PRESERVATIVE
Regulations: EC permitted for surface treatment of citrus fruits, maximum level: 12 mg/kg individually or in combination with sodium orthophenyl phenol (E232), expressed as orthophenyl phenol. Directive 95/2/EC.
What It Is: Produced in the reaction of sodium hydroxide with chlorobenzene, and used in the post-harvest treatment of fruits to protect against microbial damage.
What You Need To Know: The International Agency for Research on Cancer has concluded that this substance is unclassifiable as to carcinogenicity in humans. No data were available in humans, and there was inadequate evidence of carcinogenicity in animals.[466]

Oxidized starch (E1404)
FOOD ADDITIVE: EMULSIFIER; THICKENING AGENT; BINDER; CARRIER
Regulations: EC permitted for all foodstuffs following the *quantum satis* principle (except those specified in Table 2 on pp. 15–16 and in Appendix B on pp. 469ff).
EC permitted as carrier. Restricted use: none. Directive 95/2/EC.
Acceptable Daily Intake: Not specified.
What It Is: A chemically modfied starch, made by treating starch granules (e.g. from cornflour) suspended in water with sodium hypochlorite. This reduces the starch's natural ten-

dency to thicken when cooled, and it may be used as a filler in those foods (e.g. salad dressings) where a thick, viscous starch would not be appropriate.

Oxygen (E948)

FOOD ADDITIVE

Regulations: EC permitted for all foodstuffs following the *quantum satis* principle. Directive 95/2/EC.

What It Is: Made by the liquefaction and subsequent controlled fractionation of air, or by electrolytic decomposition of water. Mainly used in steel manufacturing, and as a raw material in the chemical industry.

Oxymetazoline

MEDICINAL SUBSTANCE: DECONGESTANT

What It Is: A sympathomimetic substance used in a similar way to ephedrine (see pp. 229–30) as a decongestant in nasal products, where it acts to constrict the blood vessels and thus reduce swelling and inflammation.

What You Need To Know: See ephedrine for notes on sympathomimetics. Side-effects may include local stinging or burning, dryness of nose and throat and sneezing.[467] Headache, lightheadedness, insomnia, and palpitations have also been noted.[468] Rebound congestion less noticable than with naphazoline.[469]

Padimate

MEDICINAL SUBSTANCE: SUN SCREEN

What It Is: The first patented sun screen was para-amino-benzoic acid (PABA). Many people were found to be sensitive to PABA, and it didn't stay on very well when wet. Padimate O is a PABA ester which is less likely to cause a reaction, and stays on better. PABA and its derivatives (including Padimate A and O) protect skin from UV-B light only.[470]

Pancreatin
MEDICINAL SUBSTANCE: ENZYME
What It Is: Pancreatin is a naturally occurring digestive enzyme made by the pancreas. Oral supplements are only needed by people with diagnosed pancreatic insufficiency, although it has been included in antacids and other digestive aids. It is inactivated by gastric acid.

Papaverine
MEDICINAL SUBSTANCE: ANTISPASMODIC
What It Is: Papaverine is an alkaloid found in opium, and also produced synthetically. It lacks opium's narcotic properties.
What You Need To Know: Papaverine is an antispasmodic which relaxes the smooth muscle (lungs, the heart, and the gastro-intestinal tract). It should not be used in cases of glaucoma. Adverse reactions have included upset stomach, skin rash, headache, sweating, jaundice and dizziness. In addition, its side-effects can include nausea, abdominal discomfort, anorexia, constipation, malaise, drowsiness, vertigo, headache, diarrhoea, rash, flushing of face, increase in heart rate and slight increase in blood pressure.[471] It has not been proved to have therapeutic value in any condition, and its use is now practically obsolete.[472]

Paprika extract, capsanthin, capsorubin (E160C)
FOOD ADDITIVE: FOOD COLOUR; FLAVOURING AGENT
Regulations: EC permitted at *quantum satis* in all foods except those to which the EC only permits certain colours to be added (Appendix C, pp. 476ff) and those to which the EC forbids the adding of colours (Appendix D, pp. 482ff). Directive 94/36/EC.
Acceptable Daily Intake: No acceptable daily intake allocated.
What It Is: The red colour present in paprika is due to its

carotenoid content (capsanthin and capsorubin are the main carotenoids). Rapidly loses its colour when exposed to sunlight, perhaps due to the presence of highly oxidizable fatty acids.

Paracetamol

MEDICINAL SUBSTANCE: ANALGESIC

What It Is: Paracetamol (acetaminophen) is a synthetically-produced analgesic substance, also used as a raw material in the manufacture of azo dyes.

What You Need To Know: Similar to aspirin in its ability to relieve mild pain and to reduce fever, but it does not reduce the inflammation and stiffness of arthritis. It may, however, be less upsetting to the stomach than aspirin. In normal doses over short periods there should be no side-effects, although skin rash and other allergic reactions occur occasionally.[473]

Do not prescribe paracetamol for yourself if you have ever reacted bady to it in the past, or if you have kidney or liver disease (such as cirrhosis of the liver), or if you are taking other drugs which may affect your liver (this means that alcoholics are especially susceptible to liver damage). Taking alcohol or other drugs with it will enhance its toxicity by reducing the metabolic capacity of the liver.[474] Contact your doctor if you experience any of the following symptoms after taking paracetamol:

- Weakness or tiredness
- Yellow skin or eyes
- An allergic skin reaction such as itching or a rash
- Unusual bruising or bleeding
- Persistent fever or sore throat

In overdose, paracetamol will cause particularly nasty symptoms. About 10 g may be sufficient to cause liver damage in an adult, doses of 20 to 25 g or more are potentially fatal.[475] For a day or so after the overdose, there may be no specific symptoms, although vomiting may occur. Thereafter, there may even be some improvement – although by then, liver and/or kidney damage could be well under way. Maximum liver or kidney damage may not become apparent until two to four days after the overdose – and by then, successful treatment could be impossible.

As with all non-prescribed drugs, you should take paracetamol as a short-term solution to a short-term problem, because there is a suggestion that long-term paracetamol usage (particularly if combined with other drugs such as alcohol or barbiturates) may also damage the liver.

The International Agency for Research on Cancer has concluded that paracetamol is unclassifiable as to its carcinogenicity in humans. There is inadequate evidence for the carcinogenicity of paracetamol in humans. There is limited evidence for the carcinogenicity of paracetamol in experimental animals.[476]

Note to pet owners: cats cannot tolerate paracetamol at any dose.[477]

Patent Blue V (E131)

FOOD ADDITIVE: FOOD COLOUR

Regulations: EC permitted to be used singly or in combination with other colours in the following foods up to the total maximum level specified.

- Non-alcoholic flavoured drinks, maximum level: 100 mg/l
- Candied fruits and vegetables, Mostarda di frutta, maximum level: 200 mg/kg
- Preserves of red fruits, maximum level: 200 mg/kg
- Confectionery, maximum level: 300 mg/kg
- Decorations and coatings, maximum level: 500 mg/kg
- Fine bakery wares (e.g. viennoiserie, biscuits, cakes and wafers), maximum level: 200 mg/kg
- Edible ices, maximum level: 150 mg/kg
- Flavoured processed cheese, maximum level: 100 mg/kg

- Desserts including flavoured milk products, maximum level: 150 mg/kg
- Sauces, seasonings (for example, curry powder, tandoori), pickles, relishes, chutney and piccalilli, maximum level: 500 mg/kg
- Mustard, maximum level: 300 mg/kg
- Fish paste and crustacean paste, maximum level: 100 mg/kg; Pre-cooked crustaceans, maximum level: 250 mg/kg; Salmon substitutes, maximum level: 500 mg/kg; Surimi, maximum level: 500 mg/kg; Fish roe, maximum level: 300 mg/kg; Smoked fish, maximum level: 100 mg/kg
- Snacks: dry, savoury potato, cereal or starch-based snack products: Extruded or expanded savoury snack products, maximum level: 200 mg/kg; Other savoury snack products and savoury coated nuts, maximum level: 100 mg/kg
- Edible cheese rind and edible casings, maximum level: *quantum satis*
- Complete formulae for weight control intended to replace total daily food intake or an individual meal, maximum level: 50 mg/kg
- Complete formulae and nutritional supplements for use under medical supervision, maximum level: 50 mg/kg
- Liquid food supplements/dietary integrators, maximum level: 100 mg/l
- Solid food supplements/dietary integrators, maximum level: 300 mg/kg
- Soups, maximum level: 50 mg/kg
- Meat and fish analogues based on vegetable proteins, maximum level: 100 mg/kg
- Spirituous beverages (including products less than 15 % alcohol by volume), except those mentioned in Annex II or III, maximum level: 200 mg/l
- Aromatized wines, aromatized wine-based drinks and aromatized wine-product cocktails as mentioned in Regulation (EEC) No 1601/91, except those mentioned in Annex II or III, maximum level: 200 mg/l
- Fruit wines (still or sparkling) cider (except cidre bouche) and perry, aromatized fruit wines, cider and perry, maximum level: 200 mg/l. Directive 94/36/EC.

Acceptable Daily Intake: No acceptable daily intake allocated.
What It Is: A synthetic, bright blue triarylmethane dye.

What You Need To Know: The International Agency for Research on Cancer has concluded that this substance is unclassifiable as to carcinogenicity in humans. No data were available in humans, and there was limited evidence of carcinogenicity in animals.[478]

The Joint FAO/WHO Expert Committee on Food Additives was unable to allocate an acceptable daily intake to this substance when it was considered in 1982 because insufficient toxicological data were available.[479]

Patulin

FOOD ADDITIVE: CONTAMINANT

Acceptable Daily Intake: Provisional tolerable weekly intake: 0.007.

What It Is: A mycotoxin produced by *Aspergillus* and *Penicillium* type bacteria. Major dietary sources are apples and apple juice made from rotten or mouldy fruit; it is particularly associated with moulds such as brown rot in apples. In 1992, British Ministry of Agriculture, Fisheries and Food inspectors detected levels of patulin at eight times the permitted amount in food samples. The findings were not made public, and considerable criticism was directed at the Ministry for its secrecy when the test results finally became known, a year later.[480]

What You Need To Know: Once tested on humans as a potential cure for the common cold, it is now known that patulin can impair DNA synthesis, suppress the immune system, and inhibit the activity of many enzymes. It has an antibiotic effect on certain (Gram-positive) bacteria, which can allow other bacteria (Gram-negative) to flourish – thus producing a greater susceptibility to diseases such as pneumonia.[481]

The International Agency for Research on Cancer has concluded that this substance is unclassifiable as to carcinogenicity in humans. No data were available in humans, and there was inadequate evidence of carcinogenicity in animals.[482]

Research indicates that there are at least two ways to reduce or eliminate patulin contamination. Activated charcoal has been shown to reduce patulin in naturally contaminated cider to nondetectable levels.[483] The addition of vitamin C also appears to have an effect – in one study, patulin disappeared from apple juice when vitamin C was present.[484]

Pectins (i) pectin (ii) amidated pectin (E440)

FOOD ADDITIVE: THICKENING AGENT; STABILIZER; GELLING AGENT

Regulations: EC permitted for all foodstuffs following the *quantum satis* principle (except those specified in Table 2 on pp. 15–16 and in Appendix B on pp. 469ff).
EC permitted as carrier. Restricted use: none. Directive 95/2/EC.

Acceptable Daily Intake: Not specified.

What It Is: Functions as 'cement' in the cell walls of all plant tissues. One of the richest sources of pectin is lemon or orange rind, which contains about 30 per cent of this polysaccharide. Used as a gelling agent in jams, jellies and confections, as a toxin adsorber, as a stabilizer for milk products, for frozen desserts and soft drinks, an emulsifier for salad dressing and an ingredient in dental adhesives.

What You Need To Know: Scientific studies do not raise carcinogenic or reproductive concerns.[485]

Peppermint oil

MEDICINAL SUBSTANCE: FLAVOURING

What It Is: Peppermint oil is produced from the leaves and flowers of peppermint, and has a pleasant, cooling fragrance. Its main constituent is menthol (see p. 295), and it may be helpful in relieving indigestion, increasing gastric secretions and speeding up the passage of food through the stomach, although it may occasionally cause heartburn. It is often used as a flavouring for other drug ingredients in a mixture.

Pepsin

MEDICINAL SUBSTANCE: ENZYME

What It Is: Pepsin is a naturally-occurring digestive enzyme whose function is to break down proteins (pepsin in over-the-counter products may be made from pigs or cows).

Peru, balsam of

MEDICINAL SUBSTANCE: ANTIMICROBIAL

What It Is: Exuded from the baill tree, Peru balsam acts as a mild antiseptic. It is generally used externally on piles (haemorrhoids), bedsores, and on eczema. One survey found that about 7 per cent of the population were allergic to it.[486]

Pheniramine malleate

MEDICINAL SUBSTANCE: ANTIHISTAMINE

What It Is: An antihistamine drug. For some general information about antihistamines, see their separate entry (p. 298).

Phenol

MEDICINAL SUBSTANCE: ANTIMICROBIAL

What It Is: Phenol (carbolic acid) is an old-fashioned antiseptic and disinfectant, which has slowly fallen from favour as more modern preparations have become available. Most industrial production today is used as a raw material for the production of phenolic resins, for eventual end use in the housing, construction and automotive industries.

What You Need To Know: Highly diluted for antiseptic use: in undiluted form, it is acutely hazardous, highly corrosive to the skin and systemically toxic. When heated it emits toxic and flammable vapours. Phenol stops bacteria from multiplying at a concentration of approximately 0.2 per cent, will kill bacteria above 1 per cent, and kills fungi above 1.3 per cent.[487] Phenol can, unfortunately, be very poisonous. Ingestion of as little as 4.8 g of pure phenol has caused death in ten minutes.[488]

Some people may be hypersensitive and the effects can be serious or even lethal at very low exposures. Death or severe toxicity are usually due to effects on the central nervous system, heart, blood vessels, lungs and kidneys. Some evidence suggests that phenol is more toxic when absorbed through the skin than when taken by mouth (phenol damages skin, which increases the rate of penetration). There is a case history of an employee who accidentally spilled 4–5 litres of 78 per cent aqueous phenol on himself. The spill was immediately washed off with alcohol, and there were only superficial skin burns, but he became comatose and died shortly afterwards.[489] It is estimated that death may result even if the exposed area is as small as that of a hand or forearm.[490] For this reason, phenol should not be used over large areas of skin or on large wounds, or even on small wounds on a regular basis. People with liver or kidney diseases should not be exposed to phenol (even vapours) for any length of time.[491]

Nevertheless, we owe a debt of gratitude to this substance: in the 1860s Lord Lister showed that he could prevent septic infection in the operating theatre by using phenol as a disinfectant. Of course, medicine has progressed enormously since that time, and phenol should probably be allowed to quietly take its place in medical history.

The International Agency for Research on Cancer has concluded that this substance is unclassifiable as to carcinogenicity in humans.[492]

Phenolphthalein
MEDICINAL SUBSTANCE: LAXATIVE

What It Is: An ingredient in laxative products, phenolphthalein is thought to work by irritating the lining of the bowels and stimulating them into action.

What You Need To Know: It is quite easily absorbed into the system, and tends to re-cycle itself, so that one dose may continue to act (often unpredictably) for a day or two. Adverse effects may include abominal cramp, skin rashes, and it may dye urine and stools pink; also fluid and electrolyte deficits may result from an excessive cathartic effect.

Phenylephrine

MEDICINAL SUBSTANCE: DECONGESTANT

What It Is: Phenylephrine is a 'sympathomimetic' drug, like ephedrine, (see pp. 229–30), used to reduce nasal congestion by constricting the blood vessels in the nose, thus temporarily reducing inflammation.

What You Need To Know: Do not use products which contain phenylephrine without medical advice if you are diabetic, have thyroid problems, suffer from high blood pressure or if you are currently taking other prescribed medicines. It may irritate the nose and may produce 'rebound congestion', where the symptoms may return a few hours after initial medication, sometimes more acutely than previously. Systemic reactions to 10 per cent phenylephrine hydrochloride eyedrops have been reported in a few cases, including raised blood pressure and pulse rate, with headache, trembling, and perspiration.[493]

Phenylpropanolamine

MEDICINAL SUBSTANCE: DECONGESTANT

What It Is: Like ephedrine (see pp. 229–30) phenyl-propanolamine (PPA) is a sympathomimetic drug, whose effect is to stimulate part of the nervous system to produce changes in blood pressure and blood sugar, increase the heart rate, constriction of skin and gut blood vessels, relaxation of other blood vessels (e.g. in the lungs), and other effects. It is sometimes used in over-the-counter weight loss pills.

What You Need To Know: Like some other decongestants, PPA produces 'vasoconstriction', in other words, it constricts blood vessels. This should reduce the swelling in inflamed mucous membranes and lessen nasal congestion, thus allowing freer passage of air through blocked airways. However: 'well-controlled clinical studies supporting the decongestant effectiveness of oral phenylpropanolamine are lacking, and some clinicians question its efficacy.'[494] One of the possible disadvantages of using it as a nasal decongestant is that rebound congestion may occur; another is that your body becomes accustomed to the drug, and after a day or so may require larger doses to achieve the same effect. PPA stimulates the central nervous system: effects may include nervousness, restlessness, insomnia, dizziness, headache, nausea and palpitations. It can also raise blood pressure (hypertension), and at least one manufacturer has recommended that blood pressure be monitored regularly during PPA therapy.

A study of adverse reactions to PPA reveals that about two-thirds of all cases have occurred in women and in people under the age of 30.[495] The most frequent side-effects involved acute hypertension and associated symptoms (e.g. severe headache) but intracranial hemorrhages, seizures, and some deaths (most due to stroke) have also been associated with PPA ingestion.

Neuropsychiatric adverse effects have also been reported in patients known to be taking recommended doses.[496] A review of 37 published cases of psychiatric problems that have been attributed to PPA reveals:[497]

- more reactions followed the ingestion of combination products than preparations containing PPA alone;
- more of the cases followed ingestion of recommended doses rather than overdoses;
- groups at particular risk appear to be those with a past or family psychiatric history, children under the age of six and post-partum women.

A Swedish study of 61 reports of psychic disturbances occurring with PPA usage indicated that most were in children below 16. Symptoms included restlessness, irritability, aggression (especially in younger children) and sleep disturbances. Five cases of psychotic episodes were also noted.[498]

It has been suggested that 'withdrawal of preparations containing PPA from general use should be considered in view of their potential for adverse reactions with other commonly used drugs and their doubtful therapeutic value'.[499] In Britain, the maximum amount of phenylpropanolamine that a non-prescription product may contain has been significantly reduced in recent years.

Pholcodine
MEDICINAL SUBSTANCE: COUGH SUPPRESSANT
What It Is: Pholcodine is derived from morphine, and is similar to codeine (see pp. 210–11) in its cough-suppressant abilities.

Phosphated distarch phosphate (E1413)
FOOD ADDITIVE: STABILIZER; THICKENING AGENT; BINDER; CARRIER
Regulations: EC permitted for all foodstuffs following the *quantum satis* principle (except those specified in Table 2 on pp. 15–16 and in Appendix B on pp. 469ff).
EC permitted as carrier. Restricted use: none. Directive 95/2/EC.
Acceptable Daily Intake: Not specified.
What It Is: Another chemically modified starch, made by treating starch (e.g. from potatoes) with sodium tripolyphosphate and sodium trimetaphosphate, which produces a strengthened starch capable of withstanding many modern food processes without degrading.
What You Need To Know: Scientific studies do not raise carcinogenic concerns.

Phosphoric acid (E338)

FOOD ADDITIVE: ACIDULANT; SEQUESTRANT; SYNERGIST FOR
ANTIOXIDANTS

Regulations: EC permitted for the following foods. The indicated maximum quantities of phosphoric acid and the phosphates E339, E340, E341, E450, E451 and E452 may be added individually or in combination (expressed as P2O5).

- Non-alcoholic flavoured drinks, maximum level: 700 mg/l (E338 only)
- Sterilized and UHT milk, maximum level: 1 g/l
- Partly dehydrated milk with less than 28 % solids, maximum level: 1 g/kg
- Partly dehydrated milk with more than 28 % solids, maximum level: 1,5 g/kg
- Dried milk and dried skimmed milk, maximum level: 2,5 g/kg
- Pasteurized, sterilized and UHT creams, maximum level: 5 g/kg
- Whipped cream and vegetable fat analogues, maximum level: 5 g/kg
- Unripened cheese (except Mozzarella), maximum level: 2 g/kg
- Processed cheese and processed cheese analogues, maximum level: 20 g/kg
- Meat products, maximum level: 5g/kg
- Sport drinks and prepared table waters, maximum level: 0,5 g/l
- Dietary supplements, maximum level: *quantum satis*
- Salt and its substitutes, maximum level: 10 g/kg
- Vegetable protein drinks, maximum level: 20 g/l
- Beverage whiteners, maximum level: 30 g/kg
- Beverage whiteners for vending machines, maximum level: 50 g/kg
- Edible ices, maximum level: 1 g/kg
- Desserts, maximum level: 3 g/kg
- Dry powdered dessert mixes, maximum level: 7 g/kg
- Fine bakery wares, maximum level: 20 g/kg
- Flour, maximum level: 2,5 g/kg
- Flour, self-raising, maximum level: 20 g/kg
- Soda bread, maximum level: 20 g/kg
- Liquid egg (white, yolk or whole egg), maximum level: 10 g/kg
- Sauces, maximum level: 5g/kg
- Soups and broths, maximum level: 3 g/kg

- Tea and herbal infusions, maximum level: 2 g/l
- Cider and perry, maximum level: 2g/l
- Chewing gum, maximum level: *quantum satis* (E341 (ii) only)
- Dried powdered foodstuffs, maximum level: 10 g/kg (E341 (iii) only)
- Chocolate and malt dairy-based drinks, maximum level: 2 g/l
- Alcoholic drinks (excluding wine and beer), maximum level: 1 g/l
- Breakfast cereals, maximum level: 5 g/kg
- Snacks, maximum level: 5 g/kg
- Surimi, maximum level: 1 g/kg; Fish and crustacean paste, maximum level: 5 g/kg
- Toppings (syrups for pancakes, flavoured syrups for milkshakes and ice cream; similar products), maximum level: 3 g/kg
- Special formulae for particular nutritional uses, maximum level: 5 g/kg
- Glazings for meat and vegetable products, maximum level: 4 g/kg
- Sugar confectionery, maximum level: 5 g/kg
- Icing sugar, maximum level: 10 g/kg
- Noodles, maximum level: 2 g/kg
- Batters, maximum level: 5 g/kg
- Fillets of unprocessed fish, frozen and deep-frozen, maximum level: 5 g/kg
- Frozen and deep-frozen crustacean products, maximum level: 5 g/kg
- Processed potato products (including frozen, deep-frozen, chilled and dried processed products), maximum level: 5 mg/kg
- Directive 95/2/EC.

Acceptable Daily Intake: Maximum tolerable daily intake 70 mg expressed as phosphorous from all sources.

What It Is: Food grade phosphoric acid is usually manufactured simply by burning elemental phosphorous in air, producing phosphorous pentoxide, which is then hydrated (exposed to water) to form phosphoric acid. It is used as a solvent, and in very dilute form as a flavouring. It is both the cheapest, and the strongest, of the acidulants used in the food industry, and most of it goes into soft drinks and beverages. It possesses a flat, synthetic taste which blends more effectively with non-fruit flavours than organic acids (e.g. citric acid); and

it is therefore preferred by manufacturers of colas, root beer, sarsaparilla and similar drinks. Phosphoric acid and its salts (phosphates) are also widely used in conjuction with the major antioxidant chemicals (e.g. ascorbic acid, BHA, BHT, the tocopherols, etc) to improve their antioxidant effect: by binding with metals present in the foodstuff (sequestering) phosphoric acid can stop them from speeding up the process of oxidation which, among other things, causes oils to go rancid.
What You Need To Know: Phosphorous only comprises 1 per cent by weight of the human body but it is extensively involved in many of our metabolic functions and enzyme systems. Indeed, phosphorous is so fundamental to life that scientists have speculated that if other lifeforms are one day located elsewhere in the universe, they may well be phosphorous-based, and not carbon-based as we (and all other living things on Earth) are.

Excessive intake of dietary phosphorous may produce an imbalance of the calcium/phosphorous ratio, leading to loss of calcium from bone and calcification of soft tissues, especially the kidneys. It is estimated that the lowest level of phosphate intake that might cause calcium to accumulate in human kidneys is in the order of 6,600 mg per day. Dividing by a safety factor of 100 yields the acceptable daily intake given above.[500] A defect in phosphate metabolism occurs in a variety of diseases including osteoporosis, rickets, osteomalacia and osteitis fibrosa cystica.[501] People eating a typical western junk-food diet can consume 500 mg of phosphorous a day, mainly in the form of food additives. At this level of intake, it may be difficult to maintain an adequate calcium/phosphorous ratio, with the result that bone mineral content and density will decrease, making the onset of osteoporosis more likely.[502]

There have been a number of reports of oral or rectal phosphate laxative poisoning in healthy children. A two and a half year old girl received two enemas consisting of monosodium phosphate (3.7 g/phosphorous each). Symptoms, consisting of vomiting, lethargy, hyperpyrexia, diarrhoea, carpal spasm and coma, began after 90 minutes and were eventually relieved by the administration of calcium gluconate.[503]

Phthalates

FOOD ADDITIVE: CONTAMINANT

Acceptable Daily Intake: Lowest level technologically attainable (provisional).

What It Is: Phthalic acid diesters, commonly known as phthalates, are a group of organic chemicals that have a variety of industrial uses, including use as plasticizers in a wide range of household and consumer goods.

What You Need To Know: Concern has arisen over the health impact of certain phthalates such as DEHP, which some surveys have shown to be the most abundant phthalate in food samples analysed by Britain's Ministry of Agriculture, Fisheries and Food (MAFF). The use of phthalates in the manufacture of food contact materials has declined considerably.[504]

Nevertheless, as a result of their extensive use and their moderate resistance to degradation, phthalates are widely distributed in the environment and can be found at low levels in food. Results from British studies have suggested that the largest contributions to phthalate intakes are made by carcass meat (about 25 per cent), eggs (about 15 per cent), poultry (about 35 per cent) and milk (about 10 per cent).[505]

There was widespread concern in 1996 when MAFF released the results of another study revealing the presence of phthalates in infant formula (baby milk) – and MAFF attracted considerable criticism when, as *The Times* reported, 'ministers refused yesterday to bow to criticism of their refusal to name the 15 brands [of infant formula] that tests have shown to contain gender-bending chemicals, called phthalates, at levels that could be high enough to reduce fertility.'[506]

In a statement, MAFF implied that the concentrations of

phthalates found in infant formulae would not have any effect
in humans. MAFF cited experiments on rats showing that
intake of the phthalate BBP at 0.1 to 0.4 mg/kg bodyweight/day
caused 'small reductions in testis weight and sperm production
in the male offspring'. Referring to its own study, MAFF then
cited evidence showing that combined phthalate intake from
infant formula was not more than 0.023 mg/kg bodyweight/day
– in other words, about four times lower than the dose causing
an effect on male rats.

Whether this is reassuring or not is open to question. The
usual 'safety margin' applied to the results of animal studies is
100, not four. And extrapolating the results of animal experiments to humans (especially babies) is fraught with difficulties.
It seems wise to reduce exposure to these substances as far as
practicable, and by keeping secret the brands in which significant levels of phthalates have been detected, it appears as if the
Ministry has negected its duties to the consumer.

If blood is stored in PVC bags which contain DEHP as a
plasticizer, humans may receive exposures to DEHP during
blood transfusions due to migration of DEHP into the blood
from the blood bag.[507] Studies on DEHP have found that it can
migrate from PVC bags into blood: normal whole blood stored
at 4 degrees C contains 0.19 mg per cent DEHP on collection
and 5.84 mg per cent after 21 days of storage.[508]

DEHP (bis(2-ethylhexyl)phthalate)

The International Agency for Research on Cancer has
concluded that no data were available to assess the mutagenicity or teratogenicity of this compound to man. No
adequate epidemiological study was available to the Working
Group. There is sufficient evidence for the carcinogenicity of
di(2-ethylhexyl) phthalate in mice and rats.[509]

Classified as a probable human carcinogen by the US
Environmental Protection Agency. Orally administered
DEHP produced significant dose-related increases in liver

tumour responses in rats and mice of both sexes. Human carcinogenicity data: inadequate. Animal carcinogenicity data: sufficient.[510]

BBP (butyl benzyl phthalate)

Classified as a possible human carcinogen by the US Environmental Protection Agency. Based on statistically significant increase in mononuclear cell leukaemia in female rats; the response in male rats was inconclusive and there was no such response in mice. Human carcinogenicity data: none. Animal carcinogenicity data: limited.[511]

The International Agency for Research on Cancer has concluded that this substance is unclassifiable as to carcinogenicity in humans. No data were available in humans, and there was inadequate evidence of carcinogenicity in animals.[512]

Diethyl phthalate

Not classifiable as to human carcinogenicity by the US Environmental Protection Agency. Pertinent data regarding carcinogenicity were not located in the available literature. Human carcinogenicity data: none. Animal carcinogenicity data: inadequate.[513]

Pini sylvestris oil

MEDICINAL SUBSTANCE: INHALANT; COUNTER-IRRITANT

What It Is: Sylvestris pine oil is used as an inhalant and a rubefacient, and is made from Scots or Norwegian pine.

Plain caramel (caramel colour class I) (E150A)

FOOD ADDITIVE: FOOD COLOUR

Regulations: EC permitted at *quantum satis* in all foods except those to which the EC only permits certain colours to be added (Appendix C, pp. 476ff) and those to which the EC forbids the adding of colours (Appendix D, pp. 482ff). The term caramel relates to products of a more or less intense brown colour which are intended for colouring. It does not correspond to the sugary aromatic product obtained from heating sugars and which is used for flavouring food (e.g. confectionery, pastry, alcoholic drinks). Directive 94/36/EC.

Acceptable Daily Intake: Not specified.

What It Is: Prepared by the controlled heat treatment of carbo-hydrates with alkali or acid.

What You Need To Know: This type of caramel is not manu-factured with ammonia, and is free of the heterocyclic compounds which may be present in caramel prepared using ammonia or ammonia salts. Scientific studies do not raise carcinogenic concerns.[514]

Podophyllum
MEDICINAL SUBSTANCE: ANTI-WART

What It Is: Podophyllum consists of a mixture of resins extracted from the American mandrake, and was once used by the North American Indians as an emetic (vomit-inducing) substance, and as a cure for intestinal worms. Podophyllum resin is used for its caustic action in the surface treatment of growths such as warts.

What You Need To Know: Warts will often disappear by them-selves, given time, and professional advice should be taken before attempting treatment. Podophyllum resin can cause serious adverse effects, and should only be used by a physician. When applied to large areas or in excessive amounts, or when allowed to remain in contact with the skin or mucous membranes for prolonged periods of time, toxic effects may ensue.[515] Adverse effects include skin rash, nausea and vomiting, confusion, diarrhoea, hallucinations, and damage to the kidneys and liver. It should be avoided during pregnancy since it can cause death or mutation to the foetus.

Polychlorinated biphenyls (PCBs)

FOOD ADDITIVE: CONTAMINANT

Acceptable Daily Intake: Provisional tolerable weekly intake not established.

What It Is: Massive amounts of PCBs have been introduced into the world's environment since they were first marketed in 1929. PCBs are oily liquids that are very stable even when they get hot, and they don't conduct electricity but they do conduct heat. This made them ideal for use in electrical transformers and capacitors. For a time, carbonless carbon paper was also made with PCBs. Even though their manufacture has now virtually ceased, the threat from PCB-containing waste products will be with us for many decades to come. It is estimated that over a third of total PCB production has been discharged into waterways or leaked from improper disposal sites. Certain highly chlorinated PCBs seem to be resistant to biodegradation, which means they may endlessly recycle themselves: evaporating from ground surfaces (water or soil) into the atmosphere, and eventually coming to earth again . . . only to evaporate once again.

Because PCBs can become airborne when they are released into the environment, they have spread everywhere on earth. Between 1969 and 1984 the levels of PCBs in Arctic polar bears quadrupled. European blue-white dolphins have been found to have 833 parts per million PCBs in their fatty tissue – which means that if they ever strayed into American waters, the U.S. Environmental Protection Agency would officially classify them as 'hazardous waste'.[516]

What You Need To Know: PCBs are stored in body fat and not readily excreted except in breast milk and possibly through the placenta.[517] A recent study confirms that children exposed to low levels of PCBs in the womb grow up with low IQs, poor reading comprehension, difficulty paying attention, and memory problems.[518]

The US Environmental Protection Agency has classified PCBs as probable human carcinogens, on the basis of hepatocellular carcinomas in three strains of rats and two strains of mice and inadequate yet suggestive evidence of excess risk of liver cancer in humans by ingestion and inhalation or dermal contact. Human carcinogenicity data: inadequate. Animal carcinogenicity data: sufficient.[519]

Polydextrose (E1200)

FOOD ADDITIVE: BULKING AGENT; STABILIZER; THICKENING AGENT; HUMECTANT; TEXTURIZER; CARRIER

Regulations: EC permitted for all foodstuffs following the *quantum satis* principle (except those specified in Table 2 on pp. 15–16 and in Appendix B on pp. 469ff).
EC permitted as carrier. Restricted use: none. Directive 95/2/EC.

Acceptable Daily Intake: Not specified.

What It Is: Made by melt polycondensation in a vacuum of glucose and sorbitol, in the presence of citric acid as a catalyst.

What You Need To Know: Produces a laxative effect in humans (at around 90 g per day intake or more). Scientific studies do not raise carcinogenic or mutagenic concerns.[520]

Polyglycerol esters of fatty acids (E475)

FOOD ADDITIVE: EMULSIFIER; CARRIER

Regulations: EC permitted for the following foods:
• Fine bakery wares, maximum level: 10 g/kg
• Emulsified liqueurs, maximum level: 5 g/l
• Egg products, maximum level: 1 g/kg
• Beverage whiteners, maximum level: 0.5 g/kg
• Chewing gum, maximum level: 5 g/kg
• Fat emulsions, maximum level: 5 g/kg
• Milk and cream analogues, maximum level: 5 g/kg

- Sugar confectionery, maximum level: 2 g/kg
- Desserts, maximum level: 2 g/kg
- Dietary food supplements, maximum level: *quantum satis*
- Dietetic foods intended for special medical purposes. Dietetic formulae for weight control intended to replace total daily food intake or an individual meal, maximum level: 5 g/kg
- Granola-type breakfast cereals, maximum level: 10 g/kg
- EC permitted as carrier. Restricted use: colours and fat-soluble antioxidants. Directive 95/2/EC.

Acceptable Daily Intake: 0 – 25.

What It Is: Made by the esterification of polyglycerol with food fats, and used in sponge or cake mixtures to keep the batter light and airy, so increasing the volume of the cake.

Polyglycerol polyricinoleate (E476)
FOOD ADDITIVE: EMULSIFIER

Regulations: EC permitted for the following foods:
Low and very low fat spreads and dressings, maximum level: 4 g/kg; cocoa-based confectionery, including chocolate, maximum level: 5 g/kg.
Directive 95/2/EC.

Acceptable Daily Intake: 0 – 7.5.

What It Is: Also known as polyglycerol esters of polycondensed fatty acids of castor oil. Used to reduce the viscosity of molten chocolate, helps the chocolate set in situations where it might be contaminated with water, e.g. factory line producing chocolate ices.

Polyoxyethylene (40) stearate (E431)
FOOD ADDITIVE: EMULSIFIER

Regulations: (*pro memoria*) Wine in accordance with Regulation (EEC) No 1873/84 authorizing the offer or disposal for direct human consumption of certain imported wines which may have undergone oenological processes not provided for in Regulation (EEC) No 337/79. Directive 95/2/EC.

Acceptable Daily Intake: 0 – 25 as total of polyoxyethylene (8) and (40) stearates.

What It Is: Made by a reaction of ethylene oxide with stearic acid.

Polyphosphates (i) sodium polyphosphate (ii) potassium polyphosphate (iii) sodium calcium polyphosphate (iv) calcium polyphosphates (E452)

FOOD ADDITIVE: EMULSIFIER; SEQUESTRANT; TEXTURIZER

Regulations: EC permitted to be used similarly to phosphoric acid (E338). Directive 95/2/EC.

Acceptable Daily Intake: Maximum tolerable daily intake 70 expressed as phosphorous from all sources.

What It Is: The polyphosphates have a wide range of functions in food: in processed cheese, they combine with casein to increase the quantity of water-soluble protein, thus giving it the smoothness which manufacturers desire. In meat and meat products, they have been used to make flesh plump and firm by increasing gel strength and making protein structure more rigid.

What You Need To Know: Contribute to your total phosphorous intake – see comments under phosphoric acid, above.

Polysorbates 20, 40, 60, 65 and 80 (E432 – 436)

FOOD ADDITIVE: EMULSIFIER; DISPERSING AGENT; CARRIER

Regulations: EC permitted for the following foods, individually or in combination with E433, E434, E435 or E436:

- Fine bakery wares, maximum level: 3 g/kg
- Fat emulsions for baking purposes, maximum level: 10 g/kg
- Milk and cream analogues, maximum level: 5 g/kg

- Edible ices, maximum level: 1 g/kg
- Desserts, maximum level: 3 g/kg
- Sugar confectionery, maximum level: 1 g/kg
- Emulsified sauces, maximum level: 5 g/kg
- Soups, maximum level: 1 g/kg
- Chewing gum, maximum level: 5 g/kg
- Dietary food supplements, maximum level: *quantum satis*
- Dietetic foods intended for special medical purposes. Dietetic formulae for weight control intended to replace total daily food intake or an individual meal, maximum level: 1 g/kg
- EC permitted as carrier. Restricted use: antifoaming agents. Directive 95/2/EC.

Acceptable Daily Intake: 0 – 25 as total polyoxyethylene (20) sorbitan esters.

What It Is: This group of five compounds (E432 – E436) are produced by the action of ethylene oxide on one of the sorbitan esters (see pp. 412–15). They are complementary to the sorbitan esters (and hence often used together) in that the polysorbates produce oil-in-water emulsions, and can be excellent foamers, dispersing agents, wetting agents and detergents (e.g. polysorbates can be used in the production of low-irritancy baby shampoo). They function primarily as emulsifiers (e.g. in products with a high water content – ice-creams), although they can also be used as softeners in bread, cakes and similar products. Also known as:

Polyoxyethylene sorbitan mono-oleate (polysorbate 80)
Polyoxyethylene sorbitan tristearate (polysorbate 65)
Polyoxyethylene sorbitan monostearate (polysorbate 60)
Polyoxyethylene sorbitan monopalmitate (polysorbate 40)

Polyvinylpolypyrrolidone (PVPP) (E1202)

FOOD ADDITIVE: CARRIER

Regulations: EC permitted to be used similarly to polyvinylpyrrolidone (E1201).

Directive 95/2/EC.
Acceptable Daily Intake: Not specified.
What It Is: See Polyvinylpyrrolidone (below).
What You Need To Know: Almost completely unabsorbed when taken orally. Scientific studies do not raise mutagenic concerns.[521]

Polyvinylpyrrolidone (PVP) (E1201)

FOOD ADDITIVE: BODYING AGENT; STABILIZER; CLARIFYING AGENT; TABLETING ADJUNCT; DISPERSING AGENT; CARRIER

Regulations: EC permitted for dietary food supplements in tablet and coated tablet form, maximum level: *quantum satis.* EC permitted as carrier. Restricted use: sweeteners. Directive 95/2/EC.

Acceptable Daily Intake: 0 – 50.

What It Is: Made by the vinylation of 2-pyrrolidone with acetylene; the process of making polyvinylpolypyrrolidone (see above) goes one step further with additional polymerization involving hydrogen peroxide and ammonia. Has been used as a clarifying agent in wines, a plasma expander, tablet binder, in hair sprays and shampoos, and as a topical antimicrobial agent in burns victims.

What You Need To Know: Practically non-toxic, not absorbed from the intestinal tract. When injected or inhaled as a result of exposure to PVP-containing hair spray, it tends to be deposited by the body (thesaurismosis, or storage disease) in storage sites in the liver, spleen, lung and bone marrow.[522] The smallest molecules are the most rapidly excreted, larger ones may take several months to a year.

The International Agency for Research on Cancer has concluded that this substance is unclassifiable as to carcinogenicity in humans. No data were available in humans, and there was inadequate evidence of carcinogenicity in animals.[523]

Ponceau 4R, Cochineal Red A (E124)

FOOD ADDITIVE: FOOD COLOUR

Regulations: EC permitted to be used singly or in combination with other colours in the following foods up to the total maximum level specified. For non-alcoholic flavoured drinks, edible ices, desserts, fine bakery wares and confectionery, a combination of food colours may be used up to the maximum limit indicated below, but the amount of Ponceau 4R may not exceed 50 mg/kg or mg/l.

- Non-alcoholic flavoured drinks, maximum level: 100 mg/l
- Candied fruits and vegetables, Mostarda di frutta, maximum level: 200 mg/kg
- Preserves of red fruits, maximum level: 200 mg/kg
- Confectionery, maximum level: 300 mg/kg
- Decorations and coatings, maximum level: 500 mg/kg
- Fine bakery wares (e.g. viennoiserie, biscuits, cakes and wafers), maximum level: 200 mg/kg
- Edible ices, maximum level: 150 mg/kg
- Flavoured processed cheese, maximum level: 100 mg/kg
- Desserts including flavoured milk products, maximum level: 150 mg/kg
- Sauces, seasonings (for example, curry powder, tandoori), pickles, relishes, chutney and piccalilli, maximum level: 500 mg/kg
- Mustard, maximum level: 300 mg/kg
- Fish paste and crustacean paste, maximum level: 100 mg/kg; Pre-cooked crustaceans, maximum level: 250 mg/kg; Salmon substitutes, maximum level: 500 mg/kg; Surimi, maximum level: 500 mg/kg; Fish roe, maximum level: 300 mg/kg; Smoked fish, maximum level: 100 mg/kg
- Snacks: dry, savoury potato, cereal or starch-based snack products: Extruded or expanded savoury snack products, maximum level: 200 mg/kg
- Other savoury snack products and savoury coated nuts, maximum level: 100 mg/kg
- Edible cheese rind and edible casings, maximum level: *quantum satis*
- Complete formulae for weight control intended to replace total daily food intake or an individual meal, maximum level: 50 mg/kg

- Complete formulae and nutritional supplements for use under medical supervision, maximum level: 50 mg/kg
- Liquid food supplements/dietary integrators, maximum level: 100 mg/l
- Solid food supplements/dietary integrators, maximum level: 300 mg/kg
- Soups, maximum level: 50 mg/kg
- Meat and fish analogues based on vegetable proteins, maximum level: 100 mg/kg
- Spirituous beverages (including products less than 15 % alcohol by volume), except those mentioned in Annex II or III, maximum level: 200 mg/l
- Aromatized wines, aromatized wine-based drinks and aromatized wine-product cocktails as mentioned in Regulation (EEC) No 1601/91, except those mentioned in Annex II or III, maximum level: 200 mg/l
- Fruit wines (still or sparkling) cider (except cidre bouche) and perry, aromatized fruit wines, cider and perry, maximum level: 200 mg/l. Directive 94/36/EC.

Acceptable Daily Intake: 0 – 4.

What It Is: A synthetic, bright red monoazo dye.

What You Need To Know: People who suffer from asthma, rhinitis or urticaria may find their symptoms become worse following consumption of foods or beverages containing azo dyes. Such people may be mistakenly thought to be suffering from specific food allergies.[524]

Potassium acetate (E261)

FOOD ADDITIVE: PRESERVATIVE; BUFFER

Regulations: EC permitted for all foodstuffs following the *quantum satis* principle (except those specified in Table 2 on pp. 15–16 and in Appendix B on pp. 469ff). Directive 95/2/EC.

Acceptable Daily Intake: Not specified.

What It Is: See Calcium acetate.

Potassium adipate (E357)

FOOD ADDITIVE: ACIDITY REGULATOR

Regulations: EC permitted to be used similarly to adipic acid (E355). Directive 95/2/EC.

Acceptable Daily Intake: 0 – 5.

What It Is: Potassium salt of adipic acid (see pp.110–11)

Potassium alginate (E402)

FOOD ADDITIVE: THICKENING AGENT; STABILIZER

Regulations: EC permitted for all foodstuffs following the *quantum satis* principle (except those specified in Table 2 on pp. 15–16 and in Appendix B on pp. 469ff). Directive 95/2/EC.

Acceptable Daily Intake: Not specified.

What It Is: See Alginic acid and its sodium, potassium, calcium and ammonium salts.

Potassium aluminium silicate (E555)

FOOD ADDITIVE: ANTICAKING AGENT

Regulations: EC permitted to be used similarly to silicon dioxide (E551). Directive 95/2/EC.

Acceptable Daily Intake: No acceptable daily intake allocated.

Potassium benzoate (E212)

FOOD ADDITIVE: PRESERVATIVE

Regulations: EC permitted to be used similarly to benzoic acid (E210). Directive 95/2/EC.

Acceptable Daily Intake: 0 – 5 expressed as benzoic acid.

What It Is: Potassium salt of benzoic acid (see pp.151–3)

Potassium carbonates (i) potassium carbonate (ii) potassium hydrogen carbonate (E501)

FOOD ADDITIVE: ALKALI

Regulations: EC permitted for all foodstuffs following the

Potassium citrates (i) monopotassium citrate (ii) tripotassium citrate (E332)

FOOD ADDITIVE: BUFFER; SEQUESTRANT; STABILIZER; CARRIER

Regulations: EC permitted for all foodstuffs following the *quantum satis* principle (except those specified in Table 2 on pp. 15–16 and in Appendix B on pp. 469ff).
EC permitted as carrier. Restricted use: none. Directive 95/2/EC.

Acceptable Daily Intake: Not specified.

What It Is: Potassium salt of citric acid (see pp. 202–4) with many of the properties of citric acid except that it lacks acidity. Sometimes used to replace sodium citrate (see p. 393) in low-sodium products.

Potassium ferrocyanide (E536)

FOOD ADDITIVE: ANTICAKING AGENT

Regulations: EC permitted to be used similarly to sodium ferro-cyanide (E535). Directive 95/2/EC.

Acceptable Daily Intake: 0 – 0.025 calculated as sodium ferro-cyanide.

What It Is: See Sodium ferrocyanide.

Potassium gluconate (E577)

FOOD ADDITIVE: YEAST FOOD; CARRIER

Regulations: EC permitted for all foodstuffs following the *quantum satis* principle (except those specified in Table 2 on pp. 15–16 and in Appendix B on pp. 469ff).
EC permitted as carrier. Restricted use: none. Directive 95/2/EC.

Acceptable Daily Intake: 0 – 50.

What It Is: Made by oxidizing glucose to gluconic acid then neutralized with potassium hydroxide. Also used as an electrolyte replenisher.

Potassium hydrogen sulphite (E228)

FOOD ADDITIVE: PRESERVATIVE

Regulations: EC permitted to be used similarly to sulphur dioxide (E220). Directive 95/2/EC.

Acceptable Daily Intake: 0 – 0.7 group acceptable daily intake for sulphur dioxide and sulphites expressed as sulphur dioxide.

What It Is: A sulphiting agent similar to sulphur dioxide (see p. 422–7).

What You Need To Know: The International Agency for Research on Cancer has concluded that there is inadequate evidence that sulphites are carcinogenic in animal studies or in humans, and sulphites are therefore not classifiable as to their carcinogenicity in humans.[528]

Potassium hydroxide (E525)

FOOD ADDITIVE: ALKALI

Regulations: EC permitted for all foodstuffs following the *quantum satis* principle (except those specified in Table 2 on pp. 15–16 and in Appendix B on pp. 469ff). Directive 95/2/EC.

Acceptable Daily Intake: Not specified.

What It Is: Also known as caustic potash or lye, obtained by the electrolysis of potassium chloride. Powerfully caustic, it rapidly destroys tissue and is strong enough to remove warts and indeed to 'disbud' calves' horns. Most production used in the chemical industry, as an intermediate in the production of potassium carbonate and soap.

What You Need To Know: Potassium hydroxide is one of the strongest alkalies and is extremely corrosive – there are many reports of the devastating damage it can inflict when brought into contact with the eye.[529] When used as a neutralizer in foods in accordance with good manufacturing practice it is unlikely to pose a hazard to the consumer.

Potassium hydroxyquinoline sulphate
MEDICINAL SUBSTANCE: KERATOLYTIC

What It Is: Potassium hydroxyquinoline sulphate is a kerato-lytic agent (i.e. it softens and peels hard skin) which has antibacterial and antifungal activity. It is sometimes combined with benzoyl peroxide (see pp.154–5) in products intended to treat acne. Skin irritation, redness and dryness may sometimes occur.

Potassium lactate (E326)
FOOD ADDITIVE: ANTIOXIDANT; SYNERGIST

Regulations: EC permitted for all foodstuffs following the *quantum satis* principle (except those specified in Table 2 on pp. 15–16 and in Appendix B on pp. 469ff). Directive 95/2/EC.

Acceptable Daily Intake: Not specified.

What It Is: Potassium salt of lactic acid (see p. 272) used in confectionery, jams, jellies, marmalades and margarines; enables other antioxidants to work more effectively, but also has flavour-enhancing and humectant (i.e. keeps products moist) properties too.

Potassium malate (E351)
FOOD ADDITIVE: SEASONING AGENT; BUFFERING AGENT

Regulations: EC permitted for all foodstuffs following the *quantum satis* principle (except those specified in Table 2 on pp. 15–16 and in Appendix B on pp. 469ff). Directive 95/2/EC.

Acceptable Daily Intake: Not specified.

What It Is: Potassium salt of malic acid (see p. 291).

Potassium metabisulphite (E224)
FOOD ADDITIVE: PRESERVATIVE; ANTIBROWNING AGENT

Regulations: EC permitted to be used similarly to sulphur dioxide (E220). Directive 95/2/EC.

Acceptable Daily Intake: 0 – 0.7 group acceptable daily intake for sulphur dioxide and sulphites expressed as sulphur dioxide, including sodium and potassium metabisulphite, sodium sulphite, potassium and sodium hydrogen sulphite and sodium thiosulphate.

What It Is: A sulphiting agent similar to sulphur dioxide (see pp. 422–7).

What You Need To Know: Low toxicity.[530] The International Agency for Research on Cancer has concluded that there is inadequate evidence that metabisulphites are carcinogenic in animal studies or in humans, and metabisulphites are therefore not classifiable as to their carcinogenicity in humans.[531]

Potassium nitrate (saltpetre) (E252)

FOOD ADDITIVE: PRESERVATIVE; COLOUR FIXATIVE

MEDICINAL SUBSTANCE: DIURETIC

Regulations: EC permitted to be used similarly to sodium nitrate (E251). Directive 95/2/EC.

Acceptable Daily Intake: 0 – 5.

What It Is: Made by the direct reaction of potassium chloride with concentrated nitric acid. Used in fireworks, blasting powders, impregnating candle wicks, as an aphrodisiac, and in fertilizers for intensive crops such as tomatoes, potatoes and tobacco. Also see comments under sodium nitrate.

What You Need To Know: Generally rapidly absorbed and excreted. Under some circumstances, however, appreciable amounts of nitrate may be converted to nitrite (see potassium nitrite), a process that can occur under specific conditions in the stomach and in saliva. Nitrite acts in blood to prevent haemoglobin from performing as an oxygen carrier to the tissues.[532] Cyanosis (blue baby syndrome) is a frequently encountered clinical manifestation of nitrate toxicity among infants who drink well water.[533]

SECRET INGREDIENTS FACT FILE
HOW TO REDUCE YOUR NITRATE INTAKE

- People who smoke produce chemicals in their bodies which can interact with nitrates in the water supply to produce cancer-causing nitrosamines. Another good reason to stop smoking!
- Avoid processed meat products because they may contain a high level of nitrites which will add to your total intake.
- When you buy leafy vegetables such as spinach, cabbage and cauliflower, try to find ones which have been grown using natural organic methods. Many commercially farmed vegetables have high nitrate levels because of the enormous amounts of fertilizer used on them.
- Choose vegetables which naturally contain less nitrates like beans, peas, wheat products, and rice.
- Foods high in vitamins C and E may prevent or reduce the formation of nitrosamines in your stomach, so make sure your diet contains good sources of these.
- Installing a reverse-osmosis water treatment system can reduce nitrate levels appreciably.

Potassium nitrite (E249)

FOOD ADDITIVE: PRESERVATIVE; COLOUR FIXATIVE

Regulations: EC permitted for:
- Non-heat-treated, cured, dried meat products, residual amount: 50 mg/kg
- Other cured meat products, canned meat products, foie gras, foie gras entier, blocs de foie gras, residual amount: 100 mg/kg
- Cured bacon, residual amount: 175 mg/kg
- Directive 95/2/EC.

Acceptable Daily Intake: 0 – 0.2. Food for babies less than six months old should not contain added nitrites.

quantum satis principle (except those specified in Table 2 on pp. 15–16 and in Appendix B on pp. 469ff).
EC permitted as carrier. Restricted use: none. Directive 95/2/EC.
Acceptable Daily Intake: Not specified.
What It Is: Potassium carbonate can be obtained by treatment of potassium hydroxide with carbon dioxide. It is used in the fertilizer industry, in the manufacture of soap, glass and pottery, and in the manufacture of washing powder and hair waving preparations.
What You Need To Know: Potassium carbonate is irritating to skin, mucous membrane of eyes and upper respiratory tract. Its irritant and caustic action is similar to that of potassium hydroxide, but less severe.[525]

Potassium chloride (E508)
FOOD ADDITIVE: SEASONING AGENT; GELLING AGENT; YEAST FOOD
Regulations: EC permitted for all foodstuffs following the *quantum satis* principle (except those specified in Table 2 on pp. 15–16 and in Appendix B on pp. 469ff).
EC permitted as carrier. Restricted use: none. Directive 95/2/EC.
Acceptable Daily Intake: Not specified.
What It Is: Obtained by mining from solid ores, or solar evaporation of natural brine. Most production is used as a fertilizer component.
What You Need To Know: Large doses by mouth can cause gastrointestinal irritation, purging, weakness and circulatory disturbances.[526] Acute potassium poisoning by mouth is rare because large single doses usually induce vomiting and (unless the kidneys are impaired) potassium is rapidly excreted. However, potassium chloride in a commercial dietary salt substitute has produced a near-fatal poisoning in an eight-month-old infant.[527]

What It Is: Manufactured by a reaction of nitrous oxide and nitric oxide with potassium hydroxide. Nitrite fulfils several functions in meat products: it fixes colour by reacting with blood to form a dark red pigment, improves flavour, and inhibits the growth of botulism-forming bacteria thus extending shelf-life.

What You Need To Know: Nitrite gives rise to three main health concerns. First, it can lower the oxygen carrying capacity of the blood by oxidizing haemoglobin (methaemoglobinaemia). Babies are extremely susceptible to this, but adults may be vulnerable too: cases have been reported following consumption of meat contaminated with excessive nitrite. The second health effect concerns nitrite's ability to combine with other substances (amines) in the diet to form nitrosamines, which are carcinogenic. The third health concern focuses on nitrite's atrophying effect on that part of the adrenal gland (the zona glomerulosa) which secretes aldosterone, the hormone responsible for maintaining the concentration of sodium, potassium and chloride in the blood within the narrow limits essential for life. It has also been suggested that nitrite can have certain mutagenic effects on DNA, and may deplete body stores of vitamin A.[534]

Potassium phosphates
(i) monopotassium phosphate
(ii) dipotassium phosphate
(iii) tripotassium phosphate (E340)

FOOD ADDITIVE: BUFFER; SEQUESTRANT; STABILIZER

Regulations: EC permitted to be used similarly to phosphoric acid (E338). Directive 95/2/EC.

Acceptable Daily Intake: Maximum tolerable daily intake 70 expressed as phosphorous from all sources.

What It Is: Potassium salts of phosphoric acid (see pp. 341–4). Chemical characteristics of the potassium phosphates are said to be nearly identical to the cheaper sodium phosphates (see p. 402) – they therefore tend to be used only when there's a good reason not to use the sodium salts, e.g. monopotassium phosphate (MKP) is sometimes used in low-sodium products. Dipotassium phosphate (DKP) and tripotassium phosphate (TKP) can be used in coffee whiteners similarly to DSP and TSP.

What You Need To Know: See Phosphoric acid.

Potassium propionate (E283)

FOOD ADDITIVE: PRESERVATIVE

Regulations: EC permitted to be used similarly to propionic acid (E280). Directive 95/2/EC.

Acceptable Daily Intake: Not specified.

What It Is: Potassium salt of propionic acid (see pp. 368–9).

Potassium sorbate (E202)

FOOD ADDITIVE: PRESERVATIVE

Regulations: EC permitted to be used similarly to sorbic acid (E200). Directive 95/2/EC.

Acceptable Daily Intake: 0 – 25 as sum of sorbic acid and calcium, potassium and sodium sorbates (expressed as sorbic acid).

What It Is: Potassium salt of sorbic acid (see pp. 408–11)

Potassium sulphates (i) potassium sulphate (ii) potassium hydrogen sulphate (E515)

FOOD ADDITIVE: SALT SUBSTITUTE; CARRIER

Regulations: EC permitted for all foodstuffs following the *quantum satis* principle (except those specified in Table 2 on pp. 15–16 and in Appendix B on pp. 469ff).

EC permitted as carrier. Restricted use: none. Directive 95/2/EC.

Acceptable Daily Intake: Not specified.

What It Is: Obtained by treatment of potassium chloride either with sulphuric acid or with sulphur dioxide; or by evaporation of salt lake brines. Mainly used as a fertilizer.

Potassium tartrates (i) monopotassium tartrate (ii) dipotassium tartrate (E336)

FOOD ADDITIVE: STABILIZER; SEQUESTRANT

Regulations: EC permitted for all foodstuffs following the *quantum satis* principle (except those specified in Table 2 on pp. 15–16 and in Appendix B on pp. 469ff). Directive 95/2/EC.

Acceptable Daily Intake: 0 – 30 expressed as L (+) tartaric acid.

What It Is: The potassium salts of tartaric acid (see p. 433) also known as cream of tartar. It is quite insoluble in cold water, but dissolves easily in hot. This quality can be exploited by the baking industry to control leavening – at cool temperatures, it is quite unreactive, but as the temperature rises, it produces more and more carbon dioxide, which makes the dough rise and gives lightness and volume to the final baked product. Also used as a taste regulator in sugar icing, and to control the rate at which toffees and fondants form crystals.

Povidone-iodine

MEDICINAL SUBSTANCE: ANTIMICROBIAL

What It Is: A complex of iodine with povidone, containing 9 to 12 per cent of available iodine.

What You Need To Know: Less irritating and less toxic than water and alcoholic solutions of iodine (see pp. 266–7).[535] Application to large areas of broken skin should be avoided as excessive absorption of iodine may occur.[536] Mouthwashes containing povidone-iodine might, if used for long periods of time, produce significant increases in the amount of iodine in the body and therefore interfere with thyroid function.[537]

Propan-1,2-diol (propylene glycol)

FOOD ADDITIVE: CARRIER; HUMECTANT; WETTING AGENT

Regulations: EC permitted as carrier. Restricted use: colours, emulsifiers, antioxidants and enzymes (maximum 1 g/kg in the foodstuff). Directive 95/2/EC.

Acceptable Daily Intake: 0 – 25.

What It Is: Made by direct hydrolysis of propylene oxide with water. A polyol, or polyhydric alcohol, with a wide range of uses in the food industry. Polyols are added to food either to extend its shelf-life (e.g. propylene glycol preserves the moisture content and texture of shredded coconut) or to gain a texture or product quality that was not naturally present (e.g. sorbitol can make saccharin taste sweeter by inhibiting its bitter aftertaste). Often, you will find a polyol bringing a variety of properties to a processed food, including the control of:

- Viscosity and 'mouth-feel' (e.g. sorbitol can give wine more body and a smoother taste)
- Crystal growth (e.g. glycerine and sorbitol will both retard sugar crystal formation in fondants, creams and fudges, thus prolonging their shelf-life)
- Taste (e.g. sorbitol and mannitol give sweetness to non-sugar chewing gums)
- Moisture (polyols help moist pet foods retain their moisture and extend their shelf-life)
- Solvency (propylene glycol is the most potent solvent of the polyols, completely soluble in water and quite soluble in oil)
- Rehydration (foods purchased in dry form will rehydrate more easily when a polyol is added during manufacture)
- Preservation (propylene glycol is the most effective anti-microbial polyol)
- Bulking (polyols such as sorbitol and mannitol are the most commonly used bulking agents)
- Sugar replacement ('sugar-free' foods such as chewing gum

often contain polyols – but be aware that many polyols actually have the same calorie yield as sugar)

Many of the commonly-used polyols are actually found in nature, although the modern food industry puts them to uses which Mother Nature probably never dreamt of. For all the above reasons, polyols are a versatile ingredient in today's processed food. Depending on your point of view, they may either preserve some of the qualities in food which would otherwise be lost during processing – or they may be used to simulate a degree of taste and freshness which is downright unnatural. Also finds uses as a component of cellophane, an emollient in cosmetic and pharmaceutical creams, and a base for aircraft de-icing fluids.

What You Need To Know: Very low systemic toxicity. On the skin, propylene glycol generally produces no significant irritation, and it does not appear to be a sensitizer.[538]

Propane-1,2-diol alginate (E405)

FOOD ADDITIVE: THICKENING AGENT; EMULSIFIER; STABILIZER; CARRIER

Regulations: EC permitted for the following foods:

- Fat emulsions, maximum level: 3 g/kg
- Fine bakery wares, maximum level: 2 g/kg
- Fillings, toppings and coatings for fine bakery wares and desserts, maximum level: 5 g/kg
- Sugar confectionery, maximum level: 1,5 g/kg
- Water-based edible ices, maximum level: 3 g/kg
- Cereal- and potato-based snacks, maximum level: 3 g/kg
- Sauces, maximum level: 8 g/kg
- Beer, maximum level: 100 mg/l
- Chewing gum, maximum level: 5 g/kg
- Fruit and vegetable preparations, maximum level: 5 g/kg
- Non-alcoholic flavoured drinks, maximum level: 300 mg/l
- Emulsified liqueur, maximum level: 10 g/l
- Dietetic foods intended for special medical purposes. Dietetic

formulae for weight control intended to replace total daily food intake or an individual meal, maximum level: 1,2 g/kg
- Dietary food supplements, maximum level: 1 g/kg
- EC permitted as carrier. Restricted use: none. Directive 95/2/EC.

Acceptable Daily Intake: 0 – 70.

What It Is: Manufactured by esterification of alginic acid (see p. 113) with propylene oxide. Unlike other salts of alginic acid, it is stable in acidic environments, and therefore preferred for use in sauces and fruit-based products.

Propionic acid (E280)

FOOD ADDITIVE: PRESERVATIVE

Regulations: EC permitted for:
- Pre-packed sliced bread and rye bread, maximum level: 3 000 mg/kg expressed as propionic acid
- Energy reduced bread, Partially baked, pre-packed bread, Pre-packed fine bakery wares (including flour confectionery) with a water activity of more than 0.65, Pre-packed rolls, buns and pitta, maximum level: 2 000 mg/kg expressed as propionic acid
- Christmas pudding, Pre-packed bread, maximum level: 1 000 mg/kg expressed as propionic acid. Directive 95/2/EC.

Acceptable Daily Intake: Not specified.

What It Is: Obtained in several ways, including fermenting wood pulp waste liquor, by a reaction of ethylene and carbon monoxide to produce propionaldehyde which is then oxidized, or from natural gas. An oily liquid with a rancid, disagreeable smell – used by bakers to suppress mould growth on bread and thus extend its shelf-life. Since mould spores are destroyed by the heat of baking, the contamination of baked goods occurs afterwards, and they quickly flourish under the wrapper in the warm, humid enviroment. When propionic acid or its salts (sodium, calcium and potassium propionate) are added, however, shelf-life can be more than doubled – from less than four days to eight or more. Calcium propionate tends to be used in bread, as the calcium contributes to its nutritional enrichment. Sodium propionate is preferred for cakes and unleavened goods where the calcium would interfere with chemical leavening. Propionic acid is naturally present in quite high amounts (1 per cent) in cheese, especially Swiss, where it is produced by the *Propioni* bacteria.

What You Need To Know: Medical reports of acute exposures of workers to propionic acid show mild to moderate skin burns, mild eye redness, and one case of mild cough and asthmatic response.[539]

Propyl gallate (E310)
FOOD ADDITIVE: ANTIOXIDANT

Regulations: EC permitted for:
- Fats and oils for the professional manufacture of heat-treated foodstuffs, maximum level: 200 mg/kg (gallates and BHA, individually or in combination)
- Frying oil and frying fat, excluding olive pomace oil, maximum level: 100 mg/kg (BHT)
- Lard; fish oil; beef, poultry and sheep fat: both expressed on fat
- Cake mixes, Cereal-based snack foods, Milk powder for vending machines, Dehydrated soups and broths, Sauces, Dehydrated meat (expressed on fat), Processed nuts, Seasonings and condiments, Pre-cooked cereals, maximum level: 200 mg/kg (gallates and BHA, individually or in combination)
- Dehydrated granulated potatoes, maximum level: 25 mg/kg (gallates and BHA, individually or in combination)
- Chewing gum, Dietary supplements, maximum level: 400 mg/kg (gallates, BHT and BHA, individually or in combination)
- Directive 95/2/EC.

Acceptable Daily Intake: 0 – 1.4.

What It Is: The gallate group of antioxidants comprise the propyl, octyl and dodecyl esters of gallic acid, to which it is hydrolized in the body. Of the three, propyl gallate is the more effective antioxidant. Unlike BHA and BHT, propyl gallate works effectively on vegetable oils, and has poor 'carry through' properties. It is not very soluble in fat, and is often used in combination with BHA and BHT.

What You Need To Know: Propyl gallate is judged unlikely to be carcinogenic, although it may cause contact dermatitis in those regularly exposed to it (e.g. bakery workers).[540]

A number of animal experiments have been conducted with this substance. Some have found no carcinogenic effect, while others have. In one experiment, male (but not female) rats fed propyl gallate showed a tendency to develop preputial gland tumours, islet cell tumours of the pancreas, and pheochromocytomas of the adrenal glands.[541]

Propyl p-hydroxybenzoate (E216)
FOOD ADDITIVE: PRESERVATIVE

Regulations: EC permitted to be used similarly to ethyl p-hydroxybenzoate (E214). Directive 95/2/EC.

Acceptable Daily Intake: 0 – 10 as sum of ethyl, methyl and propyl esters of p-hydroxybenzoic acid.

What It Is: Also known as propylparaben. A closely related compound to benzoic acid (see pp.151–3), but more soluble in water, and a more effective preservative than benzoic acid in food which tends towards the alkali.

What You Need To Know: Parabens have been identified as the cause of chronic dermatitis in numerous instances.[542]

Pseudoephedrine
MEDICINAL SUBSTANCE: DECONGESTANT

What It Is: Pseudoephedrine is a sympathomimetic drug used in a similar way to ephedrine (see pp.229–30 *for uses and adverse effects*) as a nasal decongestant. It can be taken orally and is sometimes found in cough mixtures where, like other bronchodilators, it may act to suppress some types of cough.

What You Need To Know: Less likely than ephedrine to produce adverse cardiovascular, hypertensive (high blood pressure) and central nervous system stimulant effects.[543 544]

Pumilio pine oil

MEDICINAL SUBSTANCE: PERFUME; COUNTER-IRRITANT

What It Is: This scented oil is made from the twigs and needles of the pumilio pine. It is inhaled to relieve congestion in the lungs and nasal passage and is also used on the surface of the skin as a counter-irritant.

Pyrethrum

INSECTICIDE

What It Is: Obtained from chrysanthemum flowers (pyrethrum plant, *Chrysanthemum cinerariaefolium*) native to Kenya, Ecuador and Japan. The active ingredients are called pyrethrins. Pyrethroids are synthetically manufactured to reproduce the active principles of the pyrethrum plant. It is a powerful contact insecticide, causing rapid knockdown of treated insects.[545]

What You Need To Know: The least toxic of commonly used insecticides.[546] Very little injury by pyrethrum has been the result of recognized accidents. There is one report of a two-year-old girl in Montreal who died after eating about half an ounce of insect powder.[547] Since the pyrethrin concentration of pyrethrum powder is about 1–3 per cent and of insecticide sprays is usually 1–2 per cent, serious poisoning is unlikely.[548] Pyrethrum toxicity to mammals is extremely low, in part because of poor bioavailability and a large first-pass extraction by the liver. The estimated lethal dose of pyrethrum in humans is over 1 gram per kilogram body weight.[549] Large amounts may cause nausea, vomiting, tinnitus, headache, and other central nervous system disturbances. It is capable of causing severe allergic dermatitis.[550] Pyrethrum dermatitis may be made worse by exposure to sun. Several cases have shown 'local anaphylaxis', characterized by dermatitis and sudden severe swelling of face, sometimes including eyes and lips.[551] Inhalation of dust or spray mists can cause headache and nausea.[552] A 43-year-old woman with a history of asthma and ragweed allergy experienced an anaphylactoid reaction after self-medicating with a shampoo containing pyrethrins for the treatment of head lice.[553] It was concluded that people who are sensitive to airborne allergens may develop anaphylaxis when exposed to pyrethrins-based products.

Quassia

MEDICINAL SUBSTANCE: FLAVOURING

What It Is: The heartwood of the huge tropical quassia tree is dried for its bitter principle quassin. It has been used to treat worm infestation.

Quillaia extract (E999)

FOOD ADDITIVE: FOAMING AGENT

Regulations: EC permitted for water-based flavoured non-alcoholic drinks, maximum level: 200 mg/l calculated as anhydrous extract. Directive 95/2/EC.

Acceptable Daily Intake: 0 – 5.

What It Is: Obtained from the dried inner bark from the *Quillaia saponaria* (soapbark tree) grown in China, Peru and Southern California.

What You Need To Know: Powdered quillaia bark or saponin concentrate has highly local irritant and stimulatory properties. Severe toxic effects due to large oral doses include liver damage, respiratory failure, convulsion and coma. In smaller doses, however, quillaia has been shown to normalize cholesterol levels, and to decrease elevated blood pressure. Scientific studies do not raise carcinogenic concerns.[554]

Quinine

MEDICINAL SUBSTANCE: FLAVOURING

What It Is: The principal alkaloid present in the bark of the cinchona tree, indigenous to certain regions of South America. Quinine has been used as a 'bitter' ingredient in tonics, pick-me-ups, and other restoratives and appetite stimulants. It is also used for flavouring, and has been used as an analgesic, as a fever-reducing substance, to treat nocturnal cramp and, of course, as an anti-malarial drug.

What You Need To Know: Fatal oral dose for adults is approximately 2–8 grams.[555] It has been included in products in very small doses of around 1mg or so, although at this minute dose it is not clear what its function might be. Small amounts of quinine may cause quinine-sensitive people to suffer a hypersensitivity response, consisting of skin flushing, itching, skin rashes, fever, gastric distress and ringing in the ears.[556] Quinine passes through the placenta and into breast milk.

Quinoline yellow (E104)
FOOD ADDITIVE: FOOD COLOUR

Regulations: EC permitted to be used singly or in combination with other colours in the following foods up to the total maximum level specified.
- Non-alcoholic flavoured drinks, maximum level: 100 mg/l
- Candied fruits and vegetables, Mostarda di frutta, maximum level: 200 mg/kg
- Preserves of red fruits, maximum level: 200 mg/kg
- Confectionery, maximum level: 300 mg/kg
- Decorations and coatings, maximum level: 500 mg/kg
- Fine bakery wares (e.g. viennoiserie, biscuits, cakes and wafers), maximum level: 200 mg/kg
- Edible ices, maximum level: 150 mg/kg
- Flavoured processed cheese, maximum level: 100 mg/kg
- Desserts including flavoured milk products, maximum level: 150 mg/kg
- Sauces, seasonings (for example, curry powder, tandoori), pickles, relishes, chutney and piccalilli, maximum level: 500 mg/kg
- Mustard, maximum level: 300 mg/kg
- Fish paste and crustacean paste, maximum level: 100 mg/kg; Precooked crustaceans, maximum level: 250 mg/kg; Salmon substitutes, maximum level: 500 mg/kg; Surimi, maximum level: 500 mg/kg; Fish roe, maximum level: 300 mg/kg; Smoked fish, maximum level: 100 mg/kg

- Snacks: dry, savoury potato, cereal or starch-based snack products: Extruded or expanded savoury snack products, maximum level: 200 mg/kg; Other savoury snack products and savoury coated nuts, maximum level: 100 mg/kg
- Edible cheese rind and edible casings, maximum level: *quantum satis*
- Complete formulae for weight control intended to replace total daily food intake or an individual meal, maximum level: 50 mg/kg
- Complete formulae and nutritional supplements for use under medical supervision, maximum level: 50 mg/kg
- Liquid food supplements/dietary integrators, maximum level: 100 mg/l
- Solid food supplements/dietary integrators, maximum level: 300 mg/kg
- Soups, maximum level: 50 mg/kg
- Meat and fish analogues based on vegetable proteins, maximum level: 100 mg/kg
- Spirituous beverages (including products less than 15 % alcohol by volume), except those mentioned in Annex II or III, maximum level: 200 mg/l
- Aromatized wines, aromatized wine-based drinks and aromatized wine-product cocktails as mentioned in Regulation (EEC) No 1601/91, except those mentioned in Annex II or III, maximum level: 200 mg/l
- Fruit wines (still or sparkling) cider (except cidre bouche) and perry, aromatized fruit wines, cider and perry, maximum level: 200 mg/l Directive 94/36/EC.

Acceptable Daily Intake: 0 – 10.

What It Is: A synthetic, bright greenish-yellow quinophthalone dye.

What You Need To Know: After reviewing animal studies, the Joint FAO/WHO Expert Committee on Food Additives concluded that Quinoline Yellow has no effect on thyroid function and is not carcinogenic.[557]

Red 2G (E128)

FOOD ADDITIVE: FOOD COLOUR

Regulations: EC permitted for breakfast sausages with a minimum cereal content of 6 per cent, maximum level: 20 mg/kg; burger meat with a minimum vegetable and/or cereal content of 4 per cent, maximum level: 20 mg/kg. Directive 94/36/EC.

Acceptable Daily Intake: 0 – 0.1

What It Is: A synthetic, bluish-red aniline dye.

What You Need To Know: Rats fed 1–1.5 grams per kilogram body weight of Red 2G for 75 days were prone to develop anaemia and enlarged spleens. The Joint FAO/WHO Expert Committee on Food Additives have concluded that Red 2G is not carcinogenic.[558]

Rennin

FOOD ADDITIVE: ENZYME

What It Is: Rennet is obtained by extraction from dried calf stomachs and contains the milk-curdling enzyme rennin. Vegetarian cheeses use an enzyme which is derived from micro-organisms instead of calves' stomachs.

Resorcinol

MEDICINAL SUBSTANCE: ANTIMICROBIAL, KERATOLYTIC

What It Is: A chemical used in the manufacture of resorcinol-formaldehyde resins, wood adhesive resins, explosives, dyes, and in the treatment of acne, ringworm, psoriasis, eczema, dermatitis, and the removal of corns, warts, callouses, and to treat athlete's foot. It has a sweetly bitter taste and can be tasted at a concentration of 2 mg/litre and above.

What You Need To Know: Solutions of 1 per cent to 20 per cent strength have been used on the skin, will cause irritation, redness, itching, dermatitis, and loss of surface layers. Studies show resorcinol to be less toxic than phenol by ingestion or skin penetration.[559] Overdose can cause skin to turn blue, convulsions, even death.[560] Should be avoided by people with with liver, kidney, or blood diseases.[561]

The International Agency for Research on Cancer has concluded that this substance is unclassifiable as to carcinogenicity in humans. No data were available in humans, and there was inadequate evidence of carcinogenicity in animals.[562]

Rhubarb rhizome

MEDICINAL SUBSTANCE: LAXATIVE

What It Is: The tincture or extract of rhubarb is made from rhubarb (*Rheum officinale*) root or rhizome and, like cascara and senna, it is a mild purgative, sometimes used to treat diarrhoea since it also dries out secretions and slows down bowel movements.

Riboflavin, riboflavin-5'-phosphate (E101)

FOOD ADDITIVE: FOOD COLOUR

Regulations: EC permitted at *quantum satis* in all foods except those to which the EC only permits certain colours to be added (Appendix C, pp. 476ff) and those to which the EC forbids the adding of colours (Appendix D, pp. 482ff). Directive 94/36/EC.

Acceptable Daily Intake: 0 – 0.5.

What It Is: Made synthetically, or by fermentation of carbohydrate materials by bacteria, yeast, or fungi. A natural vitamin (B2) present in almost all plant and animal tissues, possessing a bright yellow colour. Unstable in sunlight, it forms a fluorescent product, lumiflavin, as it degrades.

What You Need To Know: No untoward effects of administration of riboflavin are recognized.[563] Since riboflavin is not appreciably stored in the body, excessive intake results in increased urinary excretion rather than toxicity.[564] Alcohol will impair intestinal absorption of riboflavin. Riboflavin-5'-

phosphate is rapidly dephosphorylated to free riboflavin after ingestion.

Saccharin and its Na, K and Ca salts (E954)

FOOD ADDITIVE: SWEETENER

Regulations: EC permitted for the following foods up to the total maximum usable dose specified.

- Water-based flavoured drinks, energy-reduced or with no added sugar, maximum usable dose: 80 mg/l
- Milk- and milk-derivative-based or fruit-juice-based drinks, energy-reduced or with no added sugar, maximum usable dose: 80 mg/l
- 'Gaseosa': non-alcoholic water-based drink with added carbon dioxide, sweeteners and flavourings, maximum usable dose: 100 mg/l
- Water-based flavoured desserts, energy-reduced or without added sugar, maximum usable dose: 100 mg/kg; Milk- and milk-derivative-based preparations, energy-reduced or with no added sugar, maximum usable dose: 100 mg/kg; Fruit- and vegetable-based desserts, energy-reduced or with no added sugar, maximum usable dose: 100 mg/kg; Egg-based desserts, energy-reduced or with no added sugar, maximum usable dose: 100 mg/kg; Cereal-based desserts, energy-reduced or with no added sugar, maximum usable dose: 100 mg/kg; Fat-based desserts, energy-reduced or with no added sugar, maximum usable dose: 100 mg/kg
- Snacks: certain flavours of ready to eat, pre-packed, dry savoury starch products and coated nuts, maximum usable dose: 100 mg/kg
- Confectionery with no added sugar, maximum usable dose: 500 mg/kg; Cocoa- or dried-fruit-based confectionery, energy-reduced or with no added sugar, maximum usable dose: 500 mg/kg; Starch-based confectionery, energy-reduced or with no added sugar, maximum usable dose: 300 mg/kg
- Essoblaten, maximum usable dose: 800 mg/kg
- Cocoa-, milk-, dried-fruit- or fat-based sandwich spreads, energy-reduced or with no added sugar, maximum usable dose: 200 mg/kg
- Chewing gum with no added sugar, maximum usable dose: 1 200 mg/kg

- Cider and perry, maximum usable dose: 80 mg/l
- Alcohol-free beer or with an alcohol content not exceeding 1,2% vol, maximum usable dose: 80 mg/l
- 'Biere de table/Tafelbier/Table beer' (original wort content less than 6 %) except 'Obergariges Einfachbier', maximum usable dose: 80 mg/l
- Beers with a minimum acidity of 30 milli-equivalents expressed as NaOH, maximum usable dose: 80 mg/l
- Brown beers of the 'oud bruin' type, maximum usable dose: 80 mg/l
- Edible ices, energy-reduced or with no added sugar, maximum usable dose: 100 mg/kg
- Canned or bottled fruit, energy-reduced or with no added sugar, maximum usable dose: 200 mg/kg
- Energy-reduced jams, jellies and marmalades, maximum usable dose: 200 mg/kg
- Energy-reduced fruit and vegetable preparations, maximum usable dose: 200 mg/kg
- Sweet-sour preserves of fruit and vegetables, maximum usable dose: 160 mg/kg
- Sweet-sour preserves and semi-preserves of fish and marinades of fish, crustaceans and molluscs, maximum usable dose: 160 mg/kg
- Sauces, maximum usable dose: 160 mg/kg
- Mustard, maximum usable dose: 320 mg/kg
- Fine bakery products for special nutritional uses, maximum usable dose: 170 mg/kg
- Complete formulae for weight control intended to replace total daily food intake or an individual meal, maximum usable dose: 240 mg/kg
- Complete formulae and nutritional supplements for use under medical supervision, maximum usable dose: 200 mg/kg
- Liquid food supplements/dietary integrators, maximum usable dose: 80 mg/kg
- Solid food supplements/dietary integrators, maximum usable dose: 500 mg/kg
- Vitamins and dietary preparations, maximum usable dose: 1 200 mg/kg. Directive 94/35/EC.

Acceptable Daily Intake: 0 – 5.

What It Is: Accidentally discovered in 1878 when scientist Constantine Falhberg had a laboratory accident which spilt the newly created substance onto his hands. With great foolhardiness, he neglected to wash the spillage off and, eating bread at dinner the same evening, noticed it had an unusually sweet taste (saccharin is 500 times sweeter than sugar). Synthesized from toluene, it was first used as an antiseptic and preservative. Sugar rationing in both world wars greatly increased its market.

What You Need To Know: The International Agency for Research on Cancer has concluded that this substance is possibly carcinogenic to humans. There was inadequate evidence of carcinogenicity in humans, but sufficient evidence of carcinogenicity in animals.[565]

The Human Health Assessment Group in the US Environmental Protection Agency Office of Health and Environmental Assessment has evaluated saccharin for carcinogenicity. According to their analysis, the weight of evidence for saccharin is group C, which is based on inadequate evidence in humans and limited evidence in animals. As a group C chemical, saccharin is considered to be possibly carcinogenic to humans.[566]

The US National Academy of Sciences has stated that saccharin is a weak carcinogen in animals and a potential human carcinogen.[567]

Salicylic acid
MEDICINAL SUBSTANCE: KERATOLYTIC, ANTIMICROBIAL

What It Is: Can be obtained from natural oils present in the birch tree or wintergreen, or synthetically made in several ways (e.g. by reaction of carbon dioxide on phenol). Used in the manufacture of methyl salicylates, acetylsalicylic acid, and other salicylates. It is keratoloytic, that is, it softens skin and helps it to peel, and can be used to treat corns, callouses, warts and acne.

What You Need To Know: Available in a range of concentrations – as a rule, it is best to use the lowest concentration first, and only use higher strengths if necessary. It is so irritating that it should only be used externally.[568] Should not be applied over large areas, in high concentration, or for prolonged periods to extremities, especially in diabetics, infants, young children, or in people with peripheral vascular disease.[569] Acute inflammation, ulceration and even fatalities may occur after such use. Two patients died after more than half of their body areas had been painted twice with an alcoholic solution of salicylic acid, 20.7 per cent.[570] Mild chronic salicylate poisoning is called salicylism – symptoms include headache, dizziness, ringing in the ears, difficulty in hearing, dimness of vision, mental confusion, drowsiness, sweating, thirst, hyperventilation, nausea and vomiting.[571] Hypersensitivity to salicylic acid and related substances is well known – the most common symptoms are asthma, runny nose and rashes.[572]

Selenium sulphide
MEDICINAL SUBSTANCE: ANTI-DANDRUFF

What It Is: Made by reacting selenious acid with hydrogen sulphide. Because selenium sulphide is cytostatic (it suppresses the growth and multiplication of cells) it is useful in the control of dandruff.

What You Need To Know: Selenium itself can be toxic, and although selenium sulphide is insoluble and not significantly absorbed through unbroken skin, it should not be used if there are open sores or wounds on the head or body. Has little or no toxicity when applied as directed to normal skin or hair.[573] Prolonged treatment with 2.5 per cent selenium sulphide lotion should be monitored by a physician checking urinary selenium levels.[574] It may leave an unpleasant smell and should be quickly rinsed from the eyes if accidentally splashed in them.

The International Agency for Research on Cancer has concluded that selenium and selenium compounds are unclassifiable as to carcinogenicity in humans.[575]

The US Environmental Protection Agency was unable to

classify selenium as to human carcinogenicity, based on inadequate human data and inadequate evidence of carcinogenicity in animals. The evidence for various selenium compounds in animal and mutagenicity studies is conflicting and difficult to interpret; however, evidence for selenium sulphide is sufficient for a 'probable human carcinogen' classification. Human carcinogenicity data for selenium: inadequate. Animal carcinogenicity data for selenium: inadequate.[576]

The US Environmental Protection Agency has classified selenium sulphide as a probable human carcinogen. Based on inadequate data from human studies and sufficient evidence in animals. When administered orally, selenium sulphide produced hepatocellular carcinomas in both sexes of rats and female mice and alveolar/bronchiolar carcinomas or adenomas in female mice. Human carcinogenicity data: inadequate. Animal carcinogenicity data: sufficient.[577]

Note: As the US Environmental Protection Agency points out, the scientific evidence relating to selenium and its compounds is very conflicting. Although selenium sulphide may have a carcinogenic effect in rats, available scientific data provide no suggestion that it may be carcinogenic to humans.[578]

SECRET INGREDIENTS FACT FILE
SELENIUM

Many people take selenium supplements without really understanding why they are doing so, nor what the risks and benefits might be. Here's a briefing:

- Selenium is a rare element which occurs naturally in very small amounts in sulphur deposits and sulphide ores produced as a result of volcanic activity; soil in the neighbourhood of volcanos tends to have enriched amounts of selenium.[579] These trace deposits are too small to be economically mined, and there are, in fact, no commercial deposits of selenium anywhere on earth.[580] Most

---

commercially produced selenium is extracted from sludge which is produced as a by-product in the electrolytic refining of copper.

- Until the late 1950s, selenium was mainly known for its poisonous properties. Certain plants absorb and concentrate selenium quite readily; if eaten by grazing animals, the effect can be deadly, as in the first recorded case of selenium poisoning in 1857, when cavalry horses in the Nebraska Territory died after eating naturally contaminated pasturage.[581]

- In 1973, selenium was discovered to be an essential consituent of glutathione peroxidase, an antioxidant and free radical scavenger (a free radical is an oxygen molecule which roams the body in search of an electron, sometimes damaging healthy tissue in a process called oxidation. Cell damage from free radical attack has been linked to cancer and many other degenerative diseases). It is for this reason that selenium supplements are sometimes sold in combination with other antioxidants, such as vitamins A and E.

- In areas of acid or neutral soils, the amount of biologically available selenium in food can be extremely low. The extremely selenium-deficient soils in certain parts of China yield diets that are so poor in selenium that a degenerative heart disease develops, known as Keshan disease.[582] Convincing research work using groups of Chinese suffering from very low body stores of selenium shows that adults require a selenium intake of about 40 micrograms a day to maximize their glutathione peroxidase activity.[583] A microgram is one thousandth of a milligram (i.e. very small – it would take 28 million micrograms to make one ounce!).

- In recent years, great interest has been shown in the possible anti-cancer effect of selenium supplements. However, the results of human experiments in this area have been conflicting. One much-publicized study examined the health of 1,312 volunteers residing in low-selenium areas of the United States.[584] For four and a half years, part of the group took selenium and the other was given a placebo. Ten years later, it was found that those taking selenium had 63 per cent fewer prostate cancers, 58 per cent fewer colorectal cancers, and 46 per cent fewer lung cancers than the placebo group. Set against this study is an investigation from Harvard university which measured the amount of selenium actually present in the body tissue of 1,000 women. After four years, the researchers found that women with the highest selenium intakes showed no fewer cancers than women with the lowest intakes. In fact, the small number who took selenium supplements were almost twice as likely to get cancer, though it was not clear whether selenium was to blame. Yet another study of more than 62,000 nurses has also found no connection between the development of cancer and high – or low – levels of selenium in the body.[585] And while many people assume that selenium's anti-cancer effects – if indeed they exist – are due to its antioxidant qualities, this is by no means certain. In fact, it is possible that cancer cells may be more susceptible to selenium poisoning than normal cells. 'Cancer cells are more sensitive to selenium-induced programmed cell death,' explains Clement Ip, a selenium expert at Roswell Park Memorial Cancer Center in New York.[586] 'So it's possible that selenium eliminates early precancerous lesions.'

- Selenium certainly has toxic effects, which for adult humans usually become noticeable at doses of around 1,000 micrograms – or 1 milligram – a day. Symptoms may include hair loss, fingernail changes and loss, fatigue, irritability, nausea and gastrointestinal problems, joint inflammation and a telltale 'garlic breath'. People who ignore these signs and continue to ingest selenium can get a lethal overdose.

To summarize: selenium is essential to human health in small quantities, but at high levels it is toxic. In between these extremes lies a range of uncertainties. The possible adverse effects on humans of long-term selenium use are not known. In general, dietary sources of selenium are to be preferred to nutritional supplements, partly because there is little risk of toxicity, and also because dietary selenium will be naturally present in foods combined with other important nutrients and antioxidants. The level of selenium present in foods will vary relative to the selenium content of the soil in which the foods have been grown (brazil nuts, garlic, and hard grains are likely to be good sources). Because of this, perhaps the most effective form of selenium supplementation may be adding it to crop fertilizer, as is now done in Finland.[587]

Senega

MEDICINAL SUBSTANCE: EXPECTORANT

What It Is: Senega is made from the plant *Polygala Senega* and used in extract, tincture or powder form. It can cause vomiting and has been used as an expectorant.

Senna fruit

MEDICINAL SUBSTANCE: LAXATIVE

What It Is: Senna is an older laxative whose active ingredients are similar to those found in rhubarb, cascara and aloes (the anthraquinone laxatives).

What You Need To Know: In excess dose it may produce blood in the stools. Like all laxatives, it should not be used regularly since dependence may lead to diarrhoea, loss of water and essential minerals (particularly potassium) and weight loss.

Sennosides A and B

MEDICINAL SUBSTANCE: LAXATIVE

What It Is: The active ingredients of senna (see above). They may colour the urine and stools yellow or red.

Shellac (E904)

FOOD ADDITIVE: COATING, GLAZING AND SURFACE FINISHING AGENT

Regulations: EC permitted to be used similarly to beeswax, white and yellow (E901). Directive 95/2/EC.

Acceptable Daily Intake: Acceptable.

What It Is: Obtained from the resinous secretion of the scale insect *Laccifer lacca*, found in south-east Asia and India. It is dried into sheets, pulverized into flakes, and usually supplied as a solution in alcohol. Used as a coating for sweets, pills, and fruit.

What You Need To Know: Scientific studies do not raise carcinogenic concerns.[588]

Siberian fir oil

See Abietis oil

Silicon dioxide (E551)

FOOD ADDITIVE: ANTICAKING AGENT; CARRIER

Regulations: EC permitted for the following foods, individually or in combination with E552, E553a, E553b, E554, E555, E556 or E559:

- Dried powdered foodstuffs (including sugars), maximum level: 10 g/kg
- Salt and its substitutes, maximum level: 10 g/kg
- Dietary food supplements, maximum level: *quantum satis*
- Foodstuffs in tablet and coated tablet form, maximum level: *quantum satis*
- Sliced hard cheese and sliced processed cheese, maximum level: 10 g/kg
- Chewing gum, Rice, Sausages (surface treatment only), Moulded jelly sweets (surface treatment only), maximum level: *quantum satis* (E553b only)
- EC permitted as carrier. Restricted use: emulsifiers and colours, max. 5%. Directive 95/2/EC.

Acceptable Daily Intake: Not specified.

What It Is: The element silicon is widely distributed in the natural world, although not in isolation: it only occurs in combination with other elements. When combined with oxygen, and sometimes other elements, it forms silicate minerals: more than 1,000 have been identified (the earth's crust is composed almost entirely of silicates). Silica minerals such as quartz constitute a branch of the silicate minerals, and are composed of silicon dioxide with only small amounts of other substances. Silicon exists in the hard and soft tissues of many life forms, including human teeth and bones. Small prehistoric aquatic plants related to algae (diatoms) also used silicon as a building material in their cell walls: today, their skeletons are known as diatomaceous earth (88 per cent silica). Major uses include glass manufacture, abrasives, ceramics, enamels and petroleum products. Diatomaceous earth is used as a filter aid in the clarification of sugar, filtration of fruit juices, syrups, cider, wines, beer and in water clarification.

What You Need To Know: Chemically and biologically inert. The only form of silicon dioxide known to produce adverse health effects is crystalline quartz, which can produce silicosis (similar to pneumoconiosis) in those chronically exposed, e.g. sandblasters.[589]

Silver (E174)

FOOD ADDITIVE: FOOD COLOUR

Regulations: EC permitted for external coating of confectionery, maximum level: *quantum satis*; decoration of chocolates, maximum level: *quantum satis*; Liqueurs, maximum level: *quantum satis*. Directive 94/36/EC.

Acceptable Daily Intake: Decision postponed.

What It Is: Obtained from silver-containing ores by crushing and grinding, then leaching with sodium cyanide. Silver is precipitated then treated electrolytically to separate the silver from any gold present. Although silver is used in jewellery, ornaments and coinage, its main uses lie in photographic materials and electric and electronic products.

What You Need To Know: Long-term exposure to silver metal and soluble silver compounds causes argyria, a blue-grey/ashen-grey darkening of the eyes, nose, throat, skin and nasal septum. For example, use of a silver-containing mouth-wash for ten years caused argyria to develop in one patient, with resulting damage to kidneys caused by silver deposits.[590] Blond people are considered more susceptible to argyria than others.[591] Silver is only poorly excreted from the body: its biological half-life is up to 50 days for the human liver.[592]

The US Environmental Protection Agency was unable to classify this substance as to human carcinogenicity.[593]

Sodium acetates (i) sodium acetate (ii) sodium hydrogen acetate (sodium diacetate) (E262)

FOOD ADDITIVE: BUFFER; PRESERVATIVE

Regulations: EC permitted for all foodstuffs following the *quantum satis* principle (except those specified in Table 2 on pp. 15–16 and in Appendix B on pp. 469ff). Directive 95/2/EC.

Acceptable Daily Intake: Not specified.

What It Is: Sodium salts of acetic acid (see pp.106–7), produced by the action of acetic acid on alkali such as caustic soda or soda ash. Sodium acetate has several non-food uses, princi-pally in the textile, leather, dyestuff and chemical industries; while sodium diacetate is mainly used as an inhibitor of moulds and rope-forming bacteria in bread.

What You Need To Know: It has been experimentally demon-strated that humans have a considerable capacity to rapidly and completely metabolize acetate (it is a natural breakdown product of alcohol metabolism in the liver).[594]

Sodium adipate (E356)

FOOD ADDITIVE: ACIDITY REGULATOR

Regulations: EC permitted to be used similarly to adipic acid (E355). Directive 95/2/EC.

Acceptable Daily Intake: 0 – 5.

What It Is: Sodium salt of adipic acid (see pp. 110–11)

Sodium alginate (E401)

FOOD ADDITIVE: THICKENING AGENT; STABILIZER

Regulations: EC permitted for all foodstuffs following the *quantum satis* principle (except those specified in Table 2 on pp. 15–16 and in Appendix B on pp. 469ff). Directive 95/2/EC.

Acceptable Daily Intake: Not specified.

What It Is: Sodium salt of alginic acid (see p. 113).

What You Need To Know: Apparently not decomposed or absorbed appreciably when ingested.[595] The greatest danger from ingestion of large quantities is the possibility of intestinal obstruction.[596] Used experimentally to remove radioactive strontium from the skeleton, and to reduce the body's uptake of strontium, barium, and radium (e.g. after release of radioactive material).[597] [598]

Sodium aluminium phosphate, acidic (E541)

FOOD ADDITIVE: RAISING AGENT

Regulations: EC permitted for fine bakery wares (scones and sponge wares only), maximum level: 1 g/kg (expressed as aluminium). Directive 95/2/EC.

Acceptable Daily Intake: 0 – 0.6.

What It Is: Made by reaction of hydrated alumina and sodium carbonate or hydroxide with phosphoric acid. A slow-acting leavening agent which releases most of its acid during the baking period, rather than during the initial batter preparation. The acid then reacts with sodium bicarbonate to produce carbon dioxide gas, which gives baked goods their lightness and volume.

What You Need To Know: See Aluminium.

Sodium aluminium silicate (E554)

FOOD ADDITIVE: ANTICAKING AGENT

Regulations: EC permitted to be used similarly to silicon dioxide (E551). Directive 95/2/EC.

Acceptable Daily Intake: Not specified.

Sodium ascorbate (E301)

FOOD ADDITIVE: ANTIOXIDANT

Regulations: EC permitted for all foodstuffs following the *quantum satis* principle (except those specified in Table 2 on pp. 15–16 and in Appendix B on pp. 469ff). Directive 95/2/EC.

Acceptable Daily Intake: Not specified.

What It Is: Sodium salt of ascorbic acid (see pp.137–9) used very similarly. It is more soluble in water than ascorbic acid, and lacks its acidic taste.

Sodium benzoate (E211)

FOOD ADDITIVE: PRESERVATIVE

MEDICINAL SUBSTANCE: ANTIMICROBIAL

Regulations: EC permitted to be used similarly to benzoic acid (E210). Directive 95/2/EC.

Acceptable Daily Intake: 0 – 5 expressed as benzoic acid.

What It Is: Sodium salt of benzoic acid (see pp. 151–3) and used as a preservative. Sometimes found in mouth ulcer preparations.

Sodium carbonates (i) sodium carbonate (ii) sodium hydrogen carbonate (baking soda, bicarbonate of soda, sodium bicarbonate) (iii) sodium sesquicarbonate (E500)

FOOD ADDITIVE: ALKALI; LEAVENING AGENT; BUFFER

Regulations: EC permitted for all foodstuffs following the *quantum satis* principle (except those specified in Table 2 on pp. 15–16 and in Appendix B on pp. 469ff). Directive 95/2/EC.

Acceptable Daily Intake: Not specified.

What It Is: Sodium carbonate (soda ash or washing soda) is obtained from the brine of dry lakes then heat-converted to soda ash. It can also be manufactured by the Solvay process in which a strong brine solution (common salt – sodium chloride) is treated with ammonia and carbon dioxide to yield sodium bicarbonate and ammonium chloride. Sodium bicarbonate is then heated, yielding the carbonate. It has been used for thousands of years for embalming, in ceramic pastes, as a detergent, and, when mixed with sand, in the production of glass. Today, most production is used in glass manufacturing, as raw material in chemical production, in cleaning product formulations, and pulp and paper processing. In baking, it is used to generate carbon dioxide – the rate of gas release controls the size of the bubbles in the dough and influences the grain, volume, and texture of the final product.

What You Need To Know: Frequent use of sodium carbonate on the skin may produce sensitivity reactions. Intake of large quantities may produce corrosion of the gastrointestinal tract, vomiting, diarrhoea and circulatory collapse.[599] After ingesting or inhaling laundry detergent powder containing sodium carbonate, eight children required hospital admission. Symptoms included drooling and respiratory distress. Five children were admitted to the intensive care unit, and four children needed endotracheal intubation (breathing tubes).[600]

Sodium bicarbonate has historically been used to treat a variety of medical conditions. The emergency medicine literature contains no reports of toxicity caused by the ingestion of baking soda. It is a fast-acting antacid because it is very soluble in water. This means that it quickly counteracts acute stomach acidity, but it also means that significant amounts may be absorbed through the intestine, and into the bloodstream which could produce excess alkalinity. If large amounts of milk are taken at the same time, the milk alkali syndrome is thought to occur, where larger than normal quantities of calcium accumulate in the blood, producing confused behaviour, anorexia, abdominal pain and weak muscles, possibly leading to the development of kidney stones and impaired kidney function. People with cardiac failure, high blood pressure, damaged liver or kidneys and oedema (excessive fluid in body tissue) should only use sodium salts after medical advice.

SECRET INGREDIENTS FACT FILE
ANTACIDS AND INDIGESTION RELIEF

When we eat, smell or even think about food, our stomach starts to secrete hydrochloric acid and the digestive enzyme pepsin in preparation for their task of breaking down and metabolizing food. Thus, the high acidity present in the stomach is actually *necessary* for the digestion of food. Discomfort may be caused if this stomach acid flows back or 'refluxes' into the oesophagus (the tube that carries food and liquid from the mouth to the stomach) which has a sensitive lining that may be irritated by acid. Antacids have the effect of partially neutralizing the stomach's naturally acid environment, and can sometimes produce relief from the symptoms of indigestion. There are, however, other steps that also give indigestion relief for some people, which may be worth considering:

- Fatty foods, alcohol and chocolate may all reduce the effectiveness of the valve muscle that separates stomach acid from the oesophagus. It may be worth trying to avoid them.

- Foods with a high acid content can also provoke an attack of indigestion.
- Coffee and cigarettes have also been implicated in indigestion attacks.
- If you suffer at night-time, try raising the head of your bed by about six inches. This may help to keep stomach secretions down where they belong. Also, avoid eating before bedtime.

There is nothing wrong with the occasional use of antacids to relieve the symptoms of upset stomach. However, regular dependence on them indicates that something else is wrong (for example, an ulcer) and you should consult your doctor.

Most antacids tend to be based around four main ingredients: sodium bicarbonate, calcium carbonate (chalk), aluminium compounds, and magnesium compounds. Substances such as dimethicone, simethicone and other silicones are added as antifoaming agents – in other words, they break up bubbles of gas and so aim to relieve wind (deflatulents). Peppermint oil may also provide the same effect, and may relax intestinal muscles. The acid-neutralizing capacity of antacid preparations can vary considerably from one product to another. Sodium bicarbonate and calcium carbonate are more potent neutralizers of excess stomach acidity than magnesium compounds, which in turn tend to be more potent than aluminium compounds. It is also worth bearing in mind that some antacid products can contain significant amounts of sodium and sucrose – which could be important if you are on a low-sodium or low-sugar diet. Some antacids may also contain lactose or gluten. Antacids should not be taken at the same time as other medicine because they may interfere with its absorption.

Sodium citrates (i) monosodium citrate (ii) disodium citrate (iii) trisodium citrate (E331)

FOOD ADDITIVE: EMULSION STABILIZER; BUFFER; SEQUESTRANT; CARRIER

MEDICINAL SUBSTANCE: ANTACID; EXPECTORANT

Regulations: EC permitted for all foodstuffs following the *quantum satis* principle (except those specified in Table 2 on pp. 15–16 and in Appendix B on pp. 469ff).

EC permitted as carrier. Restricted use: none. Directive 95/2/EC.

Acceptable Daily Intake: Not specified.

What It Is: Sodium salts of citric acid (see pp. 202–4) used in cheesemaking as an emulsifier, to control acidity (buffering) in carbonated beverages and preserves, to prevent precipitation of solids during storage of evaporated milk, and in 'instant' dry soup mixes, it improves the speed of re-hydration – presumably for people who'd rather not wait those extra few seconds for their soup to cook!

What You Need To Know: Sodium citrate is oxidized in the body to bicarbonate and excreted in the urine, and is therefore sometimes used to overcome excessive urinary acidity.[601] Excess intake of sodium citrate may upset the normal balance of acids and alkalies and cause tetany (muscle spasms) or depress the heart by decreasing the ionized calcium level of the blood.[602]

Sodium erythorbate (E316)

FOOD ADDITIVE: ANTIOXIDANT

Regulations: EC permitted to be used similarly to erythorbic acid (E315). Directive 95/2/EC.

Acceptable Daily Intake: Not specified.

What It Is: Sodium salt of erythorbic acid (see p. 231).

What You Need To Know: see Erythorbic acid.

Sodium ethyl p-hydroxybenzoate (E215)

FOOD ADDITIVE: PRESERVATIVE

Regulations: EC permitted to be used similarly to ethyl p-hydroxybenzoate (E214). Directive 95/2/EC.

What It Is: Sodium salt of ethyl p-hydroxybenzoate (see p. 234), related compound to benzoic acid (see pp. 151–3), but more soluble in water, and a more effective preservative than benzoic acid in food which tends towards the alkali.

Sodium ferrocyanide (E535)

FOOD ADDITIVE: ANTICAKING AGENT

Regulations: EC permitted for salt and its substitutes, maximum level: individually or in combination with E536 or E538, 20 mg/kg as anhydrous potassium ferrocyanide. Directive 95/2/EC.

Acceptable Daily Intake: 0 – 0.025.

What It Is: Also known as yellow prussiate of soda, it is added to salt to generate jagged and bulky crystals which resist caking, and thus makes it flow more freely.

What You Need To Know: Because of the strong chemical bond between the iron and the cyanide, these salts (sodium, potassium and sodium ferrocyanide) have a low toxicity.[603]

Sodium fluoride

MEDICINAL SUBSTANCE: FLUORIDATION AGENT IN DRINKING WATER

What It Is: Obtained by the reaction of hydrofluoric acid with soda ash (sodium carbonate) or caustic soda (sodium hydroxide). Apart from its uses in toothpaste and municipal water, it has also been used as a flux in the manufacture of rimmed steel, aluminium, and magnesium; a fungicide; a glass frosting agent; a component of glues and adhesives; a stainless steel pickling agent; and a component of wood preservatives.

What You Need To Know: The controversial question of fluoridation divides into two aspects. The general principle of mass medication is essentially a political question – whether it is justifiable to deny individuals their presumed right to refuse medication, in the wider interests of disease prevention (in this case, a non-infectious disease). That issue is beyond the scope of this book. The second question concerns the health impact of fluoridation. Sodium fluoride is toxic – from numerous reports of accidental and intentional poisonings, it has been estimated that the lethal dose for a 70 kg man lies between 5 and 10 grams.[604] At far lesser concentrations, fluoride appears to have a beneficial effect on the incidence of dental caries. It has been found that a concentration of about 1 part per million in the water supply results in a 50–66 per cent reduction in incidence of dental caries in permanent teeth.[605] About half the US population has fluoride deliberately added to their drinking water, at a concentration of between 0.7 to 1.2 parts per million.[606] Naturally fluoridated water may be as high as 12 parts per million. In the UK only 10 per cent of the population receives fluoride in the water.[607]

Sodium fluoride is almost completely absorbed after ingestion, and has been detected in all organs and tissues. It is deposited in the skeleton and teeth, and the degree of skeletal storage is related to intake and age.[608] It is excreted through the kidneys and to a lesser extent by sweating and through breast milk. Chronic intake of excessive amounts of fluoride leads to osteosclerosis (hardening or abnormal density of bone) and mottled tooth enamel (known as fluorosis).[609] Fluorosis affecting bone is not detectable until the water concentration exceeds at least 4 parts per million.[610] The tendency of sodium fluoride to thicken bone may be exploited as a beneficial treatment for older women with osteoporosis.[611] But while fluoride can cause an increase in bone mass, it may also cause a decrease in bone strength; there is some evidence that this may lead to an increase in risk of fracture.[612] One trial has found that although spinal bone density increased by 35 per cent in women treated with sodium fluoride, the overall rate of vertebral fractures did not drop.[613] The authors of the study concluded that sodium fluoride increased skeletal fragility.

It has been found that children who drink fluoridated water may have an increased risk of fluorosis if they brush their teeth at least twice per day with more than a pea-sized amount of toothpaste.[614] This small quantity is in marked contrast to the television commercials for toothpaste, which sometimes depict toothbrushes covered with a generous layer of paste.

Decreased testosterone concentrations have recently been found in men living in areas where fluorosis is endemic, suggesting that fluoride may have an adverse effect on the male reproductive system.[615]

The dental health benefits of fluoridation have been challenged on the basis that large reductions in tooth decay have been found in both fluoridated and unfluoridated areas of at least eight developed countries over the past 30 years.[616] This decline could, of course, be attributed to the use of fluoride toothpaste, since the incidence of fluorosis has also increased in regions where water is fluoridated and in regions where it is not, suggesting that increased availability of fluoride in supplements, vitamins, toothpastes, beverages, and other products may be a more significant source of fluoride than water.[617] Concern was expressed in 1990 when a US government-sponsored study found that high doses of fluoride might cause cancer in male rats.[618] One rat developed bone cancer after consuming fluoridated water in a concentration of 45 parts per million over two years, and four rats developed the cancer after drinking 79 ppm fluoridated water over the same period. No cancers were found in female rats, nor in mice of either sex, at these fluoride levels; nor were cancers found in any animals at lower levels.

The International Agency for Research on Cancer working

group has concluded that sodium fluoride is unclassifiable as to carcinogenicity in humans.[619]

Sodium gluconate (E576)

FOOD ADDITIVE: SEQUESTRANT; YEAST FOOD

Regulations: EC permitted for all foodstuffs following the *quantum satis* principle (except those specified in Table 2 on pp. 15–16 and in Appendix B on pp. 469ff). Directive 95/2/EC.
Acceptable Daily Intake: 0 – 50.
What It Is: Sodium salt of gluconic acid (see p. 243).

Sodium hydrogen sulphite (E222)

FOOD ADDITIVE: PRESERVATIVE

Regulations: EC permitted to be used similarly to sulphur dioxide (E220). Directive 95/2/EC.
Acceptable Daily Intake: 0 – 0.7 group acceptable daily intake for sulphur dioxide and sulphites expressed as sulphur dioxide.
What It Is: Also known as sodium-bisulphite, produced as a by-product in the manufacture of phenol and resorcinol. A sulphiting agent similar to sulphur dioxide (see pp. 422–7).
What You Need To Know: The International Agency for Research on Cancer has concluded that there is inadequate evidence that sulphites are carcinogenic in animal studies or in humans, and sulphites are therefore not classifiable as to their carcinogenicity in humans.[620]

Sodium hydroxide (lye) (E524)

FOOD ADDITIVE: ALKALI

Regulations: EC permitted for all foodstuffs following the *quantum satis* principle (except those specified in Table 2 on pp. 15–16 and in Appendix B on pp. 469ff). Directive 95/2/EC.
Acceptable Daily Intake: Not specified.
What It Is: Also known as caustic soda or soda lye, made by electrolysis of sodium chloride brines, which yield sodium hydroxide, chlorine and hydrogen. Mainly used in chemical

processing and metal processing, in paper and pulp manufacture; and in the petroleum, textile, soap and food industries.

What You Need To Know: When caustic soda comes into contact with the skin it causes immediate damage (although there is not always initial pain) and since it does not coagulate protein, it continues to penetrate. Washing the area with water must therefore be started immediately to prevent corrosive chemical burns. If it comes into contact with the eyes, washing must be started within 10 seconds and continued for at least 15 minutes to prevent permanent injury.[621] Residue in foods is unlikely to present any hazard.

Sodium lactate (E325)

FOOD ADDITIVE: ANTIOXIDANT SYNERGIST; HUMECTANT;
BODYING AGENT

Regulations: EC permitted for all foodstuffs following the *quantum satis* principle (except those specified in Table 2 on pp. 15–16 and in Appendix B on pp. 469ff). Directive 95/2/EC.
Acceptable Daily Intake: Not specified.
What It Is: Sodium salt of lactic acid (see p. 272). It is hygroscopic (i.e. in normal conditions it will attract moisture from the atmosphere) and is therefore used as an ingredient in products such as sponge cakes and Swiss rolls, where the manufacturer wishes to retain moisture within the food as long as possible, thus extending shelf-life. Also used to provide a protein plasticizing effect in biscuits, and in frankfurter-type sausages and uncured hams.

Sodium lauryl sulphate

MEDICINAL SUBSTANCE: DETERGENT
What It Is: Sodium lauryl sulphate is used as a wetting agent and a detergent. It may be found in skin-cleansing products.

Sodium malates (i) sodium malate (ii) sodium hydrogen malate (E350)

FOOD ADDITIVE: ACIDITY REGULATOR; FLAVOURING AGENT

Regulations: EC permitted for all foodstuffs following the *quantum satis* principle (except those specified in Table 2 on pp. 15–16 and in Appendix B on pp. 469ff). Directive 95/2/EC.

Acceptable Daily Intake: Not specified.

What It Is: Sodium salts of malic acid (see p. 291).

Sodium metabisulphite (E223) ⚠

FOOD ADDITIVE: PRESERVATIVE; BLEACHING AGENT

Regulations: EC permitted to be used similarly to sulphur dioxide (E220). Directive 95/2/EC.

Acceptable Daily Intake: 0 – 0.7 group acceptable daily intake for sulphur dioxide and sulphites expressed as sulphur dioxide.

What It Is: A sulphiting agent similar to sulphur dioxide (see pp. 422–7).

What You Need To Know: The International Agency for Research on Cancer has concluded that there is inadequate evidence that metabisulphites are carcinogenic in animal studies, that there is inadequate evidence for their carcinogenicity in humans, and metabisulphites are therefore not classifiable as to their carcinogenicity in humans.[622]

Sodium metabisulphite in food and drugs may provoke life-threatening asthma. In one case, a 67-year-old woman developed severe asthma almost immediately after ingesting a salad with a vinegar-based dressing (the vinegar contained sodium metabisulphite). In another case, a 23-year-old woman developed rapid deterioration of moderately severe asthma after being given an injection which contained sodium metabisulphite. It has been suggested that the use of sodium metabisulphite as a preservative and anti-oxidant may need re-evaluating.[623]

Sodium methyl p-hydroxybenzoate (E219)

FOOD ADDITIVE: PRESERVATIVE

Regulations: EC permitted to be used similarly to ethyl p-hydroxybenzoate (E214). Directive 95/2/EC.

Acceptable Daily Intake: None specifically allocated, but see methyl p-hydroxybenzoate (E218).

What It Is: Sodium salt of methyl p-hydroxybenzoate (see pp. 312–3) and a closely related compound to benzoic acid (see pp. 151–3), but more soluble in water, and a more effective preservative than benzoic acid in food which tends towards the alkali.

Sodium nitrate (E251)

FOOD ADDITIVE: PRESERVATIVE; COLOUR FIXATIVE

Regulations: EC permitted for: cured meat products, canned meat products, residual amount: 250 mg/kg; Hard, semi-hard and semi-soft cheese, dairy-based cheese analogue, residual amount: 50 mg/kg; Pickled herring and sprat, residual amount: 200 mg/kg. Directive 95/2/EC.

Acceptable Daily Intake: 0 – 5.

What It Is: Produced by reacting nitric acid with sodium carbonate. Nitrates were once thought to have significant preservative effects, but this seems to be in doubt in view of more recent studies.[624] Their function in meat products is somewhat uncertain; it is thought that their curing action is due to their partial conversion to nitrite in the foodstuff (see p. 362f).

What You Need To Know: Sodium nitrate is usually rapidly absorbed and excreted unchanged following oral intake.[625] Nitrate itself is of relatively low toxicity, although a high intake of nitrate (>730 mg/kg body weight) may inhibit the functioning of the thyroid gland. Concerns arise, however, when it is converted by micro-organisms in human saliva to nitrite (see p. 362f). This process typically accounts for 80 per cent of human nitrite exposure (between 5 and 20 per cent of ingested nitrate is converted to nitrite).[626]

Sodium nitrite (E250)

FOOD ADDITIVE: PRESERVATIVE; COLOUR FIXATIVE

Regulations: EC permitted to be used similarly to potassium nitrite (E249). Directive 95/2/EC.

Acceptable Daily Intake: 0–0.2 temporary; food for babies aged less than 6 months should not contain added nitrates.

What It Is: Made by reaction of nitrogen oxides with aqueous sodium hydroxide.

What You Need To Know: See Potassium nitrite (see p. 362f)

Sodium orthophenyl phenol (E232)

FOOD ADDITIVE: PRESERVATIVE

Regulations: EC permitted to be used similarly to orthophenyl phenol (E231). Directive 95/2/EC.

Acceptable Daily Intake: 0 – 0.2 conditional, 0.2 – 1.0.

What It Is: Sodium salt of orthophenyl phenol (see p. 328)

Sodium perborate

MEDICINAL SUBSTANCE: ANTIMICROBIAL

What It Is: Sodium perborate is an antiseptic substance some-times used in the treatment of gum inflammation and other conditions.

What You Need To Know: Borates are rapidly absorbed from mucous membranes and abraded skin, but not from intact or unbroken skin.[627] It should be used sparingly since repeated applications to mucous membranes may be irritating.[628] Should not be swallowed.[629] Toxic symptoms of prolonged absorption may include anorexia, weight loss, vomiting, mild diarrhoea, skin rash, falling hair, convulsions and anaemia.[630] Infants and young children are thought to be more susceptible to borate poisoning than are adults.[631] In a study of over 100 cases of accidental poisoning, the overall fatality rate was

55 per cent, but in infants under 1 year of age, 70 per cent of cases ended fatally.[632]

Sodium phosphates (i) Monosodium phosphate (ii) Disodium phosphate (iii) Trisodium phosphate (E339)

FOOD ADDITIVE: SEQUESTRANT; EMULSION STABILIZER; BUFFER

Regulations: EC permitted to be used similarly to phosphoric acid (E338). Directive 95/2/EC.

Acceptable Daily Intake: Maximum tolerable daily intake 70 mg expressed as phosphorous from all sources.

What It Is: The sodium salts of phosphoric acid (see p. 341–4) Monosodium phosphate (MSP) is mildly acid and most frequently used as a mild acidulant. Disodium phosphate (DSP) is mildly alkaline, and is used in quick-cook pasta and macaroni to shorten the cooking time by making the particles swell up faster. The same effect can also be used to accelerate the setting time of instant puddings. In evaporated milk and coffee whiteners it acts as a buffer – i.e. the manufacturer of your coffee whitener doesn't know precisely how acidic your cup of hot coffee is going to be; but by adding DSP, he can ensure that the whitener will perform satisfactorily (i.e. it won't feather or clump together) no matter what the acidity. Trisodium phosphate (TSP) is strongly alkaline and is used as an emulsifier in processed cheese. Combinations of MSP and DSP are often used in combination in food 'buffering' (i.e. acidity control) systems.

What You Need To Know: The estimated fatal dose of sodium phosphates is 50 g. The corrosive effect is strong irritation and erythema, blistering.[633] Also see phosphoric acid (pp. 341–4).

Sodium polymetaphosphate

MEDICINAL SUBSTANCE: DUSTING POWDER

What It Is: Sodium polymetaphosphate is used in dusting powders for the treatment of sweaty feet.

Sodium, potassium and calcium salts of fatty acids (E470a)

FOOD ADDITIVE: ANTICAKING AGENT; EMULSIFIER

Regulations: EC permitted for all foodstuffs following the *quantum satis* principle (except those specified in Table 2 on pp. 15–16 and in Appendix B on pp. 469ff). Directive 95/2/EC.

Acceptable Daily Intake: Not specified.

What It Is: Produced by the interaction of sodium potassium or calcium salts with edible oils or fats.

Sodium potassium tartrate (E337)

FOOD ADDITIVE: BUFFER; EMULSIFIER; ACIDITY REGULATOR; SEQUESTRANT

MEDICINAL SUBSTANCE: LAXATIVE

Regulations: EC permitted for all foodstuffs following the *quantum satis* principle (except those specified in Table 2 on pp. 15–16 and in Appendix B on pp. 469ff). Directive 95/2/EC.

What It Is: Salt of tartaric acid (see pp .433–4) also known as Rochelle salt, with uses as an emulsifying agent in the manufacture of processed cheese, and also in the silvering of mirrors and the electroplating industry. Also used as a saline laxative substance that increases the water content of the stools, thus making them larger and easier to pass.

What You Need To Know: People with cardiac failure, high blood pressure, damaged liver or kidneys and oedema (excessive fluid in body tissues) should only use sodium salts after medical advice. Purgatives containing sodium salts may give rise to sodium and water retention in susceptible individuals.

Sodium propionate (E281)

FOOD ADDITIVE: PRESERVATIVE

Regulations: EC permitted to be used similarly to propionic acid (E280). Directive 95/2/EC.

Acceptable Daily Intake: Not specified.

What It Is: Sodium salt of propionic acid (see pp. 368–9).

Sodium propyl p-hydroxybenzoate (E217)

FOOD ADDITIVE: PRESERVATIVE

Regulations: EC permitted to be used similarly to ethyl p-hydroxybenzoate (E214). Directive 95/2/EC.

What It Is: A compound closely related to benzoic acid (see pp. 151–3), but more soluble in water, and a more effective preservative than benzoic acid in food which tends towards the alkali.

Sodium salicylate

MEDICINAL SUBSTANCE: ANALGESIC

What It Is: Sodium salt of salicylic acid (see pp. 379–80) Similar to aspirin (see pp. 142–4) in its use and effects, although when compared dose for dose, it is probably not such an effective pain reliever.

Sodium stearoyl-2-lactylate (E481)

FOOD ADDITIVE: EMULSIFIER; STABILIZER

Regulations: EC permitted for the following foods, individually or in combination with E482:

- Fine bakery wares, maximum level: 5 g/kg
- Quick-cook rice, maximum level: 4 g/kg
- Breakfast cereals, maximum level: 5 g/kg
- Emulsified liqueur, maximum level: 8 g/l
- Spirits with less than 15 % alcohol by volume, maximum level: 8 g/l
- Cereal-based snacks, maximum level: 2 g/kg
- Chewing gum, maximum level: 2 g/kg

- Fat emulsions, maximum level: 10 g/kg
- Desserts, maximum level: 5 g/kg
- Sugar confectionery, maximum level: 5 g/kg
- Beverage whiteners, maximum level: 3 g/kg
- Cereal- and potato-based snacks, maximum level: 5 g/kg
- Minced and diced canned meat products, maximum level: 4 g/kg
- Powders for the preparation of hot beverages, maximum level: 2g/l
- Dietetic foods intended for special medical purposes. Dietetic formulae for weight control intended to replace total daily food intake or an individual meal, maximum level: 2 g/kg
- Bread (except that referred to in Annex II), maximum level: 3 g/kg
- Mostarda di frutta, maximum level: 2 g/kg
- Directive 95/2/EC.

Acceptable Daily Intake: 0 – 20.

What It Is: Sodium salts of fatty acid, prepared from edible fats.

Sodium sulphates (i) Sodium sulphate (ii) Sodium hydrogen sulphate (E514)

FOOD ADDITIVE: ACIDITY REGULATOR; CARRIER

Regulations: EC permitted for all foodstuffs following the *quantum satis* principle (except those specified in Table 2 on pp. 15–16 and in Appendix B on pp. 469ff).

EC permitted as carrier. Restricted use: none. Directive 95/2/EC.

Acceptable Daily Intake: Not specified – intake limited by laxative action.

What It Is: Sodium salts of sulphuric acid (see p. 427), also known as Glauber's salt. Obtained by purification of natural sodium sulphate from brine, or by reaction of sodium chloride and sulphuric acid. Main uses in the pulp and paper, detergents and glass industries, but may also be used to regulate acidity in beverages (e.g. malt process in beer making), caramel and chewing gum, and has been used as a scalding agent to remove hair and feathers from pig and poultry carcasses after slaughter.

What You Need To Know: Water with sulphate concentrations above 500 mg/l may result in gastrointestinal irritation.[634]

Sodium sulphite (E221)

FOOD ADDITIVE: PRESERVATIVE

Regulations: EC permitted to be used similarly to sulphur dioxide (E220). Directive 95/2/EC.

Acceptable Daily Intake: 0 – 0.7 group acceptable daily intake for sulphur dioxide and sulphites expressed as sulphur dioxide.

What It Is: Sodium salt of sulphurous acid. Made by a reaction of sulphur dioxide with sodium carbonate or bicarbonate. Mainly used in the pulp and paper industries, for water and waste treatment, and in photography (instead of 'hypo' for fixing prints). Sulphiting agents have been used to preserve food for many centuries; in wine-making, they have been used to destroy naturally-occurring yeasts before the desired fermentation yeast is added. Their main function is to liberate free sulphur dioxide (see pp. 422–7) in the food which (1) inhibits the action of enzymes in the food; (2) acts as an anti-oxidant; (3) inhibits food browning; (4) inhibits the growth of micro-organisms and (5) exerts a bleaching action on the foodstuff.

What You Need To Know: Ingestion of sulphites at the levels found in foods does not result in their accumulation in the body because they are rapidly oxidized to sulphate and excreted in the urine.[635] Sulphites have, however, been associated with triggering asthma attacks and other acute allergic responses, some of which may be life-threatening or fatal in a small number of susceptible asthmatic humans.[636] It appears that most asthmatics may be sensitive to sulphites present in medical preparations or foods.[637]

The International Agency for Research on Cancer has concluded that there is inadequate evidence that sulphites are carcinogenic in animal studies or in humans, and sulphites are therefore not classifiable as to their carcinogenicity in humans.[638]

Sodium tartrates (i) monosodium tartrate (ii) disodium tartrate (E335)

FOOD ADDITIVE: SEQUESTRANT; STABILIZER IN MEAT PRODUCTS AND SAUSAGE CASINGS

Regulations: EC permitted for all foodstuffs following the *quantum satis* principle (except those specified in Table 2 on pp. 15–16 and in Appendix B on pp. 469ff). Directive 95/2/EC.

Acceptable Daily Intake: 0 – 30 expressed as L(+)-tartaric acid.

What It Is: Sodium salts of tartaric acid (see pp. 433–4).

Sodium tetraborate (borax) (E285)

FOOD ADDITIVE: PRESERVATIVE

Regulations: EC permitted to be used similarly to boric acid (E284). Directive 95/2/EC.

Acceptable Daily Intake: No acceptable daily intake allocated.

What It Is: Sodium salt of boric acid (see pp. 159–60). Obtained from the salt deposits found in Chile, Peru, Tibet and Canada, borax was once extensively used as a food preservative, but has now been all but discarded for that purpose in favour of less toxic substances.

Solanine

FOOD ADDITIVE: CONTAMINANT

Acceptable Daily Intake: Normal glycoalkaloid levels of 20–100 mg/kg thought not to be of concern.

What It Is: The potato's natural defence to environmental stress (being exposed to light, suffering damage due to bad handling, or sprouting) is to rapidly produce glycoalkaloids – substances which act as powerful insecticides and fungicides. Solanine is one glycoalkaloid. They cannot be destroyed by cooking, baking, frying or microwaving.

What You Need To Know: The tuber of the potato is the commonest source of poisoning from solanine in farm animals in Britain, and pigs are the animals usually affected. Potatoes when exposed to light become green: during the process large quantities of solanine are formed and render the green parts extremely poisonous. Unripe and old, rotten or sprouting tubers which have been kept for a long time are also dangerous. The alkaloid is present in the greatest concentration in the 'eyes', skin and the young green sprouts.[639]

Humans absorb glycoalkaloids freely but excrete them very slowly – typically, 34 to 68 days to excrete half the dose taken in. There have been many instances of poisonings – sometimes with fatal outcome – due to the ingestion of green or otherwise damaged potatoes. Symptoms include acute stomach upset, diarrhoea, vomiting, progressing to drowsiness, apathy, confusion, weakness, vision disturbances, then unconsciousness and death. Because of the slow excretion rate, onset of symptoms can be several days after ingestion. There have been reports that neural tube defects (anencephaly and spina bifida) may be due to glycoalkaloids retained in the mother's body then released early in pregnancy.[640]

Sorbic acid (E200)

FOOD ADDITIVE: PRESERVATIVE

Regulations: EC permitted to be used singly or in combination with E202 and E203 only in the following foods up to the total maximum level specified.

- Wine-based flavoured drinks including products covered by Regulation (EEC) No 1601/91, maximum level: 200 mg/l
- Non-alcoholic flavoured drinks not including dairy-based drinks, maximum level: 300 mg/l
- Wines as referred to in Regulation (EEC) No 822/87 (2); alcohol-free wine; fruit wine (including alcohol-free); Made wine; cider and perry (including alcohol-free), maximum level: 200 mg/l
- Sod . . . Saft or Sodet . . . Saft, maximum level: 500 mg/l
- Mead, maximum level: 200 mg/l
- Spirits with less than 15 % alcohol by volume, maximum level: 200 mg/l

- Fillings of ravioli and similar products, maximum level: 1 000 mg/kg
- Dried fruit, maximum level: 1 000 mg/kg
- Frugtgrod and Rote Grutze, maximum level: 1 000 mg/kg
- Fruit and vegetable preparations including fruit-based sauces, excluding purée, mousse, compote, salads and similar products, canned or bottled, maximum level: 1 000 mg/kg
- Potato dough and pre-fried potato slices, maximum level: 2 000 mg/kg
- Gnocchi, maximum level: 1 000 m g/kg
- Polenta, maximum level: 200 mg/kg
- Olives and olive-based preparations, maximum level: 1 000 mg/kg
- Cheese, pre-packed, sliced, maximum level: 1 000 mg/kg; Unripened cheese, maximum level: 1 000 mg/kg; Processed cheese, maximum level: 2 000 mg/kg; Layered cheese and cheese with added foodstuffs, maximum level: 1 000 mg/kg
- Curdled milk, maximum level: 1 000 mg/kg
- Dehydrated, concentrated, frozen and deep-frozen egg products, maximum level: 1 000 mg/kg
- Pre-packed sliced bread and rye-bread, maximum level: 2 000 mg/kg
- Partially baked, pre-packed bakery wares intended for retail sale, maximum level: 2 000 mg/kg
- Fine bakery wares with a water activity of more than 0,65, maximum level: 2 000 mg/kg
- Batters, maximum level: 2 000 mg/kg
- Toppings (syrups for pancakes; flavoured syrups for milkshakes and ice cream; similar products), maximum level: 1 000 mg/kg
- Fat emulsions (excluding butter) with a fat content of 60% or more, maximum level: 1 000 mg/kg
- Fat emulsions with a fat content less than 60 %, maximum level: 2 000 mg/kg
- Emulsified sauces with a fat content of 60 % or more, maximum level: 1000 mg/kg
- Emulsified sauces with a fat content less than 60 %, maximum level: 2 000 mg/kg
- Aspic, maximum level: 1 000 mg/kg

- When used singly or combined with E202 or E203, and further combined with E214, E215, E216, E217, E218 or E219 may be used in the following foods up to the combined maximum level specified.

- Jelly coatings of meat products (cooked, cured or dried); Paté, maximum level: 1 000 mg/kg
- Cereal- or potato-based snacks and coated nuts, maximum level: 1000 mg/kg (of which a maximum of 300 mg/kg from E214, E215, E216, E217, E218 or E219)

- When used singly or combined with E202 or E203, and further combined with E210, E211, E212 or E213, may be used in the following foods up to the combined maximum level specified.
- Non-alcoholic flavoured drinks not including dairy-based drinks, maximum level: 250 mg/l from E200, E202 or E203 combined plus 150 mg/l from E210, E211, E212 or E213 combined
- Liquid tea concentrates and liquid fruit and herbal infusion concentrates, maximum level: 600 mg/l
- Grape juice, unfermented, for sacramental use, maximum level: 2 000 mg/l
- Spirits with less than 15 % alcohol by volume, maximum level: 400 mg/l
- Low-sugar jams, jellies, marmalades and similar low calorie or sugar-free products and other fruit-based spreads, maximum level: 1 000 mg/kg
- Candied, crystallized and glacé fruit and vegetables, maximum level: 1000 mg/kg
- Vegetables in vinegar, brine or oil (excluding olives), maximum level: 2 000 mg/kg
- Semi-preserved fish products including fish roe products, maximum level: 2 000 mg/kg; Salted, dried fish, maximum level: 200 mg/kg; Shrimps, cooked, maximum level: 2 000 mg/kg
- *Crangon crangon* and *Crangon vulgaris*, cooked, maximum level: 6 000 mg/kg
- Non-heat-treated dairy-based desserts, maximum level: 300 mg/kg
- Liquid egg (white, yolk or whole egg), maximum level: 5 000 mg/kg
- Chewing gum, maximum level: 1 500 mg/kg
- Non-emulsified sauces, maximum level: 1 000 mg/kg
- Prepared salads, maximum level: 1 500 mg/kg
- Mustard, maximum level: 1 000 mg/kg

- Seasonings and condiments, maximum level: 1 000 mg/kg
- Liquid soups and broths (excluding canned), maximum level: 500 mg/l
- Dietetic foods intended for special medical purposes excluding foods for infants and young children as referred to in Directive 89/398/EEC (1) – dietetic formulae for weight control intended to replace total daily food intake or an individual meal, maximum level: 1 500 mg/kg

- When used singly or combined with E202 or E203, further combined with E210, E211, E212 or E213, and further combined with E214, E215, E216, E217, E218 or E219, may be used in the following foods up to the combined maximum level specified.
- Surface treatment of dried meat products, maximum level: *quantum satis*
- Confectionery (excluding chocolate), maximum level: 1 500 mg/kg (of which a maximum of 300 mg/kg from E214, E215, E216, E217, E218 or E219)
- Liquid dietary food supplements, maximum level: 2 000 mg/kg
- Directive 95/2/EC.

Acceptable Daily Intake: 0 – 25 as sum of sorbic acid and calcium, potassium and sodium sorbates (expressed as sorbic acid).

What It Is: One of the most widely used food preservatives worldwide. First isolated in 1859 by German chemist A.W. von Hoffman from mountain ash berries, it is today manufactured synthetically. Possessing little flavour or sharpness of its own, sorbic acid and its salts are effective in discouraging the growth of yeasts or moulds on food, less so against bacterial infection. Like other fatty acids, it is metabolized in the human body to carbon dioxide and water.

What You Need To Know: Considered to be of low toxicity. No reports of injury in industrial handling have been noted. In experiments, ointments containing sorbic acid were said to cause itching of face, and it has caused skin irritation at a concentration of 0.15 per cent in water.[641]

411

Sorbitan monostearate (E491)

FOOD ADDITIVE: EMULSIFIER; CARRIER

Regulations: EC permitted for the following foods, individually or in combination with E492, E493, E494 or E495.

- Fine bakery wares, maximum level: 10 g/kg
- Toppings and coatings for fine bakery wares, maximum level: 5 g/kg
- Jelly marmalade, maximum level: 25 mg/kg (E493 only)
- Fat emulsions, maximum level: 10 g/kg
- Milk and cream analogues, maximum level: 5 g/kg
- Beverage whiteners, maximum level: 5 g/kg
- Liquid tea concentrates and liquid fruit and herbal infusions concentrates, maximum level: 0,5 g/l
- Edible ices, maximum level: 0,5 g/kg
- Desserts, maximum level: 5 g/kg
- Sugar confectionery, maximum level: 5 g/kg; Cocoa-based confectionery, including chocolate, maximum level: 10 g/kg (E492 only)
- Emulsified sauces, maximum level: 5 g/kg
- Dietary food supplements, maximum level: *quantum satis*
- Yeast for baking, maximum level: *quantum satis*
- Chewing gum, maximum level: 5 g/kg
- Dietetic foods intended for special medical purposes; dietetic formulae for weight control intended to replace total daily food intake or an individual meal, maximum level: 5 g/kg
- (*pro memoria*) For E 491 only, wine in accordance with Regulation (EEC) No 1873/84 authorizing the offer or disposal for direct human consumption of certain imported wines which may have undergone oenological processes not provided for in Regulation (EEC) No 337/79
- EC permitted as carrier. Restricted use: colours and anti-foaming agents. Directive 95/2/EC.

Acceptable Daily Intake: 0 – 25 group acceptable daily intake as the sum of the sorbitan esters of lauric, oleic, palmitic and stearic acid.

What It Is: The sorbitan esters (E491 – E495) consist of sorbitol (*see below*) reacted with a fatty acid at > 200°C. This produces a substance which is insoluble in water but soluble in most organic oils, an ideal water-in-oil emulsifier. Can be further processed to form polysorbates (see pp. 351–2), whose oil-in-water solubility makes them complementary in use. Sorbitan esters generally give poor wetting, foaming, dispersing and detergency.

What You Need To Know: Mainly hydrolized in the body to the fatty acid moiety (e.g. stearic acid) and anhydrides of sorbitol. Scientific studies do not raise carcinogenic concerns. At high dietary levels (10 per cent of diet or more) some sorbitan esters may cause liver enlargement, intralobular fibrosis and enlargement of the common bile duct and growth retardation.[642]

Sorbitol (i) sorbitol (ii) sorbitol syrup (E420)

FOOD ADDITIVE: SWEETENER; HUMECTANT; SEQUESTRANT; TEXTURIZER; STABILIZER; CARRIER

Regulations: Desserts and similar products, maximum usable dose: *quantum satis*

- Water-based flavoured desserts, energy-reduced or with no added sugar, maximum usable dose: *quantum satis*
- Milk- and milk-derivative-based preparations, energy-reduced or with no added sugar, maximum usable dose: *quantum satis*
- Fruit- and vegetable-based desserts, energy-reduced or with no added sugar, maximum usable dose: *quantum satis*; Egg-based desserts, energy-reduced or with no added sugar, maximum usable dose: *quantum satis*; Cereal-based desserts, energy-reduced or with no added sugar, maximum usable dose: *quantum satis*
- Breakfast cereals or cereal-based products, energy reduced or with no added sugar, maximum usable dose: *quantum satis*
- Fat-based desserts, energy-reduced or with no added sugar, maximum usable dose: *quantum satis*
- Edible ices, energy-reduced or with no added sugar, maximum usable dose: *quantum satis*
- Jams, jellies, marmalades and crystallized fruit, energy-reduced or with no added sugar, maximum usable dose: *quantum satis*
- Fruit preparations, energy-reduced or with no added sugar, with

the exception of those intended for the manufacture of fruit-juice-based drinks, maximum usable dose: *quantum satis*

- Confectionery, maximum usable dose: *quantum satis*; Confectionery with no added sugar, maximum usable dose: *quantum satis*; Dried-fruit-based confectionery, energy-reduced or with no added sugar, maximum usable dose: *quantum satis*; Starch-based confectionery, energy-reduced or with no added sugar, maximum usable dose: *quantum satis*
- Cocoa-based products, energy-reduced or with no added sugar, maximum usable dose: *quantum satis*; Cocoa-, milk-, dried-fruit- or fat-based sandwich spreads, energy-reduced or with no added sugar, maximum usable dose: *quantum satis*
- Chewing gum with no added sugar, maximum usable dose: *quantum satis*
- Sauces, maximum usable dose: *quantum satis*
- Mustard, maximum usable dose: *quantum satis*
- Fine bakery products, energy-reduced or with no added sugar, maximum usable dose: *quantum satis*
- Products intended for particular nutritional uses, maximum usable dose: *quantum satis*
- Solid food supplements/dietary integrators, maximum usable dose: *quantum satis*
- For purposes other than sweetening, EC permitted for foodstuffs in general (including frozen and deep-frozen unprocessed fish, crustaceans, molluscs and cephalopods, and liqueurs; excluding those foodstuffs referred to in Article 2(3)) Maximum level: *quantum satis*
- EC permitted as carrier. Restricted use: none. Directive 94/35/EC.

Acceptable Daily Intake: Not specified.

What It Is: A polyol, or polyhydric alcohol, produced by hydrogenation of glucose (see propan-1,2-diol [propylene glycol] for a description of their properties and functions). Sorbitol is the most widely distributed polyol in nature, first identifed in the ripe berries of the mountain ash, now detected in cherries, plums, pears, apples, seaweed and blackstrap molasses. It is used as sweetening agent for diabetics because insulin is not required for its metabolism in the human body, and widely used in food manufacture as an agent for preserving moisture and as a softener. Sorbitol is also used as a chemical intermediate in vitamin C manufacture, and as a humectant in toothpaste.

What You Need To Know: Low toxicity.[643] Most orally ingested sorbitol is converted to carbon dioxide without appearing as glucose in the blood.[644] When used as a laxative, it has osmotic diuretic properties, exerting a hygroscopic and/or a local irritant action, drawing water from the tissues into the faeces and thus stimulating evacuation.[645]

Stannous chloride (E512)

FOOD ADDITIVE: ANTIOXIDANT; COLOUR RETENTION AGENT

Regulations: EC permitted for canned and bottled white asparagus, maximum level: 25 mg/kg as Sn (tin). Directive 95/2/EC.

Acceptable Daily Intake: 2 provisional maximum tolerable daily intake for tin, including stannous chloride and tin from food additive uses; tin levels in canned food should be as low as practicable because of possibility of gastric irritation.

What It Is: Made either by the treatment of granulated tin with hydrochloric acid, or by reduction of stannic chloride with a cathode or tin metal followed by crystallization. Mostly used as a component of tin electroplating baths.

What You Need To Know: The low toxicological risk generally associated with inorganic tin ingestion is due largely to its low degree of absorption, low tissue retention, and rapid turnover.[646]

Once tin salts have gained access to the bloodstream they are highly toxic, producing paralysis and other neurological damage.[647] Target organs are the eyes, skin and respiratory system.[648] Tin, as stannous chloride, is readily taken up by human white blood cells and can cause damage to DNA.[649]

Acute poisoning has been reported, usually following ingestion of fruit juices containing concentrations of tin greater than about 250 mg/l. The major symptoms and signs are nausea, vomiting, diarrhoea, fatigue, and headache. In a unique incident, involving 110 people who had consumed only canned peaches, intoxication was reported in the majority of those questioned. Two out of seven persons who had ingested 50 mg of tin in the peaches fell ill.[650]

It is not conclusively known whether humans have a biological requirement for tin, but if there is, the Western diet almost certainly fulfils it. Tin is generally poorly absorbed into the system, but once absorbed, it may take 30 days or more for half the absorbed amount to be excreted.[651]

Starch sodium octenyl succinate (E1450)
FOOD ADDITIVE: STABILIZER; THICKENING AGENT; BINDER; CARRIER

Regulations: EC permitted for all foodstuffs following the *quantum satis* principle (except those specified in Table 2 on pp. 15–16 and in Appendix B on pp. 469ff).
EC permitted as carrier. Restricted use: none. Directive 95/2/EC.
Acceptable Daily Intake: Not specified.
What It Is: A chemically modifed starch, obtained by reacting suspensions of starch granules in water with octenyl succinic anhydride. The resulting starch has the ability to stabilize oil in water emulsions.

Sterculia
MEDICINAL SUBSTANCE: STIMULANT; LAXATIVE
What It Is: Also called the Kola nut from the tree *Kola vera* (or *Cola vera*). Because of its caffeine content, it is a stimulant. Sterculia gum is used as a bulk laxative (i.e. it swells when it absorbs water) and can be used as an adhesive.
What You Need To Know: Occasional allergic reactions have been reported, characterized by rashes, runny nose, dermatitis, and asthma.[652]

Styrene

FOOD ADDITIVE: CONTAMINANT

Acceptable Daily Intake: Provisional maximum tolerable daily intake: 0.04 lowest level technologically attainable.

What It Is: A colourless, viscous liquid which is one of the starting materials in the manufacture of plastics (e.g. polystyrene), elastomers and resins. Styrene production requires large amounts of raw materials produced by the coal tar and petroleum industries. Since the late 1940s, has been extensively used in the production of food packaging plastics. It consumes 50 per cent of the world's production of benzene. Has also been used as a synthetic flavouring and adjuvant.

What You Need To Know: Humans can be exposed to styrene by consuming food which has been packaged in polystyrene, by ingestion of contaminated drinking water, by breathing air which has been contaminated by industrial sources, from car exhausts, by emissions by incinerators, and by inhalation of smoke from cigarettes.[653] Products such as floor waxes and polishes, paints, adhesives, putty, metal cleaners, car fillers, and varnishes may also contain styrene.[654] Plastic packaging can contain very small amounts of residual styrene which could migrate into food.[655] It is very difficult to estimate what the practical long-term effects of such exposure could be.

Styrene is easily absorbed from the gastrointestinal tract, and can be metabolized by the body to form styrene oxide, a mutagen and carcinogen. Limited human studies suggest that styrene may be hepatotoxic, a CNS (central nervous system) depressant and perhaps teratogenic.[656]

The International Agency for Research on Cancer has concluded that styrene is possibly carcinogenic to humans. There is inadequate evidence in humans for the carcinogenicity of styrene. There is limited evidence in experimental animals for the carcinogenicity of styrene.[657]

Succinic acid (E363)

FOOD ADDITIVE: FLAVOUR ENHANCER; ACIDITY REGULATOR

Regulations: EC permitted for the following foods:
Desserts, maximum level: 6 g/kg; Soups and broths, maximum level: 5 g/kg; Powders for home preparation of drinks, maximum level: 3 g/l. Directive 95/2/EC.

What It Is: The Latin for amber is *succinum*, hence the name of this substance, which was first distilled from amber. In fact, succinic acid is a normal constituent of almost all plant and animal tissues, and has even been found in meteorites. Commercially, it is obtained as by-product of the manufacture of adipic acid (see pp. 110f) and has a very sharp, slightly bitter taste. Uses of succinic acid range from scientific applications such as radiation dosimetry to uses in agriculture (as a biogenic plant growth stimulant), medicine, plastics, cosmetics, textiles, plating, and waste-gas scrubbing.

What You Need To Know: Succinic acid is a normal human metabolite; studies do not demonstrate any systemic toxic effects. Large oral doses may produce vomiting and diarrhoea.[658]

Sucroglycerides (E474)

FOOD ADDITIVE: EMULSIFIER

Regulations: EC permitted to be used similarly to sucrose esters of fatty acids (E473). Directive 95/2/EC.

Acceptable Daily Intake: 0 – 16 group acceptable daily intake based on sucrose esters contained in sucrose esters of fatty acids and sucroglycerides.

What It Is: Made by heating a mixture of sucrose with an edible fat or oil in the presence of a base (e.g. potassium carbonate) as a catalyst. Originally dimethylformamide was used as a solvent, but this has fallen into disfavour. Mainly used as a dilutent for drinks.

Sucrose

MEDICINAL SUBSTANCE: FLAVOURING

What It Is: Sugar – used by nannies and others to flavour medicines.

Sucrose acetate isobutyrate (E444)

FOOD ADDITIVE: DENSITY ADJUSTING AGENT; CLOUD-PRODUCING AGENT

Regulations: EC permitted for non-alcoholic flavoured cloudy drinks, maximum level: 300 mg/l. Directive 95/2/EC.

Acceptable Daily Intake: 0 – 10 temporary.

What It Is: A chemical mixture of esters of sucrose esterified with acetic and isobutyric acids.

What You Need To Know: Scientific studies do not raise carcinogenic concerns. [659]

Sucrose esters of fatty acids (E473)

FOOD ADDITIVE: EMULSIFIER; CARRIER

Regulations: EC permitted for the following foods, individually or in combination with E474:

- Canned liquid coffee, maximum level: 1 g/l
- Heat-treated meat products, maximum level: 5 g/kg (on fat)
- Fat emulsions for baking purposes, maximum level: 10 g/kg
- Fine bakery wares, maximum level: 10 g/kg
- Beverage whiteners, maximum level: 20 g/kg
- Edible ices, maximum level: 5 g/kg
- Sugar confectionery, maximum level: 5 g/kg
- Desserts, maximum level: 5 g/kg
- Sauces, maximum level: 10 g/kg
- Soups and broths, maximum level: 2 g/kg
- Fresh fruits, surface treatment, maximum level: *quantum satis*
- Non-alcoholic aniseed-based drinks, maximum level: 5 g/l
- Non-alcoholic coconut and almond drinks, maximum level: 5 g/l
- Spirituous beverages (excluding wine and beer), maximum level: 5 g/l
- Powders for the preparation of hot beverages, maximum level: 10 g/l

- Dairy-based drinks, maximum level: 5 g/l
- Dietary food supplements, maximum level: *quantum satis*
- Dietetic foods intended for special medical purposes; dietetic formulae for weight control intended to replace total daily food intake or an individual meal, maximum level: 5 g/kg
- Chewing gum, maximum level: 10 g/kg
- EC permitted as carrier. Restricted use: colours and fat-soluble antioxidants. Directive 95/2/EC.

Acceptable Daily Intake: 0 – 16 group acceptable daily intake based on sucrose esters contained in sucrose esters of fatty acids and sucroglycerides.

What It Is: The esters of sucrose with edible fatty acids (sometimes within a solvent such as dimethylformamide, which must be removed if the product is to be used in food).

What You Need To Know: May produce a laxative action; bloated feeling, abdominal pain, nausea and flatulence in doses of 1.5 grams or more. About a third of the amount swallowed is excreted intact, the remainder is broken down in the digestive tract into sucrose (sugar) and fatty acids. Scientific studies do not raise carcinogenic or long-term toxicity concerns.[660]

Dimethylformamide: The International Agency for Research on Cancer has concluded that dimethylformamide is possibly carcinogenic to humans. There is limited evidence for the carcinogenicity of dimethylformamide in humans. There is inadequate evidence for the carcinogenicity of dimethyl-formamide in experimental animals.[661]

Sulphite ammonia caramel (caramel colour class IV) (E150d)

FOOD ADDITIVE: FOOD COLOUR

Regulations: EC permitted at *quantum satis* in all foods except those to which the EC only permits certain colours to be added (Appendix C, pp. 476ff) and those to which the EC forbids the adding of colours (Appendix D, pp. 482ff). Directive 94/36/EC.

Acceptable Daily Intake: 0 – 200.

What It Is: Prepared by the controlled heat treatment of carbo-hydrates with ammonium-containing and sulphite-containing compounds.

What You Need To Know: Scientific studies do not raise carcinogenic concerns.[662]

Sulphur

MEDICINAL SUBSTANCE: KERATOLYTIC

What It Is: Sulphur is an element found in the volcanic regions of Italy, as well as in vast underground deposits in America. The majority of sulphur production is used as a raw material for the production of sulphuric acid (much of which is turned into fertilizer); the rest for wood pulping, rubber vulcanization, and other miscellaneous uses. It occurs naturally in the body, and is present in many proteins. Used on the surface of the skin, it tends to loosen the outer layers so that it can be rubbed away (a keratolytic action) and it has therefore been used in products for the treatment of acne, dandruff, psoriasis, and eczema dermatitis. Medical advice should be obtained for all these conditions.

What You Need To Know: Topical preparations con-taining sulphur are intended for external use only. Repeated applications may cause dermatitis, sometimes severe. In con-centrations greater than 15 per cent, sulphur is very irritating to the skin. Side-effects of headache, vomiting, muscle cramp, dizziness and collapse have apparently occurred after topical application of sulphur powder or sulphur ointment to a patient with eczema. Topical application of a 10 per cent sulphur oint-ment for 3 days on infants with scabies reportedly caused poisoning and several deaths.[663] Workers whose hands are in prolonged or repeated contact with powdered sulphur may develop eczematous lesions and signs of ulceration.[664] If you think you may be suffering from eczema – and 10 per cent of the population do at some point in their life – the best advice is to seek professional treatment.[665]

Sulphur dioxide (E220)

FOOD ADDITIVE: PRESERVATIVE

Regulations: EC permitted to be used in the following foods up to the maximum level specified.

- Burger meat with a minimum vegetable and/or cereal content of 4 %, maximum level: 450 mg/kg
- Breakfast sausages, maximum level: 450 mg/kg
- Longaniza fresca and Butifarra fresca, maximum level: 450 mg/kg
- Dried salted fish of the 'Gadidae' species, maximum level: 200 mg/kg
- Crustaceans and cephalopods: fresh, frozen and deep-frozen, maximum level: 150 mg/kg; crustaceans, *penaeidae solenceridae*, *aristeidae* family: up to 80 units, maximum level: 150 mg/kg; between 80 and 120 units, maximum level: 200 mg/kg; over 120 units, maximum level: 300 mg/kg; cooked, maximum level: 50 mg/kg
- Dry biscuit, maximum level: 50 mg/kg
- Starches (excluding starches for weaning foods, follow-on formulae and infant formulae), maximum level: 50 mg/kg
- Sago, maximum level: 30 mg/kg
- Pearl barley, maximum level: 30 mg/kg
- Dehydrated granulated potatoes, maximum level: 400 mg/kg
- Cereal- and potato-based snacks, maximum level: 50 mg/kg
- Peeled potatoes, maximum level: 50 mg/kg
- Processed potatoes (including frozen and deep-frozen potatoes), maximum level: 100 mg/kg
- Potato dough, maximum level: 100 mg/kg
- White vegetables, dried, maximum level: 400 mg/kg
- White vegetables, processed (including frozen and deep-frozen white vegetables), maximum level: 50 mg/kg
- Dried ginger, maximum level: 150 mg/kg
- Dried tomatoes, maximum level: 200 mg/kg
- Horseradish pulp, maximum level: 800 mg/kg
- Onion, garlic and shallot pulp, maximum level: 300 mg/kg

- Vegetables and fruits in vinegar, oil or brine (except olives and golden peppers in brine), maximum level: 100 mg/kg
- Golden peppers in brine, maximum level: 500 mg/kg
- Processed mushrooms (including frozen mushrooms), maximum level: 50 mg/kg
- Dried mushrooms, maximum level: 100 mg/kg
- Dried fruits: Apricots, peaches, grapes, prunes and figs, maximum level: 2 000 mg/kg; Bananas, maximum level: 1 000 mg/kg; Apples and pears, maximum level: 600 mg/kg; Other (including nuts in shell), maximum level: 500 mg/kg
- Dried coconut, maximum level: 50 mg/kg
- Candied, crystallized or glacé fruit, vegetables, angelica and citrus peel, maximum level: 100 mg/kg
- Jam, jelly and marmalade as defined in Directive 79/693/EEC (except extra jam and extra jelly) and other similar fruit spreads including low-calorie products, maximum level: 50 mg/kg
- Jams, jellies and marmalades made with sulphited fruit, maximum level: 100 mg/kg
- Fruit-based pie fillings, maximum level: 100 mg/kg
- Citrus-juice-based seasonings, maximum level: 200 mg/kg
- Concentrated grape juice for home wine-making, maximum level: 2 000 mg/kg
- Mostarda di frutta, maximum level: 100 mg/kg
- Jellying fruit extract, liquid pectin for sale to the final consumer, maximum level: 800 mg/kg
- Bottled whiteheart cherries, rehydrated dried fruit and lychees, maximum level: 100 mg/kg
- Bottled, sliced lemon, maximum level: 250 mg/kg
- Sugars as defined in Directive 73/437/EEC except glucose syrup, whether or not dehydrated, maximum level: 15 mg/kg
- Glucose syrup, whether or not dehydrated, maximum level: 20 mg/kg
- Treacle and molasses, maximum level: 70 mg/kg
- Other sugars, maximum level: 40 mg/kg
- Toppings (syrups for pancakes, flavoured syrups for milkshakes and ice-cream; similar products), maximum level: 40 mg/l
- Orange, grapefruit, apple and pineapple juice for bulk dispensing in catering establishments, maximum level: 50 mg/l
- Lime and lemon juice, maximum level: 350 mg/l

- Concentrates based on fruit juice and containing not less than 2,5 % barley (barley water), maximum level: 350 mg/l
- Other concentrates based on fruit juice or comminuted fruit; capilé groselha, maximum level: 250 mg/l
- Non-alcoholic flavoured drinks containing fruit juice, maximum level: 20 mg/l (carry-over from concentrates only)
- Non-alcoholic flavoured drinks containing at least 235 g/l glucose syrup, maximum level: 50 mg/l
- Grape juice, unfermented, for sacramental use, maximum level: 70 mg/l
- Glucose-syrup-based confectionery, maximum level: 50 mg/kg (carry-over from the glucose syrup only)
- Beer including low-alcohol and alcohol-free beer, maximum level: 20 mg/l
- Beer with a second fermentation in the cask, maximum level: 50 mg/l
- Wines, maximum level: in accordance with Regulations (EEC) No 822/87, (EEC) No 4252/88, (EEC) No 2332/92 and (EEC) No 1873/84 and their implementing regulations; (*pro memoria*) in accordance with Regulation (EEC) No 1873/84 authorizing the offer or disposal for direct human consumption of certain imported wines which may have undergone oenological processes not provided for in Regulation (EEC) No 337/79.
- Alcohol-free wine, maximum level: 200 mg/l
- Made wine, maximum level: 260 mg/l
- Cider, perry, fruit wine, sparkling fruit wine (including alcohol-free products), maximum level: 200 mg/l
- Mead, maximum level: 200 mg/l
- Fermentation vinegar, maximum level: 170 mg/l
- Mustard, excluding Dijon mustard, maximum level: 250 mg/kg
- Dijon mustard, maximum level: 500 mg/kg
- Gelatin, maximum level: 50 mg/kg
- Vegetable- and cereal-protein-based meat, fish and crustacean analogues, maximum level: 200 mg/kg. Directive 95/2/EC

Acceptable Daily Intake: 0 – 0.7 group acceptable daily intake for sulphur dioxide and sulphites expressed as sulphur dioxide.

What It Is: Obtained by roasting pyrites in special furnaces; by purifying and compressing sulphur dioxide gas from smelting operations; or by burning sulphur. Mainly used in the chemical industry, pulp and paper manufacture, food and agriculture (mainly corn processing), water and waste treatment and metal and ore refining. 'Sulphiting' is the word used by food technologists to describe the application of sulphur compounds to food. Sulphiting agents don't just prevent the growth of bacteria: they have a complex mode of action which includes inhibiting enzymes that cause food to discolour; they also have bleaching and antioxidant properties, too. In the United States, sulphiting agents are banned from use in meat products because they destroy the vitamin thiamin (vitamin B1) and may restore the colour of old meat, thus misleading consumers.[666] They are also banned from use on food recognized as a source of vitamin B1; on fruits or vegetables intended to be served raw to consumers or sold raw to consumers, or to be presented to the consumer as fresh; and on 'fresh' potatoes that are intended to be served or sold unpackaged and unlabelled to the consumer.[667]

The release of sulphur dioxide as a pollutant into the atmosphere is the cause of acid rain. On a global basis, fossil fuel combustion accounts for 75 to 85 per cent of man-made sulphur dioxide emissions, and industrial processes such as refining and smelting account for the remainder.[668] Northwestern Europe, an area about 1 per cent of the earth's surface, accounts for an estimated 20 per cent of the total global sulphur dioxide emission.[669] It wasn't until 1972 that Eugene Likens (at Cornell University) and F. Herbert Bormann at Yale discovered the phenomenon of acid rain. Earlier pollution events – such as the infamous London smog of 1952, which killed 4,000 people – were generally seen as isolated, exceptional events.[670] Often, the official response was to build smoke stacks hundreds of feet tall, in order to 'dilute' the pollution. These tall stacks simply allowed the sulphurous pollution to travel 1,000 miles or more. Acid rain doesn't just kills trees – it affects the entire ecosystem. Soil contains a large amount of bio-unavailable aluminium in the form of aluminium silicates. When acid rain dissolves the silicates, the aluminium is suddenly made available to plants. When plants get aluminium into their roots and their vascular system, the roots clog, which prevents the plant from taking up adequate nutrients and water. Acid rain also leaches many other nutrients – calcium, magnesium, phosphorus – out of the soil.

What You Need To Know: Sulphur dioxide reacts with a wide range of substances found in foods, possibly either interfering with their absorption or increasing their rate of excretion. They include: thiamin, cyanocobalamin (vitamin B12), various enzymes, calcium, and various fatty acids. The most common adverse effect to sulphiting agents in humans is bronchoconstriction and bronchospasm, particularly among those prone to asthma. Other adverse reactions may include anaphylaxis, flushing, hypotension (low blood pressure) and tingling sensations. These can all happen at levels normally found in food. In laboratory experiments sulphiting agents have been shown to be capable of damaging DNA and can induce mutations in bacteria. After examining the use of sulphites, the Joint FAO/WHO Expert Committee on Food Additives recommended 'that the use of suitable alternative technology, where it exists, should be encouraged, particularly in those applications where the use of sulphites may lead to high levels of acute exposure and which have most commonly been associated with life-threatening adverse reactions.'[671]

The International Labour Office has concluded: 'persons suffering from chronic conjunctivitis or laryngitis, bronchitis, emphysema, bronchial asthma, any disorder inhibiting nasal respiration, or any cardiovascular disease should not be exposed to this substance.'[672]

The International Agency for Research on Cancer has concluded that there is limited evidence that sulphur dioxide is carcinogenic in animal studies, that there is inadequate evidence for its carcinogenicity in humans, and it is therefore not classifiable as to its carcinogenicity in humans.[673]

Sulphuric acid (E513)

FOOD ADDITIVE: ACID

Regulations: EC permitted for all foodstuffs following the *quantum satis* principle (except those specified in Table 2 on pp. 15–16 and in Appendix B on pp. 469ff). Directive 95/2/EC.

What It Is: A key industrial chemical with uses in many areas, including the production of fertilizers, petroleum refining, inorganic chemicals and pigments, copper leaching, synthetic rubbers and plastics, industrial organic chemicals and pulp and paper production.

What You Need To Know: A very powerful acidic oxidizer which corrodes and ulcerates skin, tissues and mucous membranes which it may contact. The poisonous effect of sulphuric acid seems to be primarily due to its acidity. A quantity of acid that would be lethal in soft water could be rendered harmless in hard or highly buffered water.[674] Sulphuric acid typically attacks tooth enamel. Workers chronically exposed may show tracheobronchitis, stomatitis, conjunctivitis, or gastritis.[675] Consumers are unlikely to face a health hazard from food products containing sulphuric acid at levels in accordance with good manufacturing practice.

Occupational exposure to strong-inorganic-acid mists containing sulphuric acid: The International Agency for Research on Cancer has concluded that occupational exposure to strong-inorganic-acid mists containing sulphuric acid is carcinogenic.[676]

Sunset Yellow FCF, Orange Yellow S (E110)

FOOD ADDITIVE: FOOD COLOUR

Regulations: EC permitted to be used singly or in combination with other colours in the following foods up to the total maximum level specified. For non-alcoholic flavoured drinks, edible ices, desserts, fine bakery wares and confectionery, a combination of food colours may be used up to the maximum limit indicated below, but the amount of Sunset Yellow may not exceed 50 mg/kg or mg/l.

- Non-alcoholic flavoured drinks, maximum level: 100 mg/l
- Candied fruits and vegetables, Mostarda di frutta, maximum level: 200 mg/kg
- Preserves of red fruits, maximum level: 200 mg/kg
- Confectionery, maximum level: 300 mg/kg
- Decorations and coatings, maximum level: 500 mg/kg
- Fine bakery wares (e.g. viennoiserie, biscuits, cakes and wafers), maximum level: 200 mg/kg
- Edible ices, maximum level: 150 mg/kg
- Flavoured processed cheese, maximum level: 100 mg/kg
- Desserts including flavoured milk products, maximum level: 150 mg/kg
- Sauces, seasonings (for example, curry powder, tandoori), pickles, relishes, chutney and piccalilli, maximum level: 500 mg/kg
- Mustard, maximum level: 300 mg/kg
- Fish paste and crustacean paste, maximum level: 100 mg/kg; Pre-cooked crustaceans, maximum level: 250 mg/kg; Salmon substitutes, maximum level: 500 mg/kg; Surimi, maximum level: 500 mg/kg; Fish roe, maximum level: 300 mg/kg; Smoked fish, maximum level: 100 mg/kg
- Snacks: dry, savoury potato, cereal or starch-based snack products: Extruded or expanded savoury snack products, maximum level: 200 mg/kg; Other savoury snack products and savoury coated nuts, maximum level: 100 mg/kg
- Edible cheese rind and edible casings, maximum level: *quantum satis*
- Complete formulae for weight control intended to replace total daily food intake or an individual meal, maximum level: 50 mg/kg
- Complete formulae and nutritional supplements for use under medical supervision, maximum level: 50 mg/kg
- Liquid food supplements/dietary integrators, maximum level: 100 mg/l

- Solid food supplements/dietary integrators, maximum level: 300 mg/kg
- Soups, maximum level: 50 mg/kg
- Meat and fish analogues based on vegetable proteins, maximum level: 100 mg/kg
- Spirituous beverages (including products less than 15 % alcohol by volume), except those mentioned in Annex II or III, maximum level: 200 mg/l
- Aromatized wines, aromatized wine-based drinks and aromatized wine-product cocktails as mentioned in Regulation (EEC) No 1601/91, except those mentioned in Annex II or III, maximum level: 200 mg/l
- Fruit wines (still or sparkling) cider (except cidre bouche) and perry, aromatized fruit wines, cider and perry, maximum level: 200 mg/l Directive 94/36/EC.

Acceptable Daily Intake: 0 – 2.5 mg / kg bw.

What It Is: A synthetic yellow-orange monoazo dye.

What You Need To Know: Probably reduced by intestinal bacteria to aromatic amines and aminosulphonic acids, which are then partly absorbed by the intestinal tract. Animal experiments do not raise carcinogenic or reproductive concerns, although some studies suggest that growth retardation and severe weight loss can occur when Sunset Yellow FCF was fed to beagles at >1 per cent of their diet. In humans, Sunset Yellow FCF has been shown to produce an eczema reaction when applied on the skin of people sensitive to quinone compounds.[677] People who suffer from asthma, rhinitis or urticaria may find their symptoms become worse following consumption of foods or beverages containing azo dyes. Such people may be mistakenly thought to be suffering from specific food allergies.[678]

The International Agency for Research on Cancer has concluded that this substance is unclassifiable as to carcinogenicity in humans. No data were available in humans, and there was inadequate evidence of carcinogenicity in animals.[679]

Talc and asbestos-free talc (E553b)

FOOD ADDITIVE: ANTICAKING AGENT; DUSTING POWDER; FILTER AID; CARRIER

MEDICINAL SUBSTANCE: DUSTING POWDER

Regulations: EC permitted to be used similarly to silicon dioxide (E551).

EC permitted as carrier. Restricted use: colours, max. 5 per cent. Directive 95/2/EC.

Acceptable Daily Intake: Not specified.

What It Is: Talc is a mineral product, natural hydrous magnesium silicate (see p. 290). Its composition varies widely from one geological deposit to another, and even within the same deposit.

What You Need To Know: Respiratory distress syndrome, which can be fatal, has been described in children following massive accidental inhalation of talcum powder. Acute bronchitis and bronchiolitis were found in a 22-month-old boy who died following accidental inhalation of talc. The long-term effects of baby powder inhalation remain unknown, since serial follow-up studies are not available.[680] Acute inhalation of talc causes symptoms such as coughing, dyspnoea, sneezing, vomiting, and cyanosis (turning blue). Talc, which is water insoluble, dries up the mucous membranes of the lungs. Inhaling large amounts of talc can also result in obstruction of the small airways, leading to respiratory distress syndrome or death. It is estimated that there are probably a few thousand cases of infants inhaling talc each year – these could be prevented by using creams and lotions in place of powder. Clinical studies of intravenous drug abusers have shown that intravenous injection of pills containing psychoactive agents and talc as a binder can result in blockages forming in the small arteries of the lungs, arterioles, and capillaries. This can result in granuloma formation, impaired lung function, and even death. Intravenous injection of talc-containing formulations has been shown to predispose users to infections.[681]

Four distinct types of talc-associated lung disease have been identifed, usually in workers with occupational exposure. The first form, talcosilicosis, is caused by talc mined with high silica content mineral – the symptoms are identical with those of silicosis. Talcoasbestosis is similar to asbestosis and is produced by talc inhaled with asbestos fibres. The third form, talcosis, is caused by inhalation of pure talc, and may include acute or chronic bronchitis. The fourth form, due to intravenous administration of talc, is usually associated with abuse of oral medications.[682]

An experiment was conducted to see whether the use of talc in genital hygiene might increase the risk for epithelial ovarian cancer. Two hundred and thirty-five Caucasian women diagnosed with epithelial ovarian cancer and 239 population-based controls of similar race, age and residence were interviewed. Overall, 49 per cent of cases and 39 per cent of controls reported exposure to talc, via direct application to the perineum or to undergarments, sanitary napkins, or diaphragms. The greatest ovarian cancer risk associated with perineal talc use was observed in those women estimated to have made more than 10,000 applications during the years when they were ovulating and had an intact genital tract. The experiment supports the concept that a lifetime pattern of perineal talc use may increase the risk for epithelial ovarian cancer, but is unlikely to be the sole cause of the majority of epithelial ovarian cancers.[683]

The International Agency for Research on Cancer has concluded that there is inadequate evidence that asbestos-free talc is carcinogenic in humans, but that there is sufficient evidence that talc containing asbestos fibres is carcinogenic to humans.[684]

Tannic acid

MEDICINAL SUBSTANCE: ASTRINGENT

What It Is: Tannic acid was once made from 'galls' – a growth appearing on oak trees caused by insect larvae. Gathered and used in the preparation of ink and dye for cloth, they have also been used in various medicinal ways for hundreds of years. The term 'tannin' was originally created to describe any substance which could convert animal skin to leather. Tannic acid occurs naturally in coffee and tea, and has been used as a flavouring agent in beverages, ice-cream, sweets, baked goods and liqueurs, also as a clarifying agent in brewing and wine. The astringent properties of tannic acid means that it has been used in skin preparations, gargles and throat lozenges, for diarrhoea and as a drying agent used in the treatment of cold sores.

What You Need To Know: Practically all wood and vegetation contain small amounts of some form of natural tannin in leaves, twigs, bark, wood or fruit. In more substantial amounts, tannic acid has proven to be toxic by ingestion and inhalation – it has been shown to have a damaging effect on the liver – and for this reason it is seldom used.

The International Agency for Research on Cancer has concluded that this substance is unclassifiable as to carcinogenicity in humans. No data were available in humans, and there was limited evidence of carcinogenicity in animals.[685]

Tara gum (E417)

FOOD ADDITIVE: THICKENING AGENT; STABILIZER

Regulations: EC permitted for all foodstuffs following the *quantum satis* principle (except those specified in Table 2 on pp. 15–16 and in Appendix B on pp. 469ff). May not be used to produce dehydrated foodstuffs intended to rehydrate on ingestion. Directive 95/2/EC.

Acceptable Daily Intake: Not specified.

What It Is: Derived from the tara bush (*caesalpinia spinosa*), native to Peru, Ecuador and now also grown in Kenya. Similar in viscosity to guar gum (see p. 252)

What You Need To Know: In experiments with human gastric and duodenal juice there was no evidence that tara seed meal is digestible or degradable.[686]

Tartaric acid esters of mono- and diglycerides of fatty acids (E472d)

FOOD ADDITIVE: EMULSIFIER; STABILIZER; SEQUESTRANT

Regulations: EC permitted for all foodstuffs following the *quantum satis* principle (except those specified in Table 2 on pp. 15–16 and in Appendix B on pp. 469ff). Directive 95/2/EC.

Acceptable Daily Intake: Not specified.

What It Is: Consists of esters of glycerol with tartaric acid and fatty acids. Its constituents are also components of DATEM (E472e).

What You Need To Know: In 1992 the British government's Food Advisory Committee recommended that this substance be provisionally acceptable for use in food, pending receipt of toxicity studies on DATEM.[687]

Tartaric acid (L(+)-) (E334)

FOOD ADDITIVE: ACIDULANT; SEQUESTRANT; SYNERGIST FOR ANTIOXIDANTS

Regulations: EC permitted for all foodstuffs following the *quantum satis* principle (except those specified in Table 2 on pp. 15–16 and in Appendix B on pp. 469ff). Directive 95/2/EC.

Acceptable Daily Intake: 0 – 30 group acceptable daily intake for tartaric acid and its sodium, potassium salts.

What It Is: First isolated in 1769 from the waste products of the wine industry, and still obtained from the same source today. Tartaric acid has a strongly tart taste, and gives a characteristic flavour to the acid foods – such as grapes, currants, raspberries, lemons and oranges – in which it is naturally present. Both tartaric acid (see p. 433) and monopotassium tartrate (see p. 365) are common ingredients of baking powders. Apart from flavouring natural and artificial beverages, jellies and preserves, tartaric acid will 'mop up' undesirable oxidants in foods, by chemically combining with them and thus rendering them inactive. It has been used in this way to stabilize beef, mutton tallow and lard, and has also been successfully used on soya bean oil, ground dry spices, milk products and cheese.

Tartrazine (E102)
FOOD ADDITIVE: FOOD COLOUR

Regulations: EC permitted to be used singly or in combination with other colours in the following foods up to the total maximum level specified.

- Non-alcoholic flavoured drinks, maximum level: 100 mg/l
- Candied fruits and vegetables, Mostarda di frutta, maximum level: 200 mg/kg
- Preserves of red fruits, maximum level: 200 mg/kg
- Confectionery, maximum level: 300 mg/kg
- Decorations and coatings, maximum level: 500 mg/kg
- Fine bakery wares (e.g. viennoiserie, biscuits, cakes and wafers), maximum level: 200 mg/kg
- Edible ices, maximum level: 150 mg/kg
- Flavoured processed cheese, maximum level: 100 mg/kg
- Desserts including flavoured milk products, maximum level: 150 mg/kg
- Sauces, seasonings (for example, curry powder, tandoori), pickles, relishes, chutney and piccalilli, maximum level: 500 mg/kg
- Mustard, maximum level: 300 mg/kg
- Fish paste and crustacean paste, maximum level: 100 mg/kg; Pre-cooked crustaceans, maximum level: 250 mg/kg; Salmon substitutes, maximum level: 500 mg/kg; Surimi, maximum level: 500 mg/kg; Fish roe, maximum level: 300 mg/kg; Smoked fish, maximum level: 100 mg/kg
- Snacks: dry, savoury potato, cereal or starch-based snack products: Extruded or expanded savoury snack products, maximum

level: 200 mg/kg; Other savoury snack products and savoury coated nuts, maximum level: 100 mg/kg
- Edible cheese rind and edible casings, maximum level: *quantum satis*
- Complete formulae for weight control intended to replace total daily food intake or an individual meal, maximum level: 50 mg/kg
- Complete formulae and nutritional supplements for use under medical supervision, maximum level: 50 mg/kg
- Liquid food supplements/dietary integrators, maximum level: 100 mg/l
- Solid food supplements/dietary integrators, maximum level: 300 mg/kg
- Soups, maximum level: 50 mg/kg
- Meat and fish analogues based on vegetable proteins, maximum level: 100 mg/kg
- Spirituous beverages (including products less than 15 % alcohol by volume), except those mentioned in Annex II or III, maximum level: 200 mg/l
- Aromatized wines, aromatized wine-based drinks and aromatized wine-product cocktails as mentioned in Regulation (EEC) No 1601/91, except those mentioned in Annex II or III, maximum level: 200 mg/l
- Fruit wines (still or sparkling) cider (except cidre bouche) and perry, aromatized fruit wines, cider and perry, maximum level: 200 mg/l. Directive 94/36/EC.

Acceptable Daily Intake: 0 – 7.5.

What It Is: A synthetic yellow monoazo dye.

What You Need To Know: Perhaps the most reviled food additive of recent years, tartrazine may cause allergic reactions in sensitive individuals (perhaps 15 per cent of the population), may be a cause of asthmatic attacks, and has been implicated in bouts of hyperactivity disorder in children.[688]

People who suffer from asthma, rhinitis or urticaria may find their symptoms become worse following consumption of foods or beverages containing azo dyes. Such people may be mistakenly thought to be suffering from specific food allergies.[689]

Terebene

MEDICINAL SUBSTANCE: FLAVOURING; EXPECTORANT;
ANTIMICROBIAL

What It Is: A chemical combination of turpentine oil and
sulphuric acid, used similarly to turpentine oil (see p. 442).

Thaumatin (E957)

FOOD ADDITIVE: SWEETENER; FLAVOUR ENHANCER

Regulations: EC permitted for the following foods up to the
total maximum usable dose specified.

- Confectionery with no added sugar, maximum usable dose:
  50 mg/kg; Cocoa- or dried-fruit-based confectionery, energy-
  reduced or with no added sugar, maximum usable dose: 50 mg/kg
- Chewing gum with no added sugar, maximum usable dose:
  50 mg/kg
- Vitamins and dietary preparations, maximum usable dose:
  400 mg/kg
- EC permitted for chewing gum with added sugars, maximum level:
  10 mg/kg. Directive 94/35/EC.

Acceptable Daily Intake: Not specified.

What It Is: A mixture of extremely sweet proteins (leaving a
liquorice aftertaste) extracted from the fruit of the West
African plant *Thaumatococcus daniellii.*

What You Need To Know: A long history of use by inhabitants
of Ghana and the Côte d'Ivoire, without observed adverse
effects, suggests thaumatin's safety. Scientific studies do not
raise carcinogenic or reproductive concerns.[690]

Thermally oxidized soya bean oil interacted with mono- and diglycerides of fatty acids (TOSOM) (E479b)

FOOD ADDITIVE: EMULSIFIER; ANTISPATTERING AGENT

Regulations: EC permitted for fat emulsions for frying
purposes, maximum level: 5 g/kg. Directive 95/2/EC.

Acceptable Daily Intake: 0 – 30.

What It Is: Made by oxidizing refined soya bean oil in air at 190–250°C. Used to impart anti-spattering properties to oleo-margarine when used for frying.

What You Need To Know: Scientific studies do not raise carcinogenic concerns.[691]

Thiabendazole (E233)

FOOD ADDITIVE: PRESERVATIVE

Regulations: EC permitted for surface treatment of: citrus fruit, maximum level: 6 mg/kg; bananas, maximum level: 3 mg/kg. Directive 95/2/EC.

Acceptable Daily Intake: 0 – 0.1.

What It Is: Made by reaction of 4-thiazolecarboxamide with o-phenylenediamine in polyphosphoric acid. Used as a fungicide in the post-harvest treatment of fruits to protect against microbial damage, has also been used in the treatment of Dutch elm disease in trees.

What You Need To Know: Has also been used as anthelmintic (anti-worm) medication. When used in this way (i.e. administered in therapeutic doses) adverse effects of thiabendazole are usually mild and transient, generally occurring 3–4 hours after administration of the drug and lasting 2–8 hours. Up to one-third of patients treated with the recommended dosage of thiabendazole have experienced one or more adverse effects for several hours. The most frequent adverse effects are anorexia, nausea, vomiting, and dizziness. Diarrhoea, epigastric distress, weariness, drowsiness, and headache occur less frequently. Giddiness, seizures, vertigo, paresthesia, and psychic disturbances may also occur. Hypersensitivity reactions consisting of pruritus, fever, facial flush, chills, conjunctival infection, rashes, anaphylaxis, erythema multiforme (including Stevens-Johnson syndrome, which may be fatal), and lymphaden-opathy have been reported in some patients receiving thiabendazole.[692]

Thymol

MEDICINAL SUBSTANCE: ANTISEPTIC AND ANTIFUNGAL

What It Is: A menthol-like compound which was originally extracted from the volatile oil of the herb thyme, now produced synthetically. It has been used in ointments, inhalants, decongestants, lozenges and mouthwashes, once also used to expel worms and other intestinal parasites, to preserve documents, art objects, and urine.

What You Need To Know: It is a mild local irritant on the skin. Resembles phenol (see pp. 336–7) in its systemic actions but is less toxic. If consumed in toxic amounts, adverse effects may include stomach-ache, nausea, vomiting, hyperactivity; uncommonly convulsions, coma, cardiac and respiratory collapse.[693]

Tin

See Stannous chloride

Titanium dioxide (E171)

FOOD ADDITIVE: FOOD COLOUR

Regulations: EC permitted at *quantum satis* in all foods except those to which the EC only permits certain colours to be added (Appendix C, pp. 476ff) and those to which the EC forbids the adding of colours (Appendix D, pp. 482ff). Directive 94/36/EC.

Acceptable Daily Intake: Not specified.

What It Is: Can be obtained by extraction from ilmenite (a mineral composed of iron and titanium oxide). The unrefined ores are used in the manufacture of titanium metal and alloys. Titanium dioxide is used principally as a pigment in paints, varnishes, plastics, lacquers, enamels and glazes, and in ointments or lotions as a sun block. In food, its intensely white colouring can be used in the panning of sugar confectionery.

What You Need To Know: Titanium compounds are generally considered to be poorly absorbed upon ingestion and inhalation. However, detectable amounts of titanium can be found in the blood, brain and parenchymatous organs of individuals in the general population; the highest concentrations are found in the hilar lymph nodes and the lungs. Titanium is excreted with urine.[694] An analysis of elements present in minor or trace quantities in various toothpastes has shown that the intake of titanium from toothpaste could exceed that obtained from food by a factor of five.[695]

The International Agency for Research on Cancer has concluded that this substance is unclassifiable as to carcinogenicity in humans. There was inadequate evidence for the carcinogenicity of titanium dioxide in humans, and there was limited evidence of carcinogenicity in animals.[696]

A bioassay for titanium dioxide for possible carcinogenicity was conducted on behalf of the US Department of Health, Education and Welfare (National Toxicology Program). It was concluded that under the conditions of the bioassay, titanium dioxide was not carcinogenic by the oral route for rats or mice.[697]

Tocopherol-rich extract (E306)
FOOD ADDITIVE: ANTIOXIDANT
Regulations: EC permitted for all foodstuffs following the *quantum satis* principle (except those specified in Table 2 on pp. 15–16 and in Appendix B on pp. 469ff). Directive 95/2/EC.
Acceptable Daily Intake: 0.15 – 2 group acceptable daily intake for tocopherols.
What It Is: See Alpha-tocopherol.

Tragacanth (E413)
FOOD ADDITIVE: THICKENING AGENT; STABILIZER; EMULSIFIER; CARRIER
Regulations: EC permitted for all foodstuffs following the *quantum satis* principle (except those specified in Table 2 on pp. 15–16 and in Appendix B on pp. 469ff).

EC permitted as carrier. Restricted use: none. Directive 95/2/EC.

Acceptable Daily Intake: Not specified.

What It Is: One of the oldest natural emulsifiers known, tragacanth gum has been used for at least two thousand years. Made from the dried gummy exudate of *Astragalus*, a small thorny bush native to the dry mountainous areas of Syria, Turkey and Iran (the largest producer). It is the most viscous of all the plant gums, and thus finds uses in salad dressings, ice-creams, sauces, and confectionery and bakery goods.

What You Need To Know: Capable of causing allergic reactions, which may occur as a result of inhalation or oral ingestion. It has a laxative action, and tends to increase the size and water content of stools. When taken with cholesterol-rich foods, it will tend to decrease the absorption of cholesterol into the system. Scientific studies do not raise mutagenic or reproductive concerns.[698]

Triammonium citrate (E380)

FOOD ADDITIVE: BUFFERING AGENT

Regulations: EC permitted for all foodstuffs following the *quantum satis* principle (except those specified in Table 2 on pp. 15–16 and in Appendix B on pp. 469ff). Directive 95/2/EC.

Acceptable Daily Intake: Not specified.

What It Is: A salt of citric acid (see pp. 202–4) used to stabilize the desired degree of acidity in products.

Triclocarban

MEDICINAL SUBSTANCE: ANTIMICROBIAL

What It Is: Also called 3,4,4'-trichlorocarbanilide (or TCC), triclocarban is effective against a broad spectrum of bacteria and also against fungi. Its main use is in deodorant soaps.

What You Need To Know: Does not appear to be a major irritant or sensitizer.[699] Absorption through human skin appears to be very low, although there is a report of two cases of convulsions attributed to antiseptic soap containing trichloro-carbanilide.[700] [701]

Triethyl citrate (E1505)

FOOD ADDITIVE: CARRIER

Regulations: EC permitted for dried egg white, maximum level: *quantum satis.*

EC permitted as carrier. Restricted use: none. Directive 95/2/EC.

What It Is: Made by a reaction of citric acid and ethyl alcohol. A whipping aid for egg whites, used to restore the bounce they lose during processing (e.g. freezing, pasteurization, etc). It increases the final volume of the whipped white – useful for meringues etc. Also used as a plasticizer for cellulose, a solvent for nitrocellulose and natural resins, in paint removers, and as a perfume base.

What You Need To Know: See citric acid (see pp. 202–4).

Triphosphates (i) pentasodium triphosphate (ii) pentapotassium triphosphate (E451)

FOOD ADDITIVE: TEXTURIZER

Regulations: EC permitted to be used similarly to phosphoric acid (E338). Directive 95/2/EC.

Acceptable Daily Intake: Maximum tolerable daily intake 70 expressed as phosphorous from all sources.

What It Is: Polyphosphates and salts of tripolyphosphoric acid. Pentasodium triphosphate (STPP) is used to improve the whipping qualities of egg-containing products, e.g. angel food cake mix, tenderizes tinned peas and beans, and helps to retain moisture in meat products. Pentapotassium triphosphate (KTPP) is completely interchangeable with STPP and is generally only used for low-sodium products, or where the astringent flavour of STPP would be unacceptable. Most pentasodium triphosphate production is used as a phosphate builder (conditioner) for home laundry detergents and for automatic dishwashing detergents.

What You Need To Know: Adverse effects following ingestion of large amounts of pentasodium triphosphate (e.g. after consuming detergents) include nausea, vomiting, and diarrhoea, fall of blood pressure, slow pulse, cyanosis (turning blue), coma and sometimes tetany as a result of the reduction in ionic calcium.[702][703] Even though patients recover from immediate damage from acute poisoning by ingestion, eosophageal stricture can occur weeks, months, or years later to make swallowing difficult.

Turpentine oil

MEDICINAL SUBSTANCE: COUNTER-IRRITANT

What It Is: Turpentine oil is produced from pine trees, and used externally as a rub or ointment to relieve deep-seated pain.

What You Need To Know: The vapours can cause eye irritation, headache, dizziness and nausea.[704] Men exposed to a concentration of 720 to 1,100 parts per million complain of chest pain, and visual disturbances.[705] It is a skin irritant and can cause dermatitis or chemical burns; capable of penetrating the skin to cause systemic effects.[706] When consumed, as little as 15 ml has proven fatal to a child, but a few children have survived 3 ounces. The mean lethal dose for adults probably lies between 4 and 6 ounces.[707]

Urea

See Carbamide.

Vegetable carbon (E153)

Regulations: EC permitted at *quantum satis* in all foods except those to which the EC only permits certain colours to be added (Appendix C, p. 476) and those to which the EC forbids the adding of colours (Appendix D, p. 482). Directive 94/36/EC. See Carbon Black.

Wintergreen

MEDICINAL SUBSTANCE: COUNTER-IRRITANT

What It Is: The small, shrubby creeping evergreen Wintergreen plant (*Gaultheria procumbens*) produces a fragrant oil which is approximately 99 per cent methyl salicylate (see p. 313).

Xanthan gum (E415)

FOOD ADDITIVE: THICKENING AGENT; STABILIZER; CARRIER

Regulations: EC permitted for all foodstuffs following the *quantum satis* principle (except those specified in Table 2 on pp. 15–16 and in Appendix B on pp. 469ff). May not be used to produce dehydrated foodstuffs intended to rehydrate on ingestion.

EC permitted as carrier. Restricted use: none. Directive 95/2/EC.

Acceptable Daily Intake: Not specified.

What It Is: The gum that made Peoria famous, xanthan was developed there by the US Department of Agriculture as part of a programme to find bold new uses for corn products. It is made by fermenting dextrose (from corn) with bacteria normally found on cabbage leaves. The result is a cream-coloured powder which, uniquely among gums, does not alter its viscosity (thickness) at any temperature from freezing to boiling point – a gum that doesn't thicken upon cooling is God's gift to the food-processing industry. Widely used in salad dressings and chocolate syrup (pour them straight from the fridge), gravy (prevents it from over-thickening) and in sauces, desserts and baked goods. Low-calorie dressings are especially suitable for xanthan, since it passes through the human digestive system unabsorbed and unmetabolized (no calories) while giving the dressing an oily mouth-feel.

What You Need To Know: It has been used as a bulking agent in experiments which have sought to produce weight loss by replacing calorie-yielding foods with xanthan gum. No adverse effects at up to 10 – 13 g daily intake. Scientific studies do not raise carcinogenic or reproductive concerns.[708]

Xylitol (E967)

FOOD ADDITIVE: SWEETENER; HUMECTANT; CARRIER

Regulations: EC permitted for the following foods up to the total maximum usable dose specified.

- Desserts and similar products, maximum usable dose: *quantum satis*; Water-based flavoured desserts, energy-reduced or with no added sugar, maximum usable dose: *quantum satis*; Milk- and milk-derivative-based preparations, energy-reduced or with no added sugar, maximum usable dose: *quantum satis*
- Fruit- and vegetable-based desserts, energy-reduced or with no added sugar, maximum usable dose: *quantum satis*; Egg-based desserts, energy-reduced or with no added sugar, maximum usable dose: *quantum satis*; Cereal-based desserts, energy-reduced or with no added sugar, maximum usable dose: *quantum satis*; Fat-based desserts, energy-reduced or with no added sugar, maximum usable dose: *quantum satis*
- Breakfast cereals or cereal-based products, energy-reduced or with no added sugar, maximum usable dose: *quantum satis*
- Edible ices, energy-reduced or with no added sugar, maximum usable dose: *quantum satis*
- Jams, jellies, marmalades and crystallized fruit, energy-reduced, maximum usable dose: *quantum satis;* reduced or with no added sugar, maximum usable dose: *quantum satis*
- Fruit preparations, energy-reduced or with no added sugar, with the exception of those intended for the manufacture of fruit-juice-based drinks, maximum usable dose: *quantum satis*
- Confectionery, maximum usable dose: *quantum satis*; Confectionery with no added sugar, maximum usable dose: *quantum satis*; Dried-fruit-based confectionery, energy-reduced or with no added sugar, maximum usable dose: *quantum satis*; Starch-based confectionery, energy-reduced or with no added sugar, maximum usable dose: *quantum satis*
- Cocoa-based products, energy-reduced or with no added sugar,

maximum usable dose: *quantum satis*; Cocoa-, milk-, dried-fruit- or fat-based sandwich spreads, energy-reduced or with no added sugar, maximum usable dose: *quantum satis*

- Chewing gum with no added sugar, maximum usable dose: *quantum satis*
- Sauces, maximum usable dose: *quantum satis*
- Mustard, maximum usable dose: *quantum satis*
- Fine bakery products, energy-reduced or with no added sugar, maximum usable dose: *quantum satis*
- For purposes other than sweetening, EC permitted for foodstuffs in general (including frozen and deep-frozen unprocessed fish, crustaceans, molluscs and cephalopods, and liqueurs; excluding those foodstuffs referred to in Article 2(3)). Maximum level: *quantum satis*
- EC permitted as carrier. Restricted use: none. Directive 94/35/EC.

Acceptable Daily Intake: Not specified.

What It Is: A polyol, or polyhydric alcohol, produced by hydrogenation of xylose (wood sugar, often from birch trees). See Propylene glycol for a description of the polyols.

Zinc chloride

MEDICINAL SUBSTANCE: ASTRINGENT

What It Is: Made by the action of hydrochloric acid on zinc or zinc oxide. A caustic agent which is sometimes used on the skin, often formulated with other keratolytic substances in products such as corn and callous removers. In very dilute form it is sometimes used as a mouthwash.

What You Need To Know: Zinc chloride appears to be more corrosive and more toxic than zinc sulphate.[709] Seventy workers were exposed to an accidental release of zinc chloride from smoke generators. Ten died immediately or within a few hours and 25 experienced severe respiratory inflammation. The toxicity of zinc chloride is probably due to the formation of hydrochloric acid.[710]

Zinc oxide

MEDICINAL SUBSTANCE: ASTRINGENT

What It Is: Made by oxidizing metallic zinc, used on the surface of the skin to reduce irritation. Calamine consists of pink powder containing zinc oxide (not less than 98 per cent) and a small amount of ferric oxide for colour. Has a mild astringent and antiseptic action, has been used in skin diseases and infections such as eczema, impetigo, ringworm, varicose ulcers, pruritus, and psoriasis.

What You Need To Know: Zinc oxide powder produces relatively little systemic disturbance.[711] Inhaling fumes of zinc oxide, on the other hand, results in a malaria-like illness whose symptoms include chills and fever, nausea, and vomiting, dryness of the throat, cough, fatigue, yawning, weakness, and aching of the head and body. The condition lasts a day and is never fatal. Workers are more susceptible on Mondays, and on weekdays following a holiday, than on other workdays.[712]

Zinc pyrithione

MEDICINAL SUBSTANCE: FUNGICIDE; BACTERICIDE

What It Is: An ingredient of anti-dandruff shampoos.

What You Need To Know: It is effective in controlling dandruff, although its mode of action is not certain. If dandruff is caused by yeast-like micro-organisms, then zinc pyrithione may work by reducing the number of organisms on the scalp. Alternatively, zinc pyrithione may work by reducing the rate at which cells grow and multiply. It prolongs its action by residually adhering to the skin after shampoo and rinse.[713] Results from patch-testing with a zinc pyrithione hair-dressing cream (0.25 per cent) suggest that 72 hours after application the product possessed an extremely low index of sensitization in humans.[714]

BRIEF GLOSSARY OF TERMS

ACID   Substance which increases the acidity of a foodstuff and/or imparts a sour taste to it. Also see alkali.

ACIDITY REGULATOR   Substance which alters or controls the acidity or alkalinity of a foodstuff.

ADJUVANT   Substance which aids another to accomplish its function.

ALKALI   Alkalis (also known as bases) and acids can react with each other to produce a neutral solution. The strength of a solution of an acid or alkali is designated by its pH on a scale of 0 to 14. A pH of 7 is defined as neutral; solutions with a lower pH are acidic, and those with a higher pH are basic, or alkaline. In food processing, acids and alkalis are carefully used together to control the overall acidity or alkalinity of the finished product.

ANALGESIC   Substance which relieves pain.

ANTICAKING AGENT   Substance which reduces the tendency of individual particles of a foodstuff to adhere to one another.

ANTIFOAMING AGENT   Substance which prevents or reduces foaming.

ANTIINFLAMMATORY   Substance which counteracts inflammation.

ANTIBACTERIAL   Substance which kills or inhibits the growth of bacteria.

ANTIBIOTIC   Substance that literally 'kills life', but is used in medicine to describe a chemical that is produced by a micro-organism which can kill or inhibit the growth of other micro-organisms. Penicillin is an example of an antibiotic produced from the *Penicillium* family of fungi, which is effective against the bacteria causing a wide range of infections.

ANTIEMETIC   Substance which prevents or allieviates sickness and vomiting.

ANTIFLATULENT   Substance which relieves or prevents flatulence (internal air or gas).

ANTIFUNGAL   Substance which can kill or inhibit the growth of fungi.

ANTIMICROBIAL   Substance which can kill or inhibit the growth of micro-organisms.

ANTIOXIDANT   Substance which prolongs the shelf-life of foodstuffs by protecting them against deterioration caused by oxidation, such as fat rancidity and colour changes.

ANTIPRURITIC   Substance which relieves or prevents itching.

ANTIPYRETIC   Substance which reduces fever.

ANTISECRETORY   Substance which inhibits or diminishes secretions.

ANTISEPTIC   Literally, a substance which 'prevents decay or putrefaction': antiseptics are usually applied to the skin in order to kill or inhibit the growth of disease-causing micro-organisms.

ANTISPASMODIC   Substance which relieves muscle spasm.

ANTITUSSIVE   Substance which relieves or prevents coughing.

BACTERICIDE   Substance that kills bacteria.

BACTERIOSTATIC   Substance which inhibits the growth of, but doesn't necessarily kill, bacteria.

BACTERIUM   One-celled micro-organism, not having a nucleus, that reproduces by dividing itself (plural – bacteria).

BULKING AGENT   Substance which contributes to the volume of a foodstuff without contributing significantly to its available energy value (calories).

CARRIER, INCLUDING CARRIER SOLVENT   Substance used to dissolve, dilute, disperse or otherwise physically modify a food additive without altering its technological function (and without exerting any technological effect itself) in order to facilitate its handling, application or use.

CATALYST   A substance that enables, or speeds up, a chemical reaction while not being changed itself. Catalysts that slow down reactions are called inhibitors.

COUNTER-IRRITANT   Substance which when applied to the skin stimulates it, resulting in reduced perception of deeper-seated pain.

DISINFECTANT   Substance used to disinfect (i.e. render free from infectious organisms) objects such as surgical instruments – or the kitchen floor.

EMETIC   Substance which produces vomiting.

EMULSIFIER   Substance which makes it possible to form or maintain a homogenous mixture of two or more immiscible phases such as oil and water in a foodstuff.

EMULSIFYING SALT   Substance which converts proteins contained in cheese into a dispersed form and thereby brings about homogenous distribution of fat and other components.

ESTER   Esters are organic compounds formed by the reaction of an alcohol with an acid. Simple esters occur in fruits and flowers – most have a pleasant, fruity odour or a waxy appearance and touch. Naturally occurring vegetable oils and fats are esters of glycerol. Esters can be hydrolysized to restore the acid and alcohol. They may be used as solvents for paints and lacquers, in drugs, cosmetics, perfumes, food flavours, plasticizers, plastics and explosives.

EXCIPIENT Substance which acts as a vehicle for a drug, not usually an active ingredient.

EXPECTORANT Substance which is intended to help you cough up sputum and so clear the bronchial airways.

FIRMING AGENT Substance which makes or keeps tissues of fruit or vegetables firm or crisp, or interacts with gelling agents to produce or strengthen a gel.

FLAVOUR ENHANCER Substance which enhances the existing taste and/or odour of a foodstuff.

FLOUR TREATMENT AGENT (OTHER THAN EMULSIFIERS) Substance which is added to flour or dough to improve its baking quality.

FOAMING AGENT Substance which makes it possible to form a homogenous dispersion of a gaseous phase in a liquid or solid foodstuff.

FUNGUS Single-celled organism whose cells include a true nucleus. The group includes yeasts, mushrooms, moulds, etc.

GELLING AGENT Substance which gives a foodstuff texture through formation of a gel.

GERM General name applied to any disease-causing micro-organism.

GERMICIDE Substance which kills disease-causing micro-organisms.

GLAZING AGENT (INCLUDING LUBRICANTS) Substance which, when applied to the external surface of a foodstuff, imparts a shiny appearance or provides a protective coating.

HUMECTANT Substance which prevents foodstuffs from drying out by counteracting the effect of an atmosphere having a low degree of humidity, or promotes the dissolution of a powder in an aqueous medium.

HYDROLYSIS The word comes from Greek words meaning 'water' and 'dissolution' – hydrolysis is therefore generally a decomposition process in which the water breaks apart another substance to yield two or more different compounds (in some hydrolysis reactions, a water molecule reacts with the other compound by adding on to it). Catalysts are often used to bring about hydrolysis.

INORGANIC In chemistry, inorganic substances do not contain chains of connected carbon atoms, i.e. everything that is not classified as organic chemistry (see below).

KERATOLYTIC Substance which is a keratolye, i.e. which makes the horny layer of the skin soften and peel away.

MODIFIED STARCH Substance obtained by one or more chemical treatment of edible starches, which may have undergone a physical or enzymatic treatment, and may be acid or alkali thinned or bleached.

ORGANIC In chemistry, organic substances contain chains of connected carbon atoms. More than 2 million organic compounds are known – many are compounds found in nature. Also see inorganic.

PACKAGING GAS Gas other than air, introduced into a container before, during or after the placing of a foodstuff in that container.

PRESERVATIVE   Substance which prolongs the shelf-life of foodstuffs by protecting them against deterioration caused by micro-organisms.

PROPELLANT   Gas other than air which expels a foodstuff from a container.

QUANTUM SATIS   Means that no maximum level is specified. However, additives shall be used in accordance with good manufacturing practice, at a level not higher than is necessary to achieve the intended purpose and provided that the manufacturers do not mislead the consumer.

RAISING AGENT   Substance or combinations of substances which liberates gas and thereby increase the volume of a dough or a batter.

RUBEFACIENT   Substance which reddens the skin.

SALT   In chemistry, a salt is the result of a reaction between acids and alkalis (bases), and can be either an inorganic or organic chemical compound. Salts are abundant in the earth's crust and in the oceans.

SEQUESTRANT   Substance which forms chemical complexes with metallic ions.

STABILIZER   Substance which makes it possible to maintain the physico-chemical state of a foodstuff; stabilizers include substances which enable the maintenance of a homogenous dispersion of two or more immiscible substances in a foodstuff and include also substances which stabilize, retain or intensify an existing colour of a foodstuff.

SYMPATHOMIMETIC   A substance which influences the functioning of the sympathetic nervous system, the involuntary part of the nervous system that controls automatic functions such as blood vessel constriction, heart rate, gastrointestinal movements, pupil dilation, and glucose metabolism.

THICKENING AGENT   Substance which increases the viscosity of a foodstuff.

TOPICAL   Relating to a surface – usually the skin.

VIRUS   An infectious agent generally invisible even under the most powerful optical microscopes, which can only reproduce itself while resident in a living 'host' cell. There are three main categories – animal viruses, plant viruses, and bacterial viruses – according to their host cells.

APPENDIX A

WHAT THOSE E-NUMBERS REALLY MEAN:

**YOUR AT-A-GLANCE GUIDE TO WHAT THEY ARE
AND WHAT THEY DO**

You can use the following chart to quickly identify any E-number, and then refer to its entry in Part Two to learn more. An 'X' in the column under 'Health Concern' indicates that there is some relevant information in the 'What You Need To Know' section in Part Two.

E NUMBER	WHAT IT IS	WHAT IT DOES	HEALTH CONCERN
E100	Curcumin	colour	
E101	Riboflavin, Riboflavin-5'-phosphate	colour	
E102	Tartrazine	colour	
E104	Quinoline Yellow	colour	
E110	Sunset Yellow FCF, Orange Yellow S	colour	
E120	Cochineal, Carminic acid, Carmines	colour	

451

E NUMBER	WHAT IT IS	WHAT IT DOES	HEALTH CONCERN
E122	Azorubine, Carmoisine	colour	✖
E123	Amaranth	colour	✖
E124	Ponceau 4R, Cochineal Red A	colour	
E127	Erythrosine	colour	✖
E128	Red 2G	colour	
E129	Allura Red AC	colour	
E131	Patent Blue V	colour	✖
E132	Indigotine, Indigo carmine	colour	
E133	Brilliant Blue FCF	colour	✖
E140	Chlorophylls and Chlorophyllins: (i) Chlorophylls (ii) Chlorophyllins	colour	
E141	Copper complexes of chlorophylls and chlorophyllins (i) Copper complexes of chlorophylls (ii) Copper complexes of chlorophyllins	colour	
E142	Green S	colour	✖
E150a	Plain caramel (caramel colour class I)	colour	
E150b	Caustic sulphite caramel (caramel colour class II)	colour	
E150c	Ammonia caramel (caramel colour class III)	colour	✖
E150d	Sulphite ammonia caramel (caramel colour class IV)	colour	
E151	Brilliant Black BN	colour	✖
E153	Vegetable carbon (carbon black)	colour	✖
E154	Brown FK	colour	✖
E155	Brown HT (Chocolate Brown HT)	colour	
E160a	Carotenes (i) Mixed carotenes (ii) Beta-carotene	colour	

E NUMBER	WHAT IT IS	WHAT IT DOES	HEALTH CONCERN
E160b	Annatto, bixin, norbixin	colour	
E160c	Paprika extract, capsanthin, capsorubin	colour; flavouring agent	
E160d	Lycopene	colour	
E160e	Beta-apo-8'-carotenal (C 30) (apocarotenal)	colour	
E160f	Ethyl ester of beta-apo-8'-carotenic acid (C 30)	colour	
E161b	Lutein	colour	
E161g	Canthaxanthin	colour	
E162	Beetroot Red, betanin(e)	colour	
E163	Anthocyanins	colour	
E170	Calcium carbonate	colour; carrier; anticaking agent; stabilizer	
E171	Titanium dioxide	colour	✖
E172	Iron oxides and hydroxides	colour	
E173	Aluminium	colour	
E174	Silver	colour	
E175	Gold	colour	
E180	Litholrubine BK	colour	
E200	Sorbic acid	preservative	
E202	Potassium sorbate	preservative	
E203	Calcium sorbate	preservative	
E210	Benzoic acid	preservative	✖
E211	Sodium benzoate	preservative	
E212	Potassium benzoate	preservative	
E213	Calcium benzoate	preservative	
E214	Ethyl p-hydroxybenzoate	preservative	
E215	Sodium ethyl p-hydroxybenzoate	preservative	

E NUMBER	WHAT IT IS	WHAT IT DOES	HEALTH CONCERN
E216	Propyl p-hydroxybenzoate	preservative	
E217	Sodium propyl p-hydroxybenzoate	preservative	
E218	Methyl p-hydroxybenzoate	preservative	
E219	Sodium methyl p-hydroxybenzoate	preservative	
E220	Sulphur dioxide	preservative	✖
E221	Sodium sulphite	preservative	
E222	Sodium hydrogen sulphite	preservative	
E223	Sodium metabisulphite	preservative; bleaching agent	✖
E224	Potassium metabisulphite	preservative; antibrowning agent	
E226	Calcium sulphite	preservative	
E227	Calcium hydrogen sulphite	combined preservative and firming agent	
E228	Potassium hydrogen sulphite	preservative	
E230	Biphenyl (Diphenyl) (Phenyl benzene)	preservative	
E231	Orthophenyl phenol (2-hydroxybiphenyl)	preservative	
E232	Sodium orthophenyl phenol	preservative	✖
E233	Thiabendazole	preservative	
E234	Nisin	preservative	
E235	Natamycin (pimaricin)	preservative	
E239	Hexamethylene tetramine (hexamine)	preservative	
E242	Dimethyl dicarbonate	preservative; cold sterilizing agent	
E249	Potassium nitrite	preservative; colour fixative	✖

APPENDIX A

E NUMBER	WHAT IT IS	WHAT IT DOES	HEALTH CONCERN
E250	Sodium nitrite	preservative; colour fixative	
E251	Sodium nitrate	preservative; colour fixative	
E252	Potassium nitrate (saltpetre)	preservative; colour fixative	
E260	Acetic acid	flavouring agent; acidifier; preservative	
E261	Potassium acetate	preservative; buffer	
E262	Sodium acetates (i) Sodium acetate (ii) Sodium hydrogen acetate (sodium diacetate)	buffer; preservative	
E263	Calcium acetate	preservative; stabilizer; acidity regulator; carrier	
E270	Lactic acid	acidity regulator	
E280	Propionic acid	preservative	
E281	Sodium propionate	preservative	
E282	Calcium propionate	preservative	
E283	Potassium propionate	preservative	
E284	Boric acid	preservative	✖
E285	Sodium tetraborate (borax)	preservative	✖
E290	Carbon dioxide	carbonating agent; packaging gas; preservative; freezing agent; extraction solvent	
E296	Malic acid	acidifier; flavouring agent	
E297	Fumaric acid	acidulant; flavouring agent	

455

E NUMBER	WHAT IT IS	WHAT IT DOES	HEALTH CONCERN
E300	Ascorbic acid	antioxidant	
E301	Sodium ascorbate	antioxidant	
E302	Calcium ascorbate	antioxidant	
E304	Fatty acid esters of ascorbic acid (i) Ascorbyl palmitate (ii) Ascorbyl stearate	antioxidant	
E306	Tocopherol-rich extract	antioxidant	
E307	Alpha-tocopherol	antioxidant	
E308	Gamma-tocopherol	antioxidant	
E309	Delta-tocopherol	food additive	
E310	Propyl gallate	antioxidant	
E311	Octyl gallate	antioxidant	
E312	Dodecyl gallate	antioxidant	
E315	Erythorbic acid	antioxidant	
E316	Sodium erythorbate	antioxidant	
E320	Butylated hydroxyanisole (BHA)	antioxidant	✖
E321	Butylated hydroxytoluene (BHT)	antioxidant	✖
E322	Lecithins	antioxidant; emulsifier; carrier	
E325	Sodium lactate	antioxidant synergist; humectant; bodying agent	
E326	Potassium lactate	antioxidant	
E327	Calcium lactate	buffer; dough conditioner; yeast food	
E330	Citric acid	acidulant; antioxidant; sequestrant; synergist; flavouring agent	

E NUMBER	WHAT IT IS	WHAT IT DOES	HEALTH CONCERN
E331	Sodium citrates (i) Monosodium citrate (ii) Disodium citrate (iii) Trisodium citrate	emulsion stabilizer; buffer; sequestrant; carrier	
E332	Potassium citrates (i) Monopotassium citrate (ii) Tripotassium citrate	buffer; sequestrant; stabilizer; carrier	
E333	Calcium citrates (i) Monocalcium citrate (ii) Dicalcium citrate (iii) Tricalcium citrate	acidity regulator; firming agent; sequestrant	
E334	Tartaric acid (L(+)-)	acidulant; sequestrant; synergist for antioxidants	
E335	Sodium tartrates (i) Monosodium tartrate (ii) Disodium tartrate	sequestrant; stabilizer in meat products and sausage casings	
E336	Potassium tartrates (i) Monopotassium tartrate (ii) Dipotassium tartrate	stabilizer; sequestrant	
E337	Sodium potassium tartrate	buffer; emulsifier acidity regulator; sequestrant	
E338	Phosphoric acid	acidulant; sequestrant; synergist for antioxidants	✖
E339	Sodium phosphates (i) Monosodium phosphate (ii) Disodium phosphate (iii) Trisodium phosphate	sequestrant; emulsion stabilizer; buffer	
E340	Potassium phosphates (i) Monopotassium phosphate (ii) Dipotassium phosphate (iii) Tripotassium phosphate	buffer; sequestrant; stabilizer	

E NUMBER	WHAT IT IS	WHAT IT DOES	HEALTH CONCERN
E341	Calcium phosphates (i) Monocalcium phosphate (ii) Dicalcium phosphate (iii) Tricalcium phosphate	buffer; anticaking agent; carrier	
E350	Sodium malates (i) Sodium malate (ii) Sodium hydrogen malate	acidity regulator; flavouring agent	
E351	Potassium malate	seasoning agent; buffering agent	
E352	Calcium malates (i) Calcium malate (ii) Calcium hydrogen malate	seasoning agent; buffering agent	
E353	Metatartaric acid	other additive	
E354	Calcium tartrate	acidity regulator	
E355	Adipic acid	neutralizing agent; buffer	
E356	Sodium adipate	acidity regulator	
E357	Potassium adipate	acidity regulator	
E363	Succinic acid	flavour enhancer; acidity regulator	
E380	Triammonium citrate	buffering agent	
E385	Calcium disodium ethylene diamine tetra-acetate (Calcium disodium EDTA)	antioxidant; preservative; sequestrant	
E401	Sodium alginate	thickening agent; stabilizer	
E402	Potassium alginate	thickening agent; stabilizer	
E404	Calcium alginate	thickening agent; stabilizer	
E405	Propane-1,2-diol alginate	thickening agent; emulsifier; stabilizer; carrier	

E NUMBER	WHAT IT IS	WHAT IT DOES	HEALTH CONCERN
E406	Agar	thickening agent; gelling agent; stabilizer; carrier	
E407	Carrageenan	carrier; thickening agent; gelling agent; stabilizer	✖
E410	Locust bean gum	carrier; thickening agent; stabilizer	
E412	Guar gum	thickening agent; stabilizer; carrier	
E413	Tragacanth	thickening agent; stabilizer; emulsifier; carrier	
E414	Acacia gum (gum arabic)	carrier; thickening agent; stabilizer; emulsifier	
E415	Xanthan gum	thickening agent; stabilizer; carrier	
E416	Karaya gum (gum sterculia)	emulsifier; stabilizer; thickening agent	
E417	Tara gum	thickening agent; stabilizer	
E418	Gellan gum	thickening agent; stabilizer; gelling agent	
E420	Sorbitol (i) Sorbitol (ii) Sorbitol syrup	sweetener; humectant; sequestrant; texturizer; stabilizer; carrier	
E421	Mannitol	sweetener; humectant; stabilizer; carrier	
E422	Glycerol	humectant; bodying agent; solvent; plasticizer	
E431	Polyoxyethylene (40) stearate	emulsifier	
E440	Pectins (i) pectin (ii) amidated pectin	thickening agent; stabilizer; gelling agent	

E NUMBER	WHAT IT IS	WHAT IT DOES	HEALTH CONCERN
E442	Ammonium phosphatides	emulsifier; carrier	
E444	Sucrose acetate isobutyrate	density adjusting agent; cloud-producing agent	
E445	Glycerol esters of wood rosins	density adjustment agent for flavouring oils in beverage	
E450	Diphosphates (i) Disodium diphosphate (ii) Trisodium diphosphate (iii) Tetrasodium diphosphate (iv) Dipotassium diphosphate (v) Tetrapotassium diphosphate (vi) Dicalcium diphosphate (vii) Calcium dihydrogen diphosphate	buffering agent; sequestrant; leavening agent	
E451	Triphosphates (i) Pentasodium triphosphate (ii) Pentapotassium triphosphate	texturizer	
E452	Polyphosphates (i) Sodium polyphosphate (ii) Potassium polyphosphate (iii) Sodium calcium polyphosphate (iv) Calcium polyphosphates	emulsifier; sequestrant; texturizer	
E460	Cellulose (microcrystalline or powdered)	carrier; emulsifier; anticaking agent; stabilizer; dispersing agent	
E461	Methyl cellulose	thickening agent; emulsifier; stabilizer; carrier	
E463	Hydroxypropyl cellulose	emulsifier; thickening agent; stabilizer; binder; film coating; suspension agent; carrier	

E NUMBER	WHAT IT IS	WHAT IT DOES	HEALTH CONCERN
E464	Hydroxypropyl methyl cellulose	thickening agent; emulsifier; stabilizer; carrier	
E465	Ethyl methyl cellulose	thickening agent; emulsifier; stabilizer; foaming agent; carrier	
E466	Carboxy methyl cellulose, Sodium carboxy methyl cellulose	thickening agent; stabilizer; carrier	
E470a	Sodium, potassium and calcium salts of fatty acids	anticaking agent; emulsifier	
E470b	Magnesium salts of fatty acids	anticaking agent; emulsifier; carrier	
E471	Mono- and diglycerides of fatty acids	emulsifier; stabilizer; carrier	
E472a	Acetic acid esters of mono- and diglycerides of fatty acids	emulsifier; carrier	
E472b	Lactic acid esters of mono- and diglycerides of fatty acids	emulsifier	✖
E472c	Citric acid esters of mono- and diglycerides of fatty acids	emulsifier; stabilizer; dough conditioner; antioxidant; synergist; carrier	✖
E472d	Tartaric acid esters of mono- and diglycerides of fatty acids	emulsifier; stabilizer; sequestrant	
E472e	Mono- and diacetyl tartaric acid esters of mono- and diglycerides of fatty acids (DATEM)	emulsifier; carrier	
E472f	Mixed acetic and tartaric acid esters of mono- and diglycerides of fatty acids	emulsifier	
E473	Sucrose esters of fatty acids	emulsifier; carrier	✖

E NUMBER	WHAT IT IS	WHAT IT DOES	HEALTH CONCERN
E474	Sucroglycerides	emulsifier	
E475	Polyglycerol esters of fatty acids	emulsifier; carrier	
E476	Polyglycerol polyricinoleate	emulsifier	
E477	Propane-1,2-diol esters of fatty acids	emulsifier	
E479b	Thermally oxidized soya bean oil interacted with mono- and diglycerides of fatty acids (TOSOM)	emulsifier; antispattering agent	
E481	Sodium stearoyl-2-lactylate	emulsifier; stabilizer	
E482	Calcium stearoyl-2-lactylate	emulsifier; stabilizer	
E483	Stearyl tartrate	dough strengthening agent	
E500	Sodium carbonates (i) Sodium carbonate (ii) Sodium hydrogen carbonate (baking soda, bicarbonate of soda, sodium bicarbonate) (iii) Sodium sesquicarbonate	alkali; leavening agent; buffer	
E501	Potassium carbonates (i) Potassium carbonate (ii) Potassium hydrogen carbonate	alkali	
E503	Ammonium carbonates (i) Ammonium carbonate (ii) Ammonium hydrogen carbonate (ammonium bicarbonate)	acidity regulator; raising agent	
E504	Magnesium carbonates (i) Magnesium carbonate (ii) Magnesium hydroxide carbonate (syn.: Magnesium hydrogen carbonate)	anticaking and antibleaching agent; carrier	
E507	Hydrochloric acid	acid	

E NUMBER	WHAT IT IS	WHAT IT DOES	HEALTH CONCERN
E508	Potassium chloride	seasoning agent; gelling agent; yeast food	
E509	Calcium chloride	firming agent; carrier	
E511	Magnesium chloride	firming agent; colour retention agent; carrier	
E512	Stannous chloride	antioxidant; colour retention agent	✖
E513	Sulphuric acid	acid	
E514	Sodium sulphates (i) Sodium sulphate (ii) Sodium hydrogen sulphate	acidity regulator; carrier	
E515	Potassium sulphates (i) Potassium sulphate (ii) Potassium hydrogen sulphate	salt substitute; carrier	
E516	Calcium sulphate	yeast food; dough conditioner; sequestrant; firming agent; carrier	
E517	Ammonium sulphate	carrier; flour treatment agent; stabilizer	
E520	Aluminium sulphate	firming agent	
E521	Aluminium sodium sulphate	buffering agent; neutralizing agent; firming agent	
E522	Aluminium potassium sulphate	acidity regulator; stabilizer	
E523	Aluminium ammonium sulphate	stabilizer; firming agent	
E524	Sodium hydroxide (lye)	alkali	
E525	Potassium hydroxide	alkali	
E526	Calcium hydroxide	neutralizing agent; buffer; firming agent	
E527	Ammonium hydroxide	acidity regulator	
E528	Magnesium hydroxide	alkali; colour adjunct	

E NUMBER	WHAT IT IS	WHAT IT DOES	HEALTH CONCERN
E529	Calcium oxide	alkali; dough conditioner; yeast food	
E530	Magnesium oxide	anticaking agent; neutralizing agent	
E535	Sodium ferrocyanide	anticaking agent	
E536	Potassium ferrocyanide	anticaking agent	
E538	Calcium ferrocyanide	anticaking agent	
E541	Sodium aluminium phosphate, acidic	raising agent	
E551	Silicon dioxide	anticaking agent; carrier	
E552	Calcium silicate	anticaking agent; carrier	
E553a	Magnesium silicate (i), Magnesium trisilicate (ii) (asbestos-free)	anticaking agent	
E553b	Talc (asbestos-free)	anticaking agent; dusting powder; filter aid; carrier	✖
E554	Sodium aluminium silicate	anticaking agent	
E555	Potassium aluminium silicate	anticaking agent	
E556	Calcium aluminium silicate	anticaking agent	
E558	Bentonite	carrier; anticaking agent	
E559	Aluminium silicate (Kaolin)	anticaking agent; carrier	
E570	Fatty acids	defoaming agent; lubricant	
E574	Gluconic acid	acidity regulator; raising agent	
E575	Glucono-delta-lactone	acidulant; leavening agent; sequestrant	
E576	Sodium gluconate	sequestrant; yeast food	
E577	Potassium gluconate	yeast food; carrier	

E NUMBER	WHAT IT IS	WHAT IT DOES	HEALTH CONCERN
E578	Calcium gluconate	acidity regulator; firming agent; sequestrant	
E579	Ferrous gluconate	colouring adjunct	
E585	Ferrous lactate	colouring adjunct; nutrient	
E620	Glutamic acid	flavour enhancer; salt substitute	
E621	Monosodium glutamate	flavour enhancer	✖
E622	Monopotassium glutamate	flavour enhancer; salt substitute	
E623	Calcium diglutamate	flavour enhancer; salt substitute	
E624	Monoammonium glutamate	flavour enhancer; salt substitute	
E625	Magnesium diglutamate	flavour enhancer; salt substitute	
E626	Guanylic acid	flavour enhancer	✖
E627	Disodium guanylate	flavour enhancer	
E628	Dipotassium guanylate	flavour enhancer	
E629	Calcium guanylate	flavour enhancer	
E630	Inosinic acid	flavour enhancer	
E631	Disodium inosinate	flavour enhancer	
E632	Dipotassium inosinate	flavour enhancer	
E633	Calcium inosinate	flavour enhancer	
E634	Calcium 5'-ribonucleotides	flavour enhancer	
E635	Disodium 5'-ribonucleotides	flavour enhancer	
E640	Glycine and its sodium salt (aminoacetic acid)	food additive; carrier	
E900	Dimethyl polysiloxane (simethicone)	antifoaming agent; anticaking agent	

E NUMBER	WHAT IT IS	WHAT IT DOES	HEALTH CONCERN
E901	Beeswax, white and yellow	other additive; carrier	
E902	Candelilla wax	glazing agent; component of chewing gum base; surface finishing agent; carrier for flavour	
E903	Carnauba wax	glazing agent; component of chewing gum; carrier for flavour; surface treating agent	
E904	Shellac	coating, glazing and surface finishing agent	
E912	Montan acid esters	other additive	
E914	Oxidized polyethylene wax	other additive	
E927b	Carbamide (urea)	texturizer in chewing gum; yeast nutrient	
E938	Argon	food additive	
E939	Helium	processing aid	
E941	Nitrogen	packing gas; cryogenic freezant	
E942	Nitrous oxide	propellant	✖
E948	Oxygen	food additive	
E950	Acesulfame K	sweetener	
E951	Aspartame	sweetener	
E952	Cyclamic acid and its Na and Ca salts	sweetener	
E953	Isomalt	sweetener; carrier	
E954	Saccharin and its Na, K and Ca salts	sweetener	✖
E957	Thaumatin	sweetener; flavour enhancer	
E959	Neohesperidine DC	sweetener	

E NUMBER	WHAT IT IS	WHAT IT DOES	HEALTH CONCERN
E965	Maltitol	sweetener; humectant; stabilizer; carrier	
E966	Lactitol	sweetener; texturizer; carrier	
E967	Xylitol	sweetener; humectant; carrier	
E999	Quillaia extract	foaming agent	
E1105	Lysozyme	preservative	
E1200	Polydextrose	bulking agent; stabilizer; thickening agent; humectant; texturizer; carrier	
E1201	Polyvinylpyrrolidone (PVP)	bodying agent; stabilizer; clarifying agent; tableting adjunct; dispersing agent; carrier	
E1202	Polyvinylpolypyrrolidone (PVPP)	additive; carrier	
E1404	Oxidized starch	emulsifier; thickening agent; binder; carrier	
E1410	Monostarch phosphate	stabilizer; thickening agent; binder; carrier	
E1412	Distarch phosphate	stabilizer; thickening agent; binder; carrier	
E1413	Phosphated distarch phosphate	stabilizer; thickening agent; binder; carrier	
E1414	Acetylated distarch phosphate	emulsifier; thickening agent; binder; carrier	
E1420	Acetylated starch	stabilizer; thickening agent; binder; carrier	
E1422	Acetylated distarch adipate	stabilizer; thickening agent; binder; carrier	
E1440	Hydroxy propyl starch	emulsifier; thickening agent; binder; carrier	✖

E NUMBER	WHAT IT IS	WHAT IT DOES	HEALTH CONCERN
E1442	Hydroxy propyl distarch phosphate	stabilizer; thickening agent; binder; carrier	
E1450	Starch sodium octenyl succinate	stabilizer; thickening agent; binder; carrier	
E1505	Triethyl citrate	other additive; carrier	
E1518	Glyceryl triacetate (triacetin)	carrier; humectant	
E400 – 404	Alginic acid and its sodium, potassium, calcium and ammonium salts	thickening agent; stabilizer; carrier	
E432 – 436	Polysorbates 20, 40, 60, 65 and 80	emulsifier; dispersing agent; carrier	
E491 – 495	Sorbitan monostearate	emulsifier; carrier	

APPENDIX B

FOODSTUFFS IN WHICH A LIMITED NUMBER OF ADDITIVES MAY BE USED[715]

COCOA AND CHOCOLATE PRODUCTS

Additive: E330 Citric acid   **Maximum level:** 0.5 %

Additive: E322 Lecithins   **Maximum level:** *quantum satis*

Additive: E334 Tartaric acid   **Maximum level:** 0.5%

Additives: E422 Glycerol, E471 Mono- and diglycerides of fatty acids **Maximum level:** *quantum satis*

Additives: E170 Calcium carbonates, E500 Sodium carbonates, E501 Potassium carbonates, E503 Ammonium carbonates, E504 Magnesium carbonates, E524 Sodium hydroxide, E525 Potassium hydroxide, E526 Calcium hydroxide, E527 Ammonium hydroxide, E528 Magnesium hydroxide, E530 Magnesium oxide
Maximum level: 7% on dry matter without fat expressed as potassium carbonates

Additives: E414 Acacia gum, E440 Pectins
Maximum level: glazing agents only, *quantum satis*

FRUIT JUICES AND NECTARS

Additive: E300 Ascorbic acid   **Maximum level:** *quantum satis*

PINEAPPLE JUICE
Additive: E296 Malic acid   **Maximum level:** 3 g/l

NECTARS
Additive: E330 Citric acid   **Maximum level:** 5 g/l

Additive: E270 Lactic acid   **Maximum level:** 5 g/l

GRAPE JUICE
Additives: E170 Calcium carbonates, E336 Potassium tartrates
Maximum level: *quantum satis*

FRUIT JUICES
Additive: E330 Citric acid   **Maximum level:** 3 g/l

EXTRA JAM AND EXTRA JELLY
Additives: E440 Pectins, E270 Lactic acid, E296 Malic acid,
E300 Ascorbic acid, E327 Calcium lactate, E330 Citric acid,
E331 Sodium citrates, E333 Calcium citrates, E334 Tartaric acid,
E335 Sodium tartrates, E350 Sodium malates, E471 Mono- and
diglycerides of fatty acids
Maximum level: *quantum satis*

JAM, JELLIES AND MARMALADES AND OTHER SIMILAR FRUIT SPREADS INCLUDING LOW-CALORIE PRODUCTS
Additives: E440 Pectins, E270 Lactic acid, E296 Malic acid,
E300 Ascorbic acid, E327 Calcium lactate, E330 Citric acid,
E331 Sodium citrates, E333 Calcium citrates, E334 Tartaric acid,
E335 Sodium tartrates, E350 Sodium malates
Maximum level: *quantum satis*

Additives: E400 Alginic acid, E401 Sodium alginate, E402
Potassium alginate, E403 Ammonium alginate, E404 Calcium

470

alginate, E406 Agar, E407 Carrageenan, E410 Locust bean gum, E412 Guar gum, E415 Xanthan gum, E418 Gellan gum
Maximum level: 10 g/kg (individually or in combination)

Additives: E509 Calcium chloride, E524 Sodium hydroxide
Maximum level: *quantum satis*

PARTIALLY DEHYDRATED AND DEHYDRATED MILK

Additives: E300 Ascorbic acid, E301 Sodium ascorbate, E304 Fatty acid esters of ascorbic acid, E322 Lecithins, E331 Sodium citrates, E332 Potassium citrates, E407 Carrageenan, E500 (ii) Sodium bicarbonate, E501 (ii) Potassium bicarbonate, E509 Calcium chloride
Maximum level: *quantum satis*

STERILIZED, PASTEURIZED AND UHT CREAM, LOW-CALORIE CREAM AND PASTEURIZED LOW-FAT CREAM

Additives: E270 Lactic acid, E322 Lecithins, E325 Sodium lactate, E326 Potassium lactate, E327 Calcium lactate, E330 Citric acid, E331 Sodium citrates, E332 Potassium citrates, E333 Calcium citrates, E400 Alginic acid, E401 Sodium alginate, E402 Potassium alginate, E403 Ammonium alginate, E404 Calcium alginate, E406 Agar, E407 Carrageenan, E410 Locust bean gum, E415 Xanthan gum, E440 Pectins, E460 Celluloses, E461 Methyl cellulose, E463 Hydroxypropyl cellulose, E464 Hydroxypropyl methyl cellulose, E465, Ethyl methyl cellulose, E466 Carboxy methyl cellulose, Sodium carboxy methyl cellulose, E471 Mono- and diglycerides of fatty acids, E508 Potassium chloride, E509 Calcium chloride, E1404 Oxidized starch, E1410 Monostarch phosphate, E1412 Distarch phosphate, E1413 Phosphated distarch phosphate, E1414 Acetylated distarch phosphate, E1420 Acetylated starch, E1422 Acetylated distarch adipate, E1440 Hydroxy propyl starch, E1442 Hydroxy propyl distarch phosphate, E1450 Starch sodium octenyl succinate
Maximum level: *quantum satis*

FROZEN AND DEEP-FROZEN UNPROCESSED FRUIT AND VEGETABLES

Additives: E300 Ascorbic acid, E301 Sodium ascorbate, E302 Calcium ascorbate, E330 Citric acid
Maximum level: *quantum satis*

FRUIT COMPOTE, UNPROCESSED FISH, CRUSTACEANS AND MOLLUSCS, INCLUDING SUCH PRODUCTS FROZEN AND DEEP-FROZEN

Additives: E331 Sodium citrates, E332 Potassium citrates, E333 Calcium citrates
Maximum level: *quantum satis*

QUICK-COOK RICE

Additives: E471 Mono- and diglycerides of fatty acids, E472a Acetic acid esters of mono- and diglycerides of fatty acids
Maximum level: *quantum satis*

NON-EMULSIFIED OILS AND FATS OF ANIMAL OR VEGETABLE ORIGIN (EXCEPT VIRGIN OILS AND OLIVE OILS)

Additives: E304 Fatty acid esters of ascorbic acid, E306 Tocopherol-rich extract, E307 Alpha-tocopherol, E308 Gamma-tocopherol, E309 Delta-tocopherol
Maximum level: *quantum satis*

Additive: E322 Lecithins   **Maximum level:** 30 g/l

Additives: E471 Mono- and diglycerides of fatty acids
Maximum level: 10 g/l

Additives: E330 Citric acid, E331 Sodium citrates, E332 Potassium citrates, E333 Calcium citrates
Maximum level: *quantum satis*

REFINED OLIVE OIL, INCLUDING OLIVE POMACE OIL

Additive: E307 Alpha-tocopherol
Maximum level: 200 mg/l

RIPENED CHEESE

Additives: E170 Calcium carbonates, E504 Magnesium carbonates, E509 Calcium chloride, E575 Glucono-delta-lactone
Maximum level: *quantum satis*

MOZZARELLA AND WHEY CHEESE

Additives: E270 Lactic acid, E330 Citric acid, E575 Glucono-delta-lactone
Maximum level: *quantum satis*

CANNED AND BOTTLED FRUIT AND VEGETABLES

Additives: E260 Acetic acid, E261 Potassium acetate, E262 Sodium acetates, E263 Calcium acetate, E270 Lactic acid, E300 Ascorbic acid, E301 Sodium ascorbate, E302 Calcium ascorbate, E325 Sodium lactate, E326 Potassium lactate, E327 Calcium lactate, E330 Citric acid, E331 Sodium citrates, E332 Potassium citrates, E333 Calcium citrates, E334 Tartaric acid, E335 Sodium tartrates, E336 Potassium tartrates, E337 Sodium potassium tartrate, E509 Calcium chloride, E575 Glucono-delta-lactone
Maximum level: *quantum satis*

GEHAKT

Additives: E330 Citric acid, E331 Sodium citrates, E332 Potassium citrates, E333 Calcium citrates
Maximum level: *quantum satis*

PRE-PACKED PREPARATIONS OF FRESH MINCED MEAT

Additives: E300 Ascorbic acid, E301 Sodium ascorbate, E302 Calcium ascorbate, E330 Citric acid, E331 Sodium citrates, E332 Potassium citrates, E333 Calcium citrates
Maximum level: *quantum satis*

BREAD PREPARED SOLELY WITH THE FOLLOWING INGREDIENTS: WHEAT-FLOUR, WATER, YEAST OR LEAVEN, SALT

Additives: E260 Acetic acid, E261 Potassium acetate, E262 Sodium acetates, E263 Calcium acetate, E270 Lactic acid, E300 Ascorbic acid, E301 Sodium ascorbate, E302 Calcium ascorbate, E304 Fatty acid esters of ascorbic acid, E322 Lecithins, E325 Sodium lactate, E326 Potassium lactate, E327 Calcium lactate, E471 Mono- and diglycerides of fatty acids, E472a Acetic acid esters of mono- and diglycerides of fatty acids, E472d Tartaric acid esters of mono- and diglycerides of fatty acids, E472e Mono- and diacetyl tartaric acid esters of mono- and diglycerides of fatty acids, E472f Mixed acetic and tartaric acid esters of mono- and diglycerides of fatty acids
Maximum level: *quantum satis*

PAIN COURANT FRANÇAIS

Additives: E260 Acetic acid, E261 Potassium acetate, E262 Sodium acetates, E263 Calcium acetate, E270 Lactic acid, E300 Ascorbic acid, E301 Sodium ascorbate, E302 Calcium ascorbate, E304 Fatty acid esters of ascorbic acid, E322 Lecithins, E325 Sodium lactate, E326 Potassium lactate, E327 Calcium lactate, E471 Mono- and diglycerides of fatty acids
Maximum level: *quantum satis*

FRESH PASTA

Additives: E270 Lactic acid, E300 Ascorbic acid, E301 Sodium ascorbate, E322 Lecithins, E330 Citric acid, E334 Tartaric acid, E471 Mono- and diglycerides of fatty acids, E575 Glucono-delta-lactone
Maximum level: *quantum satis*

WINES AND SPARKLING WINES AND PARTIALLY FERMENTED GRAPE MUST

Additives: authorized in accordance with Regulations (EEC) No 822/87 (1), (EEC) No 4252/88 (2), (EEC) No 2332/92 (3) and (EEC) No 1873/84 (4) and their implementing regulations, in

accordance with Regulation (EEC) No 1873/84 authorizing the offer or disposal for direct human consumption of certain imported wines which may have undergone oenological processes not provided for in Regulation (EEC) No 337/79
pro memoria

BEER

Additives: E270 Lactic acid, E300 Ascorbic acid, E301 Sodium ascorbate, E330 Citric acid, E414 Acacia gum
Maximum level: *quantum satis*

FOIE GRAS, FOIE GRAS ENTIER, BLOCS DE FOIE GRAS

Additives: E300 Ascorbic acid, E301 Sodium ascorbate
Maximum level: *quantum satis*

APPENDIX C

FOODSTUFFS WHICH ARE ONLY PERMITTED CERTAIN COLOURS[716]

Foodstuff: Malt bread
  Permitted Colours: E150a Plain caramel, E150b Caustic sulphite caramel, E150c Ammonia caramel, E150d Sulphite ammonia caramel
  Maximum level: *quantum satis*

Foodstuffs: Beer, cidre bouché
  Permitted Colours: E150a Plain caramel, E150b Caustic sulphite caramel, E150c Ammonia caramel, E150d Sulphite ammonia caramel
  Maximum level: *quantum satis*

Foodstuffs: Butter (including reduced-fat butter and concentrated butter)
  Permitted Colour: E160a Carotenes
  Maximum level: *quantum satis*

Foodstuffs: Margarine, minarine, other fat emulsions, and fats essentially free from water
  Permitted Colours: E160a Carotenes, E100 Curcumin
  Maximum level: *quantum satis*

Permitted Colours: E160b Annatto, Bixin, Norbixin
Maximum level: 10 mg/kg

Foodstuff: Sage Derby cheese
Permitted Colours: E140 Chlorophylls, Chlorophyllins E141
Copper complexes of chlorophylls and chlorophyllins
Maximum level: *quantum satis*

Foodstuffs: Ripened Orange, Yellow and broken white cheese;
unflavoured processed cheese
Permitted Colours: E160a Carotenes E160c, Paprika extract
Maximum level: *quantum satis*

Permitted Colours: E160b Annatto, Bixin, Norbixin
Maximum level: 15 mg/kg

Foodstuff: Red Leicester cheese
Permitted Colours: E160b Annatto, Bixin, Norbixin
Maximum level: 50 mg/kg

Foodstuff: Mimolette cheese
Permitted Colours: E160b Annatto, Bixin, Norbixin
Maximum level: 35 mg/kg

Foodstuff: Morbier cheese
Permitted Colour: E153 Vegetable carbon
Maximum level: *quantum satis*

Foodstuff: Red marbled cheese
Permitted Colours: E120 Cochineal,Carminicacid, Carmines
Maximum level: 125 mg/kg

Permitted Colour: E163 Anthocyanins
Maximum level: *quantum satis*

Foodstuff: Vinegar
Permitted Colours: E150a Plain caramel, E150b Caustic
sulphite caramel, E150c Ammonia caramel, E150d Sulphite
ammonia caramel   **Maximum level:** *quantum satis*

Foodstuffs: Whisky, Whiskey, grain spirit (other than Korn or Kombrand or Eau de vie de seigle Marque nationale Luxembourgeoise), wine spirit, rum, Brandy, Weinbrand, grape marc, grape marc spirit (other than Tsikoudia and Tsipouro and Eau de vie de marc Marque nationale Luxembourgeoise), Grappa invecchiata, Bagaceira velba as mentioned in Regulation (EEC) No 1576/89

    Permitted Colours: E150a Plain caramel, E150b Caustic sulphite caramel, E150c Ammonia caramel, E150d Sulphite ammonia caramel   **Maximum level:** *quantum satis*

Foodstuffs: Aromatized wine-based drinks (except bitter soda) and aromatized wines as mentioned in Regulation (EEC No 1601/91

    Permitted Colours: E150a Plain caramel, E150b Caustic sulphite caramel, E150c Ammonia caramel, E150d Sulphite ammonia caramel   **Maximum level:** *quantum satis*

Foodstuff: Americano

    Permitted Colours: E150a Plain caramel, E150b Caustic sulphite caramel, E150c Ammonia caramel, E150d Sulphite ammonia caramel, E163 Anthocyanins
    Maximum level: *quantum satis*

    Permitted Colours: E100 Curcumin, E101 (i) Riboflavin (ii) Riboflavin-5'-phosphate, E102 Tartrazine, E104 Quinoline Yellow, E120 Cochineal, Carminic acid, Carmines, E122 Azorubine carmoisine, E123 Amaranth, E124 Ponceau 4R
    Maximum level: 100 mg/l (individually or in combination)

Foodstuffs: Bitter soda, bitter vino as mentioned in Regulation (EEC) No 1601/91

    Permitted Colours: 150a Plain caramel, E150b Caustic sulphite caramel, E150c Ammonia caramel, E150d Sulphite ammonia caramel   **Maximum level:** *quantum satis*

    Permitted Colours: E100 Curcumin, E101 (i) Riboflavin (ii) Riboflavin-5'-phosphate, E102 Tartrazine, E104 Quinoline Yellow, E110 Sunset Yellow FCF Orange Yellow S, E120 Cochineal, Carminic acid, Carmines, E122 Azorubine,

Carmoisine, E123 Amaranth, E124 Ponceau, 4R, Cochineal
Red A, E129 Allura Red AC
Maximum level: 100 mg/l (individually or in combination)

Foodstuffs: Liqueur wines and quality liqueur wines produced in specified regions
Permitted Colours: 150a Plain caramel, E150b Caustic sulphite caramel, E150c Ammonia caramel, E150d Sulphite ammonia caramel   **Maximum level:** *quantum satis*

Foodstuffs: Vegetables in vinegar, brine or oil (excluding olives)
Permitted Colours: E101 (i) Riboflavin (ii) Riboflavin-5'-phosphate, E140 Chlorophylls, Chlorophyllins, E150a Plain caramel, E150b Caustic sulphite caramel, E150c Ammonia caramel, E150d Sulphite ammonia caramel, E141 Copper complexes of chlorophylls and chlorophyllins, E160a Carotenes: (i) Mixed carotenes (ii) Beta-carotene, E162 Beerroot Red, betanin, E163 Anthocyanins
Maximum level: *quantum satis*

Foodstuffs: Extruded, puffed and/or fruit-flavoured breakfast cereals
Permitted Colours: E150c Ammonia caramel, E160a Carotenes, E160c Paprika extract, Capsanthin, Capsorubin
Maximum level: *quantum satis*

Permitted Colours: E160b Annatto, Bixin, Norbixin
Maximum level: 25 mg/kg

Foodstuffs: Fruit-flavoured breakfast cereals
Permitted Colours: E120 Cochineal, Carminic acid, Carmines, E162 Beetroot Red, betanin, E163 Anthocyanins
Maximum level: 200 mg/kg (individually or in combination)

Foodstuffs: Jam, jellies and marmalades as mentioned in Directive 79/693/EEC and other similar fruit preparations including low calorie products
Permitted Colours: E100 Curcumin, E140 Chlorophylls and chlorophyllins, E141 Copper complexes of chlorophylls and chlorophyllins, E150a Plain caramel, E150b Caustic sulphite

caramel, E150c Ammonia caramel, E150d Sulphite ammonia caramel, E160a Carotenes: (i) Mixed carotenes (ii) Beta-carotene, E160c Paprika extract, Capsanthin, Capsorubin, E162 Beetroot Red, betanin, E163 Anthocyanins.
Maximum level: *quantum satis*

Permitted Colours: E104 Quinoline Yellow, E110 Sunset Yellow, E120 Cochineal, Carminic acid, Carmines, E124 Ponceau 4R, Cochineal, E142 Green S, E160d Lypcopene, E161b Lutein
Maximum level: 100 mg/kg (individually or in combination)

Foodstuffs: Sausages, patés and terrines
Permitted Colour: E100 Curcumin
Maximum level: 20 mg/kg

Permitted Colour: E120 Cochineal, Carminic acid, Carmines
Maximum level: 100 mg/kg

Permitted Colours: E150a Plain caramel, E150b Caustic sulphite caramel, E150c Ammonia caramel, E150d Sulphite ammonia caramel, E162 Beetroot Red, betanin
Maximum level: *quantum satis*

Permitted Colour: E160a Carotenes
Maximum level: 20 mg/kg

Permitted Colour: E160c Paprika extract, Capsanthin, Capsorubin   **Maximum level:** 10 mg/kg

Foodstuff: Luncheon meat
Permitted Colour: E129 Allura Red AC
Maximum level: 25 mg/kg

Foodstuff: Breakfast sausages with a minimum cereal content of 6%
Permitted Colour: E129 Allura Red AC
Maximum level: 25 mg/kg

Foodstuff: Burger meat with a minimum vegetable and/or cereal content of 4%
   Permitted Colour: E120 Cochineal, Carminic acid, Carmines
   Maximum level: 100 mg/kg

   Permitted Colours: E150a Plain caramel, E150b Caustic sulphite caramel, E150c Ammonia caramel, E150d Sulphite ammonia caramel   **Maximum level:** *quantum satis*

Foodstuffs: Chorizo sausage, Salchichon
   Permitted Colour: E120 Cochineal, Carminic acid, Carmines
   Maximum level: 200 mg/kg

   Permitted Colours: E124 Ponceau 4R, Cochineal Red A
   Maximum level: 250 mg/kg

Foodstuff: Sobrasada
   Permitted Colour: E110 Sunset Yellow FCF
   Maximum level: 135 mg/kg

   Permitted Colours: E124 Ponceau 4R, Cochineal Red A
   Maximum level: 200 mg/kg

Foodstuffs: Pasturmas (edible external coating)
   Permitted Colours: E100 Curcumin, E101 (i) Riboflavin (ii) Riboflayin-5'-phosphate, E120 Cochineal, Carminic acid, Carmines **Maximum level:** *quantum satis*

Foodstuffs: Dried potato granules and flakes
   Permitted Colour: E100 Curcumin
   Maximum level: *quantum satis*

Foodstuffs: Processed mushy and garden peas (canned)
   Permitted Colour: E102 Tartrazine
   Maximum level: 100 mg/kg

   Permitted Colour: E133 Brilliant Blue
   Maximum level: 20 mg/kg

   Permitted Colour: E142 Green S
   Maximum level: 10 mg/kg

Appendix D

FOODSTUFFS WHICH MAY NOT CONTAIN ADDED COLOURS (EXCEPT AS SPECIFIED IN APPENDIX C OR AS NOTED UNDER THE COLOUR CONCERNED) (DIRECTIVE 94/36/EC)

Unprocessed foodstuffs

All bottled or packed waters

Milk, semi-skimmed and skimmed, pasteurized or sterilized (including UHT sterliization) (unflavoured)

Chocolate milk

Fermented milk (unflavoured)

Preserved milks (as mentioned in Directive 76/118/EEC)

Butter-milk (unflavoured)

Cream and cream powder (unflavoured)

Oils and fats of animal or vegetable origin

Eggs and egg products (as defined in Article 2 (1) of Directive 89/437/EEC)

Flour and other milled products and starches

Bread and similar products

Pasta and gnocchi

Sugar, including all mono- and disaccharides

Tomato paste and canned and bottled tomatoes

Tomato-based sauces

Fruit juice and fruit nectar (as mentioned in Directive 75/726/EEC) and vegetable juice

Fruit, vegetables (including potatoes) and mushrooms – canned, bottled or dried; processed fruit, vegetables (including potatoes) and mushrooms

Extra jam, extra jelly, and chestnut purée (as mentioned in Directive 79/693/EEC); crème de pruneaux

Fish, molluscs and crustaceans, meat, poultry and game as well as their preparations, but not including prepared meals containing these ingredients

Cocoa products and chocolate components in chocolate products (as mentioned in Directive 73/241/EEC)

Roasted coffee, tea, chicory; tea and chicory extracts; tea, plant, fruit and cereal preparations for infusions, as well as mixes and instant mixes of these products

Salt, salt substitutes, spices and mixtures of spices

Wine and other products defined by Regulation (EEC) No 822/87

Korn, Kombrand, fruit spirit drinks, fruit spirits, Ouzo, Grappa, Tsikoudia from Crete, Tsipouro from Macedonia, Tsipouro from Thessaly, Tsipouro from Tyrnavos, Eau de vie de marc Marque nationale Luxembourgeoise, Eau de vie de seigle Marque nationale Luxembourgeoise, London gin (as defined in Regulation (EEC) No 1576/89)

Sambuca, Maraschino and Mistra (as defined in Regulation (EEC) No 1180/91)

Sangria, Clarea and Zurra (as mentioned in Regulation (EEC) No 1601/91)

Wine vinegar

Foods for infants and young children (as mentioned in Directive 89/398/EEC) including foods for infants and young children not in good health

Honey

Malt and malt products

Ripened and unripened cheese (unflavoured)

Butter from sheep and goats' milk

ENDNOTES

1 *Registry of Toxic Effects of Chemical Substances*, National Institute for Occupational Safety and Health, 1996.
2 *US News & World Report*, 20 Feb, 1989, v106, n7, p77(2).
3 *Ibid.*
4 *New Scientist*, 8 July, 1989.
5 *Ibid.*
6 The *Guardian* 8 January, 1987.
7 Action Against Allergy, 43 The Downs, London SW20 8HG.
8 *FDA Consumer*, Feb 1989, v23, n1, p10(5).
9 *The Atlantic*, Nov 1989, v264, n5, p90(8).
10 *The Lancet*, 9 Mar 1985, 1 (8428), p540–5.
11 *I. Journal for Biosocial Research*, 1983, vol 4(2), p74–84.
12 *J Pediatr*, Feb 1995, 126(2): p171–7.
13 EC Directive 95/2/EC.
14 *Can J Neurol Sci*, Feb 1987, 14(1), p36–41.
15 The *Independent*, 18 July, 1989.
16 UPI, 7 September, 1989.
17 *Nutr Health*, 1985, 3 (4), p217–39.
18 UPI, 25 February, 1989.
19 The Associated Press, 28 June, 1993.
20 *Redbook*, May, 1989, v173, n1, p116(5).
21 UPI, 21 November, 1983.
22 *Which?*, February, 1989.
23 *Environ Health Perspect*, Oct 1985, 62, p313–8.
24 Pediatric Report's *Child Health Newsletter*, April 1992, v9 n3, p19(3).
25 *Newsline*, Summer 1994, p17(2).
26 *New Scientist*, 27 January, 1990.
27 *Chicago Tribune*, 24 June, 1990.
28 *Ibid.*
29 *Vegetarian Times*, September, 1990.

30 Foliage for Clean Air Council, Tel (USA) 091-1-703-534-5268.
31 *Impact on Human Health of Air Pollution in Europe*, World Health Organization, July 1990.
32 *The Lancet*, 7 Aug, 1982, 2 (8293).
33 *J Cancer Res Clin Oncol*, 1986, 112 (2).
34 *People's Medical Society Newsletter*, Aug, 1988.
35 Cancer Causes Control (ENGLAND) July, 1992, 3 (4).
36 *Scientific American*, Jan 1989, v260, n1, p68(8).
37 *Washington Post*, 21 Apr, 1987.
38 *Philadelphia Inquirer*, 19 September, 1988.
39 Vernon Coleman, *The Health Scandal*, Sidgwick & Jackson, 1988.
40 *Washington Post*, 16 August, 1987.
41 *Postgraduate Medical Journal*, August 1985, 61 (718) p713–6.
42 *Washington Post*, 16 August, 1987.
43 *Ibid.*
44 *Ibid.*
45 *Ibid.*
46 *British National Formulary*, published by the British Medical Association & The Pharmaceutical Society of Great Britain.
47 Vernon Coleman, *The Health Scandal*, Sidgwick & Jackson, 1988.
48 *Journal of the American Medical Association*, 21 July, 1988, cited in *Facts on File*, 28 October, 1988.
49 Vernon Coleman, *The Health Scandal*, Sidgwick & Jackson, 1988.
50 *Sunday Correspondent*, 26 November, 1989.
51 *Summary of Evaluations Performed by the Joint FAO/WHO Expert Committee on Food Additives*, ILSI Press, 1994.
52 R.E. Gosselin, H.C. Hodge, R.P. Smith, and M.N. Gleason, *Clinical Toxicology of Commercial Products*, Williams and Wilkins, Baltimore, 1976, p11–155.
53 *International Labour Office. Encyclopedia of Occupational Health and Safety*, vol I, II, McGraw-Hill Book Co, New York, 1971.
54 *WHO Food Additives Series: 26 Toxicological evaluation of certain food additives and contaminants*, World Health Organization, Geneva, 1990.
55 *Food Advisory Committee Report on the Review of The Emulsifiers and Stabilizers Regulations*, HMSO, 1992.
56 *WHO Food Additives Series: 28 Toxicological evaluation of certain food additives*, World Health Organization, Geneva, 1991.
57 G. Reineccius, *Source Book of Flavors*, Chapman & Hall, 1994.
58 F.W. Mackison, R.S. Stricoff, and L.J. Partridge, Jr (eds), *NIOSH/OSHA – Occupational Health Guidelines for Chemical Hazards, DHHS(NIOSH) Publication No. 81–123, US Government Printing Office, Washington DC, 1981.*
59 Alain Li Wan Po, *Non-prescription Drugs*, Blackwell Scientific Publications, 1982.
60 USEPA; Ambient Water Quality Criteria document for Acrylonitrile PB81–117285, 1980.
61 T.E. Graedel, *Atmospheric Chemical Compounds*, Academic Press, NY, 1986, p 398.
62 *Monographs on the Evaluation of the Carcinogenic Risk of Chemicals to Man*, World Health Organization, Geneva, International Agency for Research on Cancer, 1972–present, p. S7 56, 1987.
63 US Environmental Protection Agency's Integrated Risk Information System

(IRIS) on Acrylonitrile (107–13–1), National Library of Medicine TOXNET System, 28 March, 1994.

64 *NIOSH Pocket Guide to Chemical Hazards*, DHHS (NIOSH) Publication No. 94–116, Government Printing Office, Washington DC, June 1994.

65 J.A. Maga, A.T. Tu (eds), *Food Additive Toxicology*, Marcel Dekker Inc, 1995.

66 *MAFF Food Surveillance Information Sheet Number 81*, March 1996.

67 *Monographs on the Evaluation of the Carcinogenic Risk of Chemicals to Man*, World Health Organization, Geneva, International Agency for Research on Cancer, 1972–present, p. S7 56, 1987.

68 R.E. Gosselin, H.C. Hodge, R.P. Smith, and M.N. Gleason, *Clinical Toxicology of Commercial Products*, Williams and Wilkins, Baltimore, 1976.

69 R.H. Dreisback, *Handbook of Poisoning*, Lange Medical Publications, Los Altos, California, 1977.

70 *WHO Food Additives Series: 30 Toxicological evaluation of certain food additives*, World Health Organization, Geneva, 1993.

71 J.A. Maga, A.T. Tu (eds), *Food Additive Toxicology*, Marcel Dekker Inc, 1995.

72 Freedman B., *Clin Allergy*, 7 (5): 417, 1977.

73 *British National Formulary Number 13*, British Medical Association & The Pharmaceutical Society of Great Britain, 1987.

74 NACNE, September 1983, Health Education Council.

75 *The Lancet*, 30 December, 1972.

76 J.E.F. Reynolds, A.B. Prasad, (eds) *Martindale – The Extra Pharmacopoeia*, The Pharmaceutical Press, London, 1982.

77 *Which?* February, 1986, p102.

78 *British National Formulary Number 13*, British Medical Association & The Pharmaceutical Society of Great Britain, 1987, p166.

79 *WHO Food Additives Series: 21 Toxicological evaluation of certain food additives and contaminants*, World Health Organization, Geneva, 1987.

80 *Int J Vitam Nutr Res*, 59 (4): 430–8, 1989.

81 US Pharmacopeial Convention, US Pharmacopeia Dispensing Information (USP DI); Drug Information for the Health Care Professional v1, p 2767, 1992.

82 *WHO Food Additives Series: 17 Toxicological evaluation of certain food additives*, World Health Organization, Geneva, 1982.

83 D.R. McLachlan *et al*; *Can J Neurol Sci*, 16 (4 Suppl): 490–7 1989.

84 *Clin. Geriatr. Med*, May 1987, 3 (2) p389–402.

85 *Scand. J. Gastroenterol.*, Aug 1985, 20 (6) p741–6.

86 L. Friberg, G.F. Nordberg, E. Kessler, and V.B. Vouk, (eds), *Handbook of the Toxicology of Metals*, vols I, II, Elsevier Science Publishers BV, Amsterdam, 1986.

87 Dissolved aluminium in canned soft drinks increases in concentration during storage and may significantly exceed the EEC prescribed limits for tap water. T. Reynolds, S. Smith, A. Taylor, *Communications in Laboratory Medicine*, 1; 109–13, 1992.

88 N.I. Sax, and R.J. Lewis, Sr. (eds), *Hawley's Condensed Chemical Dictionary*, Van Nostrand Reinhold Co, New York, 1987.

89 *British National Formulary Number 13*, British Medical Association & The Pharmaceutical Society of Great Britain, 1987.

90 J.A. Maga, A.T. Tu (eds), *Food Additive Toxicology*, Marcel Dekker Inc, 1995.

91 *The Merck Index:* Merck & Co, Inc, New Jersey, 1976.

92 *Monographs on the Evaluation of the Carcinogenic Risk of Chemicals to Man*, World

Health Organization, Geneva, International Agency for Research on Cancer, 1972–present. p. S7 56, 1987.

93 B. Freedman, *Clin Allergy*, 7 (5): 417, 1977.

94 *Martindale: The Extra Pharmacopoeia*, The Pharmaceutical Press.

95 *WHO Food Additives Series: 20 Toxicological evaluation of certain food additives and contaminants*, World Health Organization, Geneva, 1987.

96 *Foreign Compound Metabolism in Mammals Volume 3*, The Chemical Society, London, 1975.

97 *WHO Food Additives Series: 17 Toxicological evaluation of certain food additives*, World Health Organization, Geneva, 1982.

98 *Martindale: The Extra Pharmacopoeia*, The Pharmaceutical Press, 1982.

99 G.G. Hawley, *The Condensed Chemical Dictionary*, Van Nostrand Reinhold Co., New York, 1981.

100 *WHO Food Additives Series: 17 Toxicological evaluation of certain food additives*, World Health Organization, Geneva, 1982.

101 *Ibid.*

102 *Martindale: The Extra Pharmacopoeia*, The Pharmaceutical Press, 1982.

103 D.V. Frost, *Sci Total Environ*, 28:·455–66, 1983.

104 L. Alessio et *al; Influence of Factors Other Than Exposure on the Levels of Biological Indicators*, p.69–75, 1987.

105 *Monographs on the Evaluation of the Carcinogenic Risk of Chemicals to Man*,World Health Organization, Geneva, International Agency for Research on Cancer, 1972–present, p. S7 57, 1987.

106 US Environmental Protection Agency's Integrated Risk Information System (IRIS) on Arsenic, inorganic (7440–38–2), National Library of Medicines TOXNET System, 5 July, 1995.

107 *NIOSH Pocket Guide to Chemical Hazards*, DHHS (NIOSH) Publication No. 94–116. US Government Printing Office, Washington DC, June 1994.

108 *Monographs on the Evaluation of the Carcinogenic Risk of Chemicals to Man*, World Health Organization, Geneva, International Agency for Research on Cancer, 1972–present, *Ibid.* p. S7 106, 1987.

109 US Environmental Protection Agency's Integrated Risk Information System (IRIS) on Asbestos (1332–21–4), National Library of Medicine TOXNET System, 1 November, 1994.

110 *Documentation of the Threshold Limit Values and Biological Exposure Indices*, American Conference of Governmental Industrial Hygienists, 1986.

111 NRCC, n17585, p54, 1980.

112 Nat'l Research Council Canada, n. 16452, p52, 1979.

113 American Hospital Formulary Service Drug Information, 1990.

114 *Med Hypotheses* 7:1359–1376.

115 V. Kyzlink, Elsevier, *Principles of Food Preservation*, 1990.

116 T.E. Furia, (ed.), *CRC Handbook of Food Additives*, vol 2, CRC Press, Inc., Florida, 1980.

117 *Am J Clin Nutr* 43 (3): 464–9, 1986.

118 *Environ Health Perspec, 75*, 53–7, 1987.

119 *Conn Med*, 53 (7): 395–400, 1989.

120 *WHO Food Additives Series: 18 Toxicological evaluation of certain food additives and contaminants*, World Health Organization, Geneva, 1983.

121 *Clin Allergy*, 7 (5): 417, 1977.

122 R.E. Gosselin, H.C. Hodge, R.P. Smith, and M.N. Gleason, *Clinical Toxicology of Commercial Products*, Williams and Wilkins, Baltimore, 1976.

123 E. Browning, *Toxicity of Industrial Metals*, Appleton-Century-Crofts, New York, 1969.

124 G.K. McEvoy, (ed.), *American Hospital Formulary Service – Drug Information 93*, American Society of Hospital Pharmacists, Inc., 1993 (plus Supplements, 1993).

125 A. Osol, (ed.), *Remington's Pharmaceutical Sciences*, Mack Publishing Co., Easton, Pennsylvania, 1980.

126 *WHO Food Additives Series: Toxicological evaluation of certain food additives*, World Health Organization, Geneva, 1991.

127 IARC *Monographs on the Evaluation of the Carcinogenic risk to Humans*, vol. 32, Suppl. 7, 1987, WHO/International Agency for Research on Cancer.

128 US Environmental Protection Agency's Integrated Risk Information System (IRIS) on Benzo(a)pyrene (BaP) (50–32–8), National Library of Medicine TOXNET System, 4 November, 1994.

129 R. Edenharder, *et al*, Antimutagene Aktivitaten von Gemuse- und Obstextrakten gegenuber Benzo[a]pyren in vitro, *Z Gesamte Hyg*, Mar 1990.

130 *Practitioner*, 1979, 222, 400.

131 *WHO Food Additives Series: 37 Toxicological evaluation of certain food additives*, World Health Organization, Geneva, 1996.

132 US Environmental Protection Agency's Integrated Risk Information System (IRIS) on Benzoic acid (65–85–0), National Library of Medicine TOXNET System, October 1996.

133 A. Osol, (ed.), *Remington's Pharmaceutical Sciences*, Mack Publishing Co., Easton, Pennsylvania, 1980.

134 AMA Drug Evaluations Annual 1991, American Medical Association, Chicago, 1991.

135 *Monographs on the Evaluation of the Carcinogenic Risk of Chemicals to Man*, World Health Organization, Geneva, International Agency for Research on Cancer, 1972–present, p. S7 58 1987.

136 R.A. Cartwright *et al*; *Br J Dermatol*, 118 (2): 239–42, 1988.

137 J. Schweizer *et al*; Carcinogenesis 8 (3): 479–82, 1987.

138 *Fenaroli's Handbook of Flavor Ingredients*, CRC Press, Burdock G.A., 1995

139 A. Hamilton, and H.L. Hardy, *Industrial Toxicology*, Publishing Sciences Group, Inc., Acton Mass., 1974.

140 *Documentation of the Threshold Limit Values and Biological Exposure Indices*, American Conference of Governmental Industrial Hygienists, 1986.

141 US Environmental Protection Agency's Integrated Risk Information System (IRIS) on 1, 1–Biphenyl (92–52–4), National Library of Medicine TOXNET System, 1 November, 1994.

142 L.S. Goodman, and A. Gilman, (eds.) *The Pharmacological Basis of Therapeutics*, Macmillan Publishing Co., Inc., New York, 1975.

143 H.G. Seiler, H. Sigel and A. Sigel (eds.), *Handbook on the Toxicity of Inorganic Compounds*. Marcel Dekker, Inc, New York, NY, 1988.

144 *WHO Food Additives Series: 16 Toxicological evaluation of certain food additives*, World Health Organization, Geneva, 1981.

145 *Clin Allergy*, 7 (5): 417, 1977.

146 *Monographs on the Evaluation of the Carcinogenic risk to Humans*, vol. 16, suppl. 7, WHO/International Agency for Research on Cancer, 1987.

147 *WHO Food Additives Series: 20 Toxicological evaluation of certain food additives and contaminants*, World Health Organization, Geneva, 1987.

148 *Clin Allergy*, 7 (5): 417, 1977.

149 *Monographs on the Evaluation of the Carcinogenic Risk of Chemicals to Man*, World Health Organization, Geneva, International Agency for Research on Cancer, 1972–present, p. S7 59, 1987.

150 *WHO Food Additives Series: 24 Toxicological evaluation of certain food additives and contaminants*, World Health Organization, Geneva, 1989.

151 M. Mizuno *et al, Mutat. Res*, 176, 1987.

152 *CRC Handbook of Food Additives*, CRC Press Inc, 1977.

153 G.D. Clayton, and F.E. Clayton (eds.), *Patty's Industrial Hygiene and Toxicology: volume 2A, 2B, 2C; Toxicology*, John Wiley Sons, New York, 1981–1982.

154 B.J.F. Hudson (ed.), *Food Antioxidants*, Elsevier Applied Science, 1990.

155 *WHO Food Additives Series: 28 Toxicological evaluation of certain food additives*, World Health Organization, Geneva, 1991.

156 *Monographs on the Evaluation of the Carcinogenic Risk of Chemicals to Man*, World Health Organization, Geneva, International Agency for Research on Cancer, 1972–present, *(multivolume work)* p. suppl. 7, 59.

157 *Independent On Sunday Magazine*, 20 March, 1994.

158 R.E. Gosselin, R.P. Smith, H.C. Hodge, *Clinical Toxicology of Commercial Products*, Williams and Wilkins, Baltimore, 1984.

159 L. Friberg, Nordberg, G.F., Kessler, E. and Vouk, V.B. (eds), *Handbook of the Toxicology of Metals*, vols I, II, Elsevier Science Publishers B.V., Amsterdam, 1986.

160 *Monographs on the Evaluation of the Carcinogenic Risk of Chemicals to Man*, World Health Organization, Geneva, International Agency for Research on Cancer, 1972–present, p.85 210 1993.

161 US Environmental Protection Agency's Integrated Risk Information System (IRIS) on Cadmium (7440–43–9), National Library of Medicine TOXNET System, 6 March, 1995.

162 A.G. Gilman, T.W. Rall, A.S. Nies and P. Taylor (eds.), *Goodman and Gilman's The Pharmacological Basis of Therapeutics.* Pergamon Press, New York, 1990.

163 *American Journal of Epidemiology AJE*, v 126, n5, p803.

164 *Handbook of Non-prescription Drugs*, American Pharmaceutical Society.

165 *British National Formulary Number 13*, BMA/PSGB, GB, 1987.

166 *Monographs on the Evaluation of the Carcinogenic Risk of Chemicals to Man*, World Health Organization, Geneva, International Agency for Research on Cancer, 1972–present, p.51 357 1991.

167 The Associated Press, 11 March, 1996.

168 *WHO Food Additives Series: 6 Toxicological evaluation of some food colours, enzymes, flavour enhancers, thickening agents and certain food additives*, World Health Organization, Geneva, 1975.

169 A.G. Gilman, L.S. Goodman, and A. Gilman. (eds.), *Goodman and Gilman's The Pharmacological Basis of Therapeutics*, Macmillan Publishing Co., Inc., New York, 1980.

170 AMA Department of Drugs. *AMA Drug Evaluations*, American Medical Association, 1980.

171 *Encyclopedia of Occupational Health and Safety*, vols I, II, International Labour Office, Geneva, 1983.

172 M.L. Clarke, D.G. Harvey and D.J. Humphreys, *Veterinary Toxicology*, Bailliere Tindall, London, 1981.
173 L.S. Goodman, and A. Gilman. (eds.) *The Pharmacological Basis of Therapeutics*, Macmillan Publishing Co., Inc., 1975.
174 *Monographs on the Evaluation of the Carcinogenic Risk of Chemicals to Man*, World Health Organization, Geneva, International Agency for Research on Cancer, 1972–present, p.54 178, 1992.
175 *Ibid.*
176 *WHO Food Additives Series: 30 Toxicological evaluation of certain food additives*, World Health Organization, Geneva, 1993.
177 *WHO Food Additives Series: 24 Toxicological evaluation of certain food additives and contaminants*, World Health Organization, Geneva, 1989.
178 *Encyclopedia of Occupational Health and Safety*, vols, I, II, International Labour Office, Geneva, 1983.
179 R.J. Lewis, *Food Additives Handbook.* Van Nostrand Reinhold, 1989.
180 *Criteria Document: Carbon Black* p.23, 1978, DHEW, NIOSH 78–204.
181 *Encyclopedia of Occupational Health and Safety*, vols I, II, International Labour Office, Geneva, 1983.
182 *Monographs on the Evaluation of the Carcinogenic Risk of Chemicals to Man*, World Health Organization, Geneva, International Agency for Research on Cancer, 1972–present, p. S7 59, 1987.
183 *NIOSH Pocket Guide to Chemical Hazards*, DHHS (NIOSH) Publication No. 94–116. US Government Printing Office, Washington, DC, June 1994.
184 *Monographs on the Evaluation of the Carcinogenic Risk of Chemicals to Man*, World Health Organization, Geneva, International Agency for Research on Cancer, 1972–present, p. S7, 59. 1987.
185 J.A. Maga, A.T. Tu (eds.) *Food Additive Toxicology*, Marcel Dekker Inc, 1995.
186 *WHO Food Additives Series: 30 Toxicological evaluation of certain food additives*, World Health Organization, Geneva, 1993.
187 J. Doull, C.D. Klaassen, and M.D. Amdur (eds.), *Casarett and Doull's Toxicology*, Macmillan Publishing Co., New York, 1980.
188 M.M. Mathews-Roth, *Toxicol Lett*, 41 (3): 185–91, 1988.
189 *NCI Cancer Weekly*, 14 August, 1989.
190 *Nutrition Health Review*, n53 Winter 1990.
191 AJCN, v53, n1 Jan 1991, p298S(7).
192 Beta-carotene and cancer prevention: the Basel study. H.B. Stahelin, et al. *American Journal of Clinical Nutrition*, Jan 1991 v53, n1.
193 The *Independent*, 3 May, 1994.
194 Nutrition Research Newsletter, v15 n2, Feb 1996.
195 *NCI Cancer Weekly*, 19 June, 1989.
196 *Cancer Res* 52 (23): 6583–7, 1992.
197 IARC Monographs on the Evaluation of Carcinogenic risk to Humans, vol 31, suppl. 7, WHOInternational Agency for Research on Cancer, 1987.
198 *WHO Food Additives Series: 20 Toxicological evaluation of certain food additives and contaminants*, World Health Organization, Geneva, 1987.
199 R.E. Gosselin, R.P. Smith, H.C. Hodge, *Clinical Toxicology of Commercial Products*, Williams and Wilkins, Baltimore, 1984, p. 11–231.
200 *BMI* 1982, 284, 385.
201 W.M. Grant, *Toxicology of the Eye*, Charles C. Thomas, Springfield Illinois, 1974.

202 *Ibid.*
203 R.E. Gosselin, H.C. Hodge, R.P. Smith, and M.N. Gleason, *Clinical Toxicology of Commercial Products*, Williams and Wilkins, Baltimore, 1976, p. 11–119.
204 K.E. Anderson, K. Hamann, *Contact Dermatitis* 11 (1): 11–20 (1984).
205 M. Sittig, *Handbook of Toxic and Hazardous Chemicals and Carcinogens*, 1985, Noyes Data Corporation, NJ, 1985.
206 *IARC Monographs on the Evaluation of Carcinogenic risk to Humans*, vol. 20, suppl. 7; 1987, WHO/International Agency for Research on Cancer.
207 US Environmental Protection Agency's Integrated Risk Information System (IRIS) on Chloroform (67–66–3), National Library of Medicine TOXNET System, 29 August, 1994.
208 G. Reineccius, *Source Book of Flavors*, Chapman & Hall, 1994.
209 *WHO Food Additives Series: 30 Toxicological evaluation of certain food additives*, World Health Organization, Geneva, 1993.
210 R.E. Gosselin, H.C. Hodge, R.P. Smith, and M.N. Gleason, *Clinical Toxicology of Commercial Products*, Williams and Wilkins, Baltimore, 1976, p. 11–168.
211 G.D. Clayton, and F.E. Clayton (eds.), *Patty's Industrial Hygiene and Toxicology: Volume 2A, 2B, 2C: Toxicology*, John Wiley Sons, New York, 1981–82.
212 *Food Advisory Committee Report on the Review of The Emulsifiers and Stabilizers Regulations*, HMSO, 1992.
213 O. Hansson, *Inside Ciba-Geigy*, IOCU Regional Office for Asia and the Pacific, PO Box 1045, 10830 Penang, Malaysia.
214 W.M. Grant, *Toxicology of the Eye*, Charles C. Thomas Publisher, Springfield, Il, 1986.
215 M.J. Ellenhorn, and D.G. Barceloux, *Medical Toxicology – Diagnosis and Treatment of Human Poisoning*, Elsevier Science Publishing Co., Inc., New York, 1988.
216 G.K. McEvoy, (ed.), *American Hospital Formulary Service – Drug Information 93*, American society of Hospital Pharmacists, Inc., 1993, 2178.
217 *Ibid.*
218 *Ibid.*
219 *Br F Dermatol*, 1970; 82:510.
220 *British Medical Journal*, 5 Oct, 1991 v303, n6806, p829(7).
221 G.K. McEvoy, (ed.), *American Hospital Formulary Service – Drug Information 94*, American Society of Hospital Pharmacists, Inc., 1994 (plus Supplements).
222 *Ibid.*
223 *Monographs on the Evaluation of the Carcinogenic Risk of Chemicals to Man*, World Health Organization, Geneva, International Agency for Research on Cancer, 1972–present, p. S7 61, 1987.
224 US Environmental Protection Agency's Integrated Risk Information System (IRIS) on coke oven emissions (8007–45–2), National Library of Medicine TOXNET System, 10 November, 1993.
225 G.K. McEvoy, (ed.), *American Hospital Formulary Service – Drug Information 94*, American Society of Hospital Pharmacists, Inc., 1994 (plus Supplements).
226 USPDI-Drug Information for the Health Care Professional, vol I. United States Pharmacopeial Convention, Inc., Rockville, MD, 1994.
227 *British National Formulary Number 13*, British Medical Association & The Pharmaceutical Society of Great Britain, 1987.
228 M.J. Ellenhorn, and D.G. Barceloux, *Medical Toxicology – Diagnosis and*

Treatment of Human Poisoning, Elsevier Science Publishing Co., Inc., New York, 1988.

229 *Drinking Water and Health*, vol 3, National Academy Press, 1980.

230 Encyclopedia of Occupational Health and Safety, vols I, II, International Labour Office, Geneva, 1983.

231 *WHO Food Additives Series: 17 Toxicological evaluation of certain food additives*, World Health Organization, Geneva, 1982.

232 *The Merck Index*, Merck Co., Inc., New Jersey, 1983.

233 E. Browning, *Toxicity of Industrial Metals*, Appleton-Century-Crofts, New York, 1969.

234 J.E.F. Reynolds, A.B. Prasad, (eds.), *Martindale –The Extra Pharmacopoeia*, The Pharmaceutical Press, London, 1982.

235 US Environmental Protection Agency's Integrated Risk Information System (IRIS) on Copper (7440–50–8), National Library of Medicine TOXNET System, 1 November, 1994.

236 *Monographs on the Evaluation of the Carcinogenic Risk of Chemicals to Man*, World Health Organization, Geneva, International Agency for Research on Cancer, 1972–present, p. S7 177, 1987.

237 US Environmental Protection Agency's Integrated Risk Information System (IRIS) on Creosote (8001–58–9), National Library of Medicine TOXNET System, 1 November, 1994.

238 *WHO Food Additives Series: 35 Toxicological evaluation of certain food additives*, World Health Organization, Geneva, 1996.

239 J.M. Arena, *Poisoning: Toxicology-Symptoms Treatments*, Charles C. Thomas, Springfield, Illinois, 1974.

240 *Monographs on the Evaluation of the Carcinogenic Risk of Chemicals to Man*, World Health Organization, Geneva, International Agency for Research on Cancer, 1972–present, p. V22.

241 R. Lefaus, *Practical Toxicology of Plastics*, CRC Press Inc., Cleveland, 1968.

242 *Documentation of the Threshold Limit Values*, 1980, American Conference of Governmental Industrial Hygienists, Inc., 1980.

243 *Monographs on the Evaluation of the Carcinogenic Risk to Humans*, vol. 22, suppl. 7, 1987, WHO/International Agency for Research on Cancer.

244 *Kirk-Othmer Encyclopedia of Chemical Technology*, vols 1–26, John Wiley and Sons, New York, 1978–1984.

245 O.H. Willoughby, *Farm Chemicals Handbook*, Meister Publishing Co., 1989.

246 *Monographs on the Evaluation of the Carcinogenic Risk of Chemicals to Man*, World Health Organization, Geneva, International Agency for Research on Cancer, 1972–present, p. 53 234, 1991.

247 US Environmental Protection Agency's Integrated Risk Information System (IRIS) on Dichlorodiphenyltrichloroethane (DDT) (50–29–3), National Library of Medicine TOXNET System, 29 August, 1994.

248 A. Osol, and J.E. Hoover, *et al.* (eds.), *Remington's Pharmaceutical Sciences*, Mack Publishing Co., Pennsylvania: 1975.

249 PRS 1978; 61:836–841.

250 *N Engl J Med*, 1992; 326:1713–1715.

251 *The Western Journal of Medicine*, May 1995, v162 n5.

252 *Monographs on the Evaluation of the Carcinogenic Risk of Chemicals to Man*, World Health Organization, Geneva, International Agency for Research on Cancer, 1972–present, p. S7 72, 1987.

253 Vols. I–III (review draft). EPA Office of Research and Development; Washington DC: 1994, Report No.: EPA/600/BP-92-001.

254 Great Lakes Water Quality Board 102nd Meeting, Chicago, Illinois, 15 July, 1993.

255 *Cancer Researcher Weekly*, 6 Sept, 1993.

256 Banbury Reports 1991; 35:121–132.

257 Banbury Reports 1991; 35:169–214.

258 *Environ Health Perspect*, 1994; 102 (9 suppl):157–167.

259 *MAFF Food Surveillance Information Sheets Number 71*, July 1995.

260 *WHO Food Additives Series: 6 Toxicological evaluation of some food colours, enzymes, flavour enhancers, thickening agents and certain food additives*, World Health Organization, Geneva, 1975.

261 *Br Med F*, 1876; ii: 819–20.

262 *British Medical Journal*, 5 Oct, 1991, v303 n6806 p829(7).

263 *Br F Dermatol*, 1980; 102–571.

264 *The Lancet*, 27 July 1991, v338, n8761, p231(4).

265 *Monographs on the Evaluation of the Carcinogenic Risk of Chemicals to Man*, World Health Organization, Geneva, International Agency for Research on Cancer, 1972–present, p. S7 13, 1987.

266 USPDI-Drug Information for the Health Care Professional, United States Pharmacopeial Convention Inc., 1994.

267 G.K. McEvoy, (ed.), *American Hospital Formulary Service – Drug Information 94*, American Society of Hospital Pharmacists, Inc., 1994. *(plus Supplements)*.

268 *American Medical Association, AMA Department of Drugs, AMA Drug Evaluations*, PSG Publishing Co., Inc., Littleton, Massachusetts, 1977.

269 *Martindale: The Extra Pharmacopoeia*, The Pharmaceutical Press, 1982.

270 *J Neurol Neurosurg Psychiatry*, 1982; 45:471–2.

271 *Am J Med*, 1990; 89:195–208.

272 *International Journal of Obesity and Related Metabolic Disorders*, 1994; 18:99103.

273 *Am J Clin Nutr*, 1985; 42:83–94.

274 *Journal of Obesity and Related Metabolic Disorders*, 1993; 17 (suppl):S41–S43.

275 *Am J Clin Nutr*, 1990; 51:759–67, 8.

276 Food and Drug Administration. Cold, cough, allergy, bronchodilator, and anti-asthamic drug products for over-the-counter human use; proposed amendment of monograph for OTC bronchodilator drug products. Notice of proposed rule-making. [21 CFR Parts 310 and 341] Fed Regist 1995; 60:38643–7.

277 The Associated Press, 1 Oct, 1995.

278 B.J.F. Hudson, *Food Antioxidants*, Elsevier Applied Science, 1990.

279 *WHO Food Additives Series: 28 Toxicological evaluation of certain food additives*, World Health Organization, Geneva, 1991.

280 *FDA Consumer*, May 1990, v24 n4, p18(4).

281 N.H. Booth, L.E. McDonald (eds.), *Veterinary Pharmacology and Therapeutics*, Iowa State University Press, 1982.

282 A. Osol, and J.E. Hoover, *et al.* (eds.), *Remington's Pharmaceutical Sciences*, Mack Publishing Co., Easton, Pennsylvania: 1975.

283 *Monographs on the Evaluation of the Carcinogenic Risk of Chemicals to Man*, World Health Organization, Geneva, International Agency for Research on Cancer, 1972–present, p. S7 63, 1987.

284 M. Grieve, *A Modern Herbal*, Jonathan Cape, 1931.

285 *New Scientist*, 16 December, 1989.

286 *Monographs on the Evaluation of the Carcinogenic Risk of Chemicals to Man*, World Health Organization, Geneva, International Agency for Research on Cancer, 1972–present, p. S7 216, 1987.

287 A.G. Gilman, T.W. Rall, A.S. Nies and P. Taylor (eds.), *Goodman and Gilman's The Pharmacological Basis of Therapeutics*, Pergamon Press, New York, 1990.

288 *Am J Emerg Med*, 1992: 10; 452–505.

289 *Morbidity and Mortality Weekly Report*, 19 Feb, 1993, v42, n6, p111 (3).

290 US Environmental Protection Agency's Integrated Risk Information System (IRIS) on Formaldehyde (50–00–0), National Library of Medicine TOXNET System, 29 August, 1994.

291 *Monographs on the Evaluation of the Carcinogenic Risk of Chemicals to Man*, World Health Organization, Geneva, International Agency for Research on Cancer, 1972–present, p. 62 336, 1995.

292 *NIOSH Pocket Guide to Chemical Hazards*, DHHS (NIOSH) Publication No. 94–116. US Government Printing Office, June 1994, 148.

293 *Am Ind Hyg Assoc J*, 38: 61, 1977.

294 *Monographs on the Evaluation of the Carcinogenic Risk of Chemicals to Man*, World Health Organization, Geneva, International Agency for Research on Cancer, 1972–present, p. 29, 370 1982.

295 *Environ Res*, 52 (2): 177–25, 1990.

296 M.J. Ellenhorn, and D.G. Barceloux, *Medical Toxicology – Diagnosis and Treatment of Human Poisoning*, Elsevier Science Publishing Co., Inc., New York, 1988.

297 *MAFF Food Surveillance Information Sheets. Number 26* May, 1994.

298 *Chicago Tribune*, 24 June, 1990.

299 G. Reineccius, *Source Book of Flavors*, Chapman & Hall, 1994.

300 *Encyclopedia of Occupational Health and Safety*, vols I, II, International Labour Office, Geneva, 1983.

301 *J Natl Cancer Inst*, 69 (6): 1317–20, 1982.

302 P. Harris (ed.), Food Gels, Elsevier Applied Science, 1990.

303 P.R. Ashhurst, *Food Flavourings*, Blackie Academic & Professional, 1991.

304 G.G. Hawley, *The Condensed Chemical Dictionary*, Van Nostrand Reinhold Co., New York, 1977.

305 *Science*, 16 Dec, 1988, v242, n4885.

306 *Science*, 7 June, 1991 v252, n5011.

307 G.D. Clayton, and F.E. Clayton (eds.), *Patty's Industrial Hygiene and Toxicology: Volume 2A, 2B, 2C: Toxicology*, John Wiley Sons, New York: 1981.

308 G.K. McEvoy, (ed), *American Hospital Formulary Service – Drug Information 93*, American Society of Hospital Pharmacists, Inc., 1993 (plus Supplements, 1993).

309 *WHO Food Additives Series: 37 Toxicological evaluation of certain food additives*, World Health Organization, Geneva, 1996.

310 *Encyclopedia of Occupational Health and Safety*, vols I, II, International Labour Office, Geneva, 1983.

311 Bureau Of Mines, Mineral Commodity Summaries, 1986.

312 A.G. Gilman, L.S. Goodman, and A. Gilman. (eds.), *Goodman and Gilman's The Pharmacological Basis of Therapeutics*, Macmillan Publishing Co., Inc., New York, 1980.

313 T.D. Luckey, and B. Venugopal, *Metal Toxicity in Mammals I*, Plenum Press, New York, 1977.

314 *WHO Food Additives Series: 6 Toxicological evaluation of some food colours,*

enzymes, flavour enhancers, thickening agents and certain food additives, World Health Organization, Geneva, 1975.

315 G.D. Clayton, and F.E. Clayton (eds.), *Patty's Industrial Hygiene and Toxicology: Volume 2A, 2B, 2C: Toxicology*, John Wiley Sons, New York: 1981–2.

316 *Ibid.*

317 American Hospital Formulary Service.

318 G. Reineccius, *Source Book of Flavors*, Chapman & Hall, 1994.

319 *WHO Food Additives Series: 32 Toxicological evaluation of certain food additives*, World Health Organization, Geneva, 1993.

320 *Toxic and Hazardous Industrial Chemicals Safety Manual*, The International Technical Information Institute, Tokyo, Japan: 1988.

321 *Philos Tran R Soc Lond (Biol)*, 304 (1118): 105–17, 1984.

322 *Monographs on the Evaluation of the Carcinogenic Risk of Chemicals to Man*, World Health Organization, Geneva, International Agency for Research on Cancer, 1972–present, p. V20 250, 1979.

323 *Ibid.*

324 W.M. Grant, *Toxicology of the Eye*, Charles C. Thomas Publisher, Springfield, Il, 1986, p480.

325 *AMA Department of Drugs, AMA Drug Evaluations*, PSG Publishing Co., Inc., Littleton, Massachusetts, 1977, p893.

326 21 CFR 250.250 (4/1/93).

327 *Monographs on the Evaluation of the Carcinogenic Risk of Chemicals to Man*, World Health Organization, Geneva, International Agency for Research on Cancer, 1972–present, p. S7 64 1987.

328 American Hospital Formulary Service, 1996.

329 *Ibid.*

330 *Chemical Products Synopsis: Hydrochloric Acid*, 1985.

331 *Threshold Limit Values and Biological Exposure Indices*, American Conference of Governmental Industrial Hygienists, 1986.

332 WHO, *Environ Health Criteria: Chlorine and Hydrogen chloride*, p.75, 1982.

333 *Ibid.*

334 29 CFR 1910.1000, 7/1/1988.

335 *Monographs on the Evaluation of the Carcinogenic Risk of Chemicals to Man*, World Health Organization, Geneva, International Agency for Research on Cancer, 1972–present, p. 54 206, 1992.

336 National Research Council. *Prudent Practices for Handling Hazardous Chemicals in Laboratories*, National Academy Press, Washington, DC, 1981.

337 M.J. Ellenhorn, and D.G. Barceloux, *Medical Toxicology – Diagnosis and Treatment of Human Poisoning*, Elsevier Science Publishing Co., Inc., New York, 1988.

338 J.E.F. Reynolds, Prasad, A.B. (eds.), *Martindale – The Extra Pharmacopoeia*, The Pharmaceutical Press, 1982.

339 *British National Formulary Number 13, British Medical Association & The Pharmaceutical Society of Great Britain, 1987.*

340 *Martindale: The Extra Pharmacopoeia*, The Pharmaceutical Press, 1982.

341 Topical Corticosteroids: General Statement. American Hospital Formulary Service, 1996.

342 G.K. McEvoy, (ed.), *American Hospital Formulary Service – Drug Information 93*, American Society of Hospital Pharmacists, Inc., 1993 (plus Supplements, 1993).

343 C. Thienes, and T.J. Haley, *Clinical Toxicology*, Lea and Febiger, Philadelphia, 1972, p.191.
344 *AMA Drug Evaluations Annual 1991*, American Medical Association, Chicago, 1991.
345 *Monographs on the Evaluation of the Carcinogenic Risk of Chemicals to Man*, World Health Organization, Geneva, International Agency for Research on Cancer, 1972–present, p. S7 64, 1987.
346 J.A. Maga, A.T. Tu, *Food Additive Toxicology*. Marcel Dekker Inc, 1995.
347 *FAO Food and Nutrition Paper No 49* (1990), Food and Agriculture Organization of the United Nations, Rome.
348 *WHO Food Additives Series: 17 Toxicological evaluation of certain food additives*, World Health Organization, Geneva, 1982.
349 A.G. Gilman, T.W. Rall, A.S. Nies and P. Taylor (eds.), *Goodman and Gilman's The Pharmacological Basis of Therapeutics*, Pergamon Press, New York, 1990.
350 US Food and Drug Administration. Labeling revisions for NSAIDs. FDA Drug Bill. 1989.
351 *Ann Intern Med*, 1991; 114:307–19.
352 *American Hospital Formulary Service*, 1996.
353 R.E. Gosselin, R.P. Smith, H.C. Hodge, *Clinical Toxicology of Commercial Products*, Williams and Wilkins, Baltimore, 1984.
354 *Encyclopedia of Occupational Health and Safety*, vols I, II, International Labour Office, Geneva, 1983.
355 R.E. Gosselin, R.P. Smith, H.C. Hodge, *Clinical Toxicology of Commercial Products*, Williams and Wilkins, Baltimore, 1984.
356 *WHO Food Additives Series: 20 Toxicological evaluation of certain food additives and contaminants*, World Health Organization, Geneva, 1987.
357 AMA Department of Drugs, AMA Drug Evaluations, PSG Publishing Co., Inc., Littleton, Massachusetts, 1977.
358 R.E. Gosselin, R.P. Smith, H.C. Hodge, *Clinical Toxicology of Commercial Products*, Williams and Wilkins, Baltimore, 1984.
359 *TLV's Threshold Limit Values for Chemical Substances and Physical Agents in the Work Environment with Intended Changes for 1983–84*, American Conference of Governmental Industrial Hygienists, 1983.
360 *Monographs on the Evaluation of Carcinogenic risk to Humans*, vol. 15, suppl. 7, 1987, WHO/International Agency for Research on Cancer.
361 G.K. McEvoy, (ed.), *American Hospital Formulary Service – Drug Information 94*, American Society of Hospital Pharmacists, Inc., Bethesda 1994 (plus Supplements).
362 A.G. Gilman, L.S. Goodman, and A. Gilman (eds.), *Goodman and Gilman's The Pharmacological Basis of Therapeutics*, Macmillan Publishing Co., Inc., New York, 1980.
363 F. Patty, (ed.), *Industrial Hygiene and Toxicology: Volume II: Toxicology*, Interscience Publishers, New York, 1963.
364 *Food Advisory Committee Report on the Review of The Emulsifiers and Stablizers Regulations*, HMSO, 1992.
365 *WHO Food Additives Series: 18 Toxicological evaluation of certain food additives and contaminants*, World Health Organization, Geneva, 1983.
366 *Isr J Med Sci*, Sep 1983, 19 (9) p806–9.
367 A. Osol, and J.E. Hoover, *et al.* (eds.), *Remington's Pharmaceutical Sciences*, Mack Publishing Co., Easton, Pennsylvania, 1975.

368 M.J. Ellenhorn, and D.G. Barceloux, *Medical Toxicology – Diagnosis and Treatment of Human Poisoning*, Elsevier Science Publishing Co., Inc., New York, 1988.

369 *JAMA*, 13 Jan, 1989, 261 (2) p242,

370 *J Pediatr*, 1952; 41:411–23.

371 *Birth*, 1987; 14(1):41–5.

372 The Associated Press, 20 May 1993.

373 *Environ Res*, Oct 1978, 17 (2).

374 *Food Additives and Contaminants*, 1996, vol 13, no 7, 747–765.

375 Association of London Chief Environmental Health Officers, 1987.

376 *The Times*, 23 October, 1987.

377 *Journal of Nutrition*, June 1995, v125 n6 p1484(6).

378 *Tufts University Diet & Nutrition Letter*, Oct 1989, v7, n8.

379 *Science News*, 1 Dec, 1990, v138, n22, p340(l).

380 R.E. Gosselin, H.C. Hodge, R.P. Smith, and M.N. Gleason, *Clinical Toxicology of Commercial Products*, Williams and Wilkins, Baltimore, 1976.

381 CA 7 (5): 417, 1977.

382 R.E. Gosselin, R.P. Smith, H.C. Hodge,*Clinical Toxicology of Commercial Products*, Williams and Wilkins, Baltimore, 1984.

383 *WHO Food Additives Series: 16 Toxicological evaluation of certain food additives*, World Health Organization, Geneva, 1981.

384 R.E. Gosselin, H.C. Hodge, R.P. Smith, and M.N. Gleason, *Clinical Toxicology of Commercial Products*, Williams and Wilkins, Baltimore, 1976, p. 11–88.

385 H.B. Heath, G. Reinecciius, *Flavour Chemistry and Technology*, AVI Publishing Co, 1986.

386 A.G. Gilman, L.S. Goodman, and A. Gilman (eds.), *Goodman and Gilman's The Pharmacological Basis of Therapeutics*, Macmillan Publishing Co., Inc., New York: 1980.

387 R.E. Gosselin, H.C. Hodge, R.P. Smith, and M.N. Gleason, *Clinical Toxicology of Commercial Products*, Williams and Wilkins, Baltimore, 1976, p. 11–88.

388 *Monographs on the Evaluation of Carcinogenic risk to Humans*, vol 42, 1986, WHO/International Agency for Research on Cancer.

389 *7th Annual Report On Carcinogens*, US Department of Health and Human Services.

390 F. Patty, (ed.), *Industrial Hygiene and Toxicology: Volume II: Toxicology*, Interscience Publishers, New York, 1963.

391 *WHO Food Additives Series: 21 Toxicological evaluation of certain food additives and contaminants*, World Health Organization, Geneva, 1987.

392 *Ibid.*

393 G.G. Hawley, *The Condensed Chemical Dictionary*, Van Nostrand Reinhold Col, New York, 1977.

394 *Drugs and Therapeutics Bulletin*, vol.23 n.22.

395 *British National Formulary Number 13*, British Medical Association & The Pharmaceutical Society of Great Britain, 1987.

396 *Ibid.*

397 *Martindale: The Extra Pharmacopoeia*, The Pharmaceutical Press, 1982.

398 A.G. Gilman, L.S. Goodman, and A. Gilman (eds.), *Goodman and Gilman's The Pharmacological Basis of Therapeutics*, Macmillan Publishing Co., Inc., New York, 1985.

399 D.L. Britt, J.M. Hushon, *Biological Effects, Criteria and Standards for Hazardous*

Pollutants Associated with Energy Technologies, p. 6–38, 1976.
400 T.H. Shepard, *Catalog of Teratogenic Agents*, The Johns Hopkins University Press, 1986.
401 NIOSH/OSHA *Occupational Health Guide for Chemical Hazards: Inorganic Mercury*, p.1 (1981) DHHS Pub. NIOSH 81–123.
402 *Monographs on the Evaluation of the Carcinogenic Risk of Chemicals to Man*, World Health Organization, Geneva, International Agency for Research on Cancer, 1972–present, p. 58 324, 1993.
403 US Environmental Protection Agency's Integrated Risk Information System (IRIS) on Mercury (Inorganic) (7439–97–6), National Library of Medicine TOXNET System, 3 May, 1995.
404 *J Basic-Microbiol*, 1986, 26(8). p 499–504.
405 M. Dermelj, *et al; Chemosphere 16:* 877–86, 1987.
406 *Environ H Pers* 68: 203–8, 1986.
407 *J Appl Tox*, 5: 113–33 1985.
408 *Monographs on the Evaluation of the Carcinogenic Risk of Chemicals to Man*, World Health Organization, Geneva, International Agency for Research on Cancer, 1972–present, p. 58 324, 1993.
409 US Environmental Protection Agency's Integrated Risk Information System (IRIS) on Methylmercury (MeHg) (22967–92–6), National Library of Medicine TOXNET System, 3 May, 1995.
410 P. Levi, *The Periodic Table*, Abacus/Sphere Ltd, 1986.
411 *Nature*, 16 Aug 1990, p615.
412 S. Ziff, *The Toxic Time Bomb*, Thorsons, 1985.
413 JADA (1991) 122; p62–65.
414 *J Apl Electrochem*, 19; p301–310.
415 World Health Organization (1991), *Environmental Health Criteria*, Vol 118, Inorganic Mercury.
416 *Dent Res*, 64: p1069–1071.
417 *Dent Res*, 64: p1072–1075.
418 *J Trace Elem Exp Med*, 3: p111–123.
419 *Fund Appl Toxicol*, 19: p320–1.
420 *Ibid.*
421 *The Lancet*, 337: p1103.
422 *Fund Appl Toxicol*, 19: p321–3.
423 *Antimicrob Agents Chemother*, 37: p825–34.
424 *Fund Appl Toxicol*, 19: p324–6.
425 *The Lancet*, 336: p1587.
426 S. Ziff, *The Toxic Time Bomb*, Thorsons, 1985.
427 R.E. Gosselin, H.C. Hodge, R.P. Smith, and M.N. Gleason, *Clinical Toxicology of Commercial Products*, Williams and Wilkins, Baltimore, 1976.
428 *American Hospital Formulary Service*, vol I, II.
429 A.G. Gilman, L.S. Goodman, and A. Gilman (eds.), *Goodman and Gilman's The Pharmacological Basis of Therapeutics*, Macmillan Publishing Co., Inc., New York, 1980.
430 M.J. Ellenhorn, and D.G. Barceloux, *Medical Toxicology – Diagnosis and Treatment of Human Poisoning*, Elsevier Science Publishing Co., Inc., New York, 1988.
431 A.G. Gilman, T.W. Rall, A.S. Nies and P. Taylor (eds.), *Goodman and Gilman's The Pharmacological Basis of Therapeutics*, Pergamon Press, New York, 1990.

432 *Food Advisory Committee Report on the Review of The Emulsifiers and Stabilizers Regulations*, HMSO, 1992.
433 *Ibid.*
434 H.B. Heath, G. Reinecciius, *Flavour Chemistry and Technology*, AVI Publishing Co, 1986.
435 *Ibid.*
436 R.H. Dreisbach, *Handbook of Poisoning*, Appleton and Lange, Norwalk, CT, 1987.
437 R.E. Gosselin, R.P. Smith, H.C. Hodge, *Clinical Toxicology of Commercial Products*, Williams and Wilkins, Baltimore, 1984.
438 M.J. Ellenhorn, and D.G. Barceloux, *Medical Toxicology – Diagnosis and Treatment of Human Poisoning*, Elsevier Science Publishing Co., Inc., New York, 1988.
439 *Biochem Biophys Res Commun*, vol 100 (3): 972, 1981.
440 *Anal Toxicol*, 11 (3): 97–9, 1989.
441 L.S. Goodman, and A. Gilman, (eds.), *The Pharmacological Basis of Therapeutics*, Macmillan Publishing Co., Inc., New York, 1975.
442 *AMA Department of Drugs, AMA Drug Evaluations*, PSG Publishing Co., Inc., Littleton, Massachusetts, 1977.
443 *American Hospital Formulary Service, vol I, II.*
444 W.M. Grant, *Toxicology of the Eye*, Charles C. Thomas Publisher, Springfield, Il, 1986.
445 J. Doull, C.D. Klassen, and M.D. Amdur (eds.), *Casarett and Doull's Toxicology*, Macmillan Publishing Co., Inc., New York, 1986.
446 *Drinking Water and Health. Volume 3*, National Academy Press, 1980.
447 *MUTAT RES*, 87 (1): 1, 1981.
448 *Monographs on the Evaluation of the Carcinogenic Risk of Chemicals to Man*, World Health Organization, Geneva, International Agency for Research on Cancer, 1972–present, p. 49 410, 1990.
449 US Environmental Protection Agency's Integrated Risk Information System (IRIS) on Nickel refinery dust (NO CAS RN), National Library of Medicine TOXNET System, 1 March, 1995.
450 *Ambient Water Quality Criteria Document: Nickel*, p C-7, 1980, EPA 400/5-80-060.
451 F. Patty, (ed.), *Industrial Hygiene and Toxicology: Volume II: Toxicology*, Interscience Publishers, New York, 1963.
452 N.H. Booth, L.E. McDonald (eds.), *Veterinary Pharmacology and Therapeutics*, Iowa State University Press, 1982.
453 *Science News*, v139, p117 (1) 23 Feb, 1991.
454 Chemioterapia 4 (5): 393–99, 1985.
455 *MTI*, (5): 362–74, 1986.
456 *American Medical Association, Department of Drugs. Drug Evaluations*, American Medical Association, 1986.
457 G.D. Clayton, and F.E. Clayton (eds.), *Patty's Industrial Hygiene and Toxicology: volume 2A, 2B, 2C; Toxicology*, John Wiley Sons, New York, 1981–2.
458 A. Osol, and J.E. Hoover, *et al.* (eds.) *Remington's Pharmaceutical Sciences*, Mack Publishing Co., Easton, Pennsylvania, 1975.
459 *American Medical Association, AMA Department of Drugs, AMA Drug Evaluations*, PSG Publishing Co., Inc., Littleton, Massachusetts, 1977.
460 EJCP 16(6) 393, 1979.

461 A. Osol, and J.E. Hoover, *et al.* (eds.), *Remington's Pharmaceutical Sciences*, Mack Publishing Co., Easton, Pennsylvania, 1975.

462 *American Medical Association, AMA Department of Drugs, AMA Drug Evaluations*, PSG Publishing Co., Inc., Littleton, Massachusetts, 1977.

463 CT 4(1) 1–4, 1971.

464 CT 12(1) 1–31, 1978.

465 *Monographs on the Evaluation of the Carcinogenic Risk of Chemicals to Man*, World Health Organization, Geneva, International Agency for Research on Cancer, 1972–present, p V56 509, 1993.

466 *Monographs on the Evaluation of the Carcinogenic Risk of Chemicals to Man*, World Health Organization, Geneva, International Agency for Research on Cancer, 1972–present, p. S7 70 1987.

467 A. Osol, and J.E. Hoover, *et al.* (eds.), *Remington's Pharmaceutical Sciences*, Mack Publishing Co., Easton, Pennsylvania, 1975.

468 *American Medical Association, AMA Department of Drugs, AMA Drug Evaluations*, PSG Publishing Co., Inc., Littleton, Massachusetts, 1977.

469 A. Osol, and J.E. Hoover, *et al.* (eds.) *Remington's Pharmaceutical Sciences*, Mack Publishing Co., Easton, Pennsylvania, 1975.

470 *Consumers' Research Magazine*, July 1994, v77, n7, p10(5).

471 *American Medical Association, AMA Department of Drugs, AMA Drug Evaluations*, PSG Publishing Co., Inc., Littleton, Massachusetts, 1977.

472 L.S. Goodman, and A. Gilman. (eds.), *The Pharmacological Basis of Therapeutics*, Macmillan Publishing Co., Inc., New York, 1975.

473 A.G. Gilman, T.W. Rall, A.S. Nies and P. Taylor (eds.), *Goodman and Gilman's The Pharmacological Basis of Therapeutics*, Pergamon Press, New York, 1990.

474 A.G. Gilman, L.S. Goodman, and A. Gilman (eds.), *Goodman and Gilman's The Pharmacological Basis of Therapeutics*, Macmillan Publishing Co., Inc., New York: 1980.

475 A.G. Gilman, T.W. Rall, A.S. Nies and P. Taylor (eds.), *Goodman and Gilman's The Pharmacological Basis of Therapeutics*, Pergamon Press, New York, 1990.

476 *Monographs on the Evaluation of the Carcinogenic Risk of Chemicals to Man*, World Health Organization, Geneva, International Agency for Research on Cancer, 1972–present, p.50 325, 1990.

477 N.H. Booth, L.E. McDonald (eds.), *Veterinary Pharmacology and Therapeutics*, Iowa State University Press, 1982.

478 *Monographs on the Evaluation of the Carcinogenic Risk of Chemicals to Man*, World Health Organization, Geneva, International Agency for Research on Cancer, 1972–present, p. S7 59, 1987.

479 *WHO Food Additives Series: 17 Toxicological evaluation of certain food additives and contaminants*, World Health Organization, Geneva, 1982.

480 Reuters World Report, 26 Mar, 1996.

481 *WHO Food Additives Series: 35 Toxicological evaluation of certain food additives*, World Health Organization, Geneva, 1996.

482 *Monographs on the Evaluation of the Carcinogenic Risk of Chemicals to Man*, World Health Organization, Geneva, International Agency for Research on Cancer, 1972–present, p. S7 69, 1987.

483 *Appl Environ Microbiol*, 32(3) 388, 1976.

484 *J Food Prot*, 42(11) 864, 1980.

485 *WHO Food Additives Series: 16 Toxicological evaluation of certain food additives*, World Health Organization, Geneva, 1981.

486 *Archs. Derm* 1972, 106. 335.
487 A.G. Gilman, L.S. Goodman, and A. Gilman (eds.), *Goodman and Gilman's The Pharmacological Basis of Therapeutics*, Macmillan Publishing Co., Inc., New York, 1985.
488 NIOSH, *Criteria Document L Phenol*, p, 65 1976, DHEW Pub NIOSH, 76–196.
489 *Ibid.* p.41.
490 *Kirk-Othmer Encyclopedia of Chemical Technology*, vols 1–26, John Wiley and Sons, New York, 1978–84, p. 17 381, 1982.
491 G.D. Clayton, and F.E. Clayton (eds.), *Patty's Industrial Hygiene and Toxicology: Volume 2A, 2B, 2C; Toxicology*, John Wiley Sons, New York, 1981–2.
492 *Monographs on the Evaluation of the Carcinogenic Risk of Chemicals to Man*, World Health Organization, Geneva, International Agency for Research on Cancer, 1972–present, p. 47 279, 1989.
493 W.M. Grant, *Toxicology of the Eye*, Charles C. Thomas Publisher, Springfield, Il, 1986.
494 American Hospital Formulary Service, 1996.
495 AJM, Aug. 1990, 89 (2) p195–208.
496 *Gen Hosp Psychiatry*, Sep, 1994, 16 (5) p358–60.
497 *Pharmacopsychiatry*, July, 1988, 21 (4) p171–81.
498 *The Lancet*, 22–29 Dec 1979, 2 (8156–8157) p1367–8.
499 *The Lancet*, 26 May, 1979, 1 (8126) p1110–1.
500 *WHO Food Additives Series: Toxicological evaluation of certain food additives*, World Health Organization, Geneva, 1982.
501 A.G. Gilman, T.W. Rall, A.S. Nies and P. Taylor (eds.), *Goodman and Gilman's The Pharmacological Basis of Therapeutics*, Pergamon Press, New York, 1990.
502 *Nutrition Today*, March–April 1994, v29, n2.
503 R.E. Gosselin, R.P. Smith, H.C. Hodge, *Clinical Toxicology of Commercial Products*, Williams and Wilkins, Baltimore, 1984.
504 *MAFF Food Surveillance Information Sheets Number 82*, March 1996.
505 *Ibid.*
506 *The Times*, 28 May, 1996.
507 *Some Industrial Chemicals and Dyestuffs*, 29: 269, IARC, 1980.
508 *Natl Heart Lung Inst*, Rep No 1, HB 5–2906, 1978.
509 *Monographs on the Evaluation of the Carcinogenic Risk of Chemicals to Man*, World Health Organization, Geneva, International Agency for Research on Cancer, 1972–present, p. V29 285, 1982–7.
510 US Environmental Protection Agency's Integrated Risk Information System (IRIS) on Di (2–ethylhexyl)phthalate (DEHP) (117–81–7), National Library of Medicine TOXNET System, 29 August, 1994.
511 US Environmental Protection Agency's Integrated Risk Information System (IRIS) on Butyl benzyl phthalate (85–68–7), National Library of Medicine TOXNET System, 1 November, 1994.
512 *Monographs on the Evaluation of the Carcinogenic Risk of Chemicals to Man*, World Health Organization, Geneva, International Agency for Research on Cancer, 1972–present, p. S7 59, 1987.
513 US Environmental Protection Agency's Integrated Risk Information System (IRIS) on Diethyl phthalate (84–66–2), National Library of Medicine TOXNET System, 1 November, 1994.
514 *WHO Food Additives Series: 20 Toxicological evaluation of certain food additives and contaminants*, World Health Organization, Geneva, 1987.

515 Podophyllum Resin. American Hospital Formulary Service, 1996.

516 *Rachel's Hazardous Waste News*, #144 29 August, 1989.

517 *Martindale – The Extra Pharmacopoeia*, The Pharmaceutical Press, 1982.

518 NEJM, vol. 335, n11, 12 September, 1996, p783–789.

519 US Environmental Protection Agency's Integrated Risk Information System (IRIS) on Polychlorinated biphenyls (PCBs) (1336–36–3), National Library of Medicine TOXNET System, 1 November, 1994.

520 *WHO Food Additives Series: 16 Toxicological evaluation of certain food additives*, World Health Organization, Geneva, 1981.

521 *WHO Food Additives Series: 18 Toxicological evaluation of certain food additives and contaminants*, World Health Organization, Geneva, 1983.

522 R.E. Gosselin, H.C. Hodge, R.P. Smith, and M.N. Gleason, *Clinical Toxicology of Commercial Products*, Williams and Wilkins, Baltimore, 1976.

523 *Monographs on the Evaluation of the Carcinogenic Risk of Chemicals to Man*, World Health Organization, Geneva, International Agency for Research on Cancer, 1972–present, p. S7 66, 1987.

524 *Clin Allergy*, 7 (5): 417, 1977.

525 *International Labour Office. Encyclopedia of Occupational Health and Safety, Volumes I and II*, McGraw-Hill Book Co., New York, 1971.

526 *The Merck Index*, Merck & Co., Inc., New Jersey, 1976.

527 R.E. Gosselin, R.P. Smith, H.C. Hodge, *Clinical Toxicology of Commercial Products*, Williams and Wilkins, Baltimore, 1984.

528 *Monographs on the Evaluation of the Carcinogenic Risk of Chemicals to Man*, World Health Organization, Geneva, International Agency for Research on Cancer, 1972–present, p. 54 178, 1992.

529 W.M. Grant, *Toxicology of the Eye*, Charles C. Thomas Publisher, Springfield, Il, 1986.

530 G.G. Hawley, *The Condensed Chemical Dictionary*, Van Nostrand Reinhold Co., 1981.

531 *Monographs on the Evaluation of the Carcinogenic Risk of Chemicals to Man*, World Health Organization, Geneva, International Agency for Research on Cancer, 1972–present, p. 54 178, 1992.

532 *Drinking Water & Health Volume I*, National Academy Press, Washington, DC: 1977.

533 R.E. Gosselin, R.P. Smith, H.C. Hodge, *Clinical Toxicology of Commercial Products*, Williams and Wilkins, Baltimore, 1984.

534 *WHO Food Additives Series: 35 Toxicological evaluation of certain food additives and contaminants*, World Health Organization, Geneva, 1996.

535 *AMA Drug Evaluations Annual 1991*, American Medical Association, 1991.

536 J.E.F. Reynolds, Prasad, A.B. (eds.), *Martindale – The Extra Pharmacopoeia*, The Pharmaceutical Press, 1982.

537 A. Li Wan Po, *Non-prescription Drugs, Blackwell Scientific Publications*, 1982.

538 G.D. Clayton, and F.E. Clayton (eds.), *Patty's Industrial Hygiene and Toxicology: Volume 2A, 2B, 2C: Toxicology*, John Wiley Sons, New York, 1981–2.

539 *Documentation of the Threshold Limit Values and Biological Exposure Indices*, American Conference of Governmental Industrial Hygienists, 1986.

540 *WHO Food Additives Series: 32 Toxicological evaluation of certain food additives*, World Health Organization, Geneva, 1993.

541 NIH Publication No. 83–1796.

542 A.G. Gilman, L.S. Goodman, and A. Gilman (eds.), *Goodman and Gilman's The Pharmacological Basis of Therapeutics*, Macmillan Publishing Co., Inc., New York: 1980.

543 *Br J Clin Pharmacol*, 6(SEP) 221–225, 1978.

544 *Morbidity and Mortality Weekly Report*, 16 August, 1996, vol 45, n.32.

545 *Farm Chemicals Handbook 1986*, Meister Publishing Co., Willoughby, Ohio: 1986.

546 M.L. Clarke, D.G. Harvey and D.J. Humphreys, *Veterinary Toxicology*, Bailliere Tindall, London, 1981.

547 W.J. Hayes, E.R. Laws (eds.), *Handbook of Pesticide Toxicology*, v2 p.593, 1991.

548 R.E. Gosselin, R.P. Smith, H.C. Hodge, *Clinical Toxicology of Commercial Products*, Williams and Wilkins, Baltimore, 1984.

549 M.J. Ellenhorn, and D.G. Barceloux, *Medical Toxicology – Diagnosis and Treatment of Human Poisoning*, Elsevier Science Publishing Co., Inc., New York, 1988.

550 S. Budavari, (ed.), *The Merck Index – Encyclopedia of Chemicals, Drugs and Biologicals.* Merck and Co., Inc., NJ, 1989.

551 J. Hayes, Wayland, Jr. *Pesticides Studied in Man*, Williams and Wilkins, Baltimore/London, 1982.

552 D. Hartley, and H. Kidd (eds.), *The Agrochemicals Handbook*, Royal Society of Chemistry/Unwin Brothers Ltd., 1983.

553 *Clin Pharm*, 7 Nov. 846–49, 1988.

554 *WHO Food Additives Series: 17 Toxicological evaluation of certain food additives*, World Health Organization, Geneva, 1982.

555 A.G. Gilman, T.W. Rall, A.S. Nies and P. Taylor (eds.), *Goodman and Gilman's The Pharmacological Basis of Therapeutics*, Pergamon Press, New York, 1990.

556 M.J. Ellenhorn, and D.G. Barceloux, *Medical Toxicology – Diagnosis and Treatment of Human Poisoning*, Elsevier Science Publishing Co., Inc., New York, 1988.

557 *WHO Food Additives Series: 19 Toxicological evaluation of certain food additives and contaminants*, World Health Organization, Geneva, 1984.

558 *WHO Food Additives Series: 16 Toxicological evaluation of certain food additives*, World Health Organization, Geneva, 1981.

559 *Documentation of the Threshold Limit Values and Biological Exposure Indices*, American Conference of Governmental Industrial Hygienists, 1986.

560 *The Merck Index*, Merck Co., Inc., 1983.

561 M. Sittig, *Handbook of Toxic and Hazardous Chemicals and Carcinogens*, Noyes Data Corporation, Park Ridge, NJ: 1985.

562 *Monographs on the Evaluation of the Carcinogenic Risk of Chemicals to Man*, World Health Organization, Geneva, International Agency for Research on Cancer, 1972–present, p. S7 71, 1987.

563 A. Osol, and R. Pratt (eds.), *The United States Dispensatory*, J.B. Lippincott, Philadelphia, 1973.

564 *Evaluations of Drug Interactions*, American Pharmaceutical Assn., 1976, 1978.

565 *Monographs on the Evaluation of the Carcinogenic Risk of Chemicals to Man*, World Health Organization, Geneva, International Agency for Research on Cancer, 1972–present, p. S7 71, 1987.

566 *Methodology for Evaluating Potential Carcinogenicity in Support of Reportable Quantity Adjustments Pursuant to Cercla Section 102* (Final), p.42, 1988, US EPA/600/8–89/053.

567 N.I. Sax, and R.J. Lewis, Sr. (eds.), *Hawley's Condensed Chemical Dictionary*, Van Nostrand Reinhold Co., New York, 1987.

568 *1989 Directory of Chemical Producers – United States of America*, SRI International, 1989.

569 *AMA Drug Evaluations Annual 1991*, American Medical Association, 1991.

570 J.E.F. Reynolds, Prasad, A.B. (eds.), *Martindale – The Extra Pharmacopoeia*, The Pharmaceutical Press, 1982.

571 A.G. Gilman, T.W. Rall, A.S. Nies and P. Taylor (eds.), *Goodman and Gilman's The Pharmacological Basis of Therapeutics*, Pergamon Press, New York, 1990.

572 *J Laryngol Otol*, May 1984, 98 (5) p547–8.

573 *Department of Drugs. Drug Evaluations*, American Medical Association, 1986.

574 *J Environ Sci Health (A)*, 21 (6): 571–82, 1986.

575 *Monographs on the Evaluation of the Carcinogenic Risk of Chemicals to Man*, World Health Organization, Geneva, International Agency for Research on Cancer, 1972–present, vol. 9, suppl. 7, 1987.

576 US Environmental Protection Agency's Integrated Risk Information System (IRIS) on Selenium and compounds (7782–49–2), National Library of Medicine TOXNET System, 1 November, 1994.

577 US Environmental Protection Agency's Integrated Risk Information System (IRIS) on Selenium sulfide (7446–34–6), National Library of Medicine's TOXNET System, 1 November, 1994.

578 *Monographs on the Evaluation of the Carcinogenic Risk of Chemicals to Man*, World Health Organization, Geneva, International Agency for Research on Cancer, 1972–present, p. V9 256, 1975.

579 *Clin Toxicol*, 17 (2): 171–230, 1980.

580 *Encyclopedia of Occupational Health and Safety*, vols I, II, International Labour Office, Geneva, 1983.

581 *Sports Illustrated*, 22 March, 1993, v78, n11, p62.

582 *Clin Med J*, 1979; 92:477–482.

583 G.F. Combs, J.e. Spallholz, O.A. Levander, J.E. Oldfield, (eds.) *Selenium in Biology and Medicine*, NY: Van Nostrand Reinhold, New York, 1987, p589–607.

584 *Journal of the American Medical Association*, 25 Dec, 1996, v276, n24, p1984.

585 *JAMA*, 5 Sept, 1990, v264, n9, p1128.

586 *Nutrition Action Healthletter*, Jan–Feb 1997, v24, n1, p8.

587 *Medical World News*, April 1993, v34, n4, p16.

588 *WHO Food Additives Series: 30 Toxicological evaluation of certain food additives*, World Health Organization, Geneva, 1993.

589 L.J. Casarett, and J. Doull, *Toxicology: The Basic Science of Poisons*, Macmillan Publishing Co., New York, 1975.

590 *Ambient Water Quality Criteria Doc:* Silver p.C–79 (1980) US EPA 440/5–80–071.

591 H.G. Seiler, H. Sigel and A. Sigel (eds.), *Handbook on the Toxicity of Inorganic Compounds*, Marcel Dekker, Inc., New York, 1988.

592 *Ibid.*

593 US Environmental Protection Agency's Integrated Risk Information System (IRIS) on Silver (7440–22–4), National Library of Medicine TOXNET System, 1 November, 1994.

594 J Oslo City Hosp, 30 (8): 101, 1980.

595 R.E. Gosselin, H.C. Hodge, R.P. Smith, and M.N. Gleason, *Clinical Toxicology of Commercial Products*, Williams and Wilkins, Baltimore, 1976.

596 R.H. Dreisbach, *Handbook of Poisoning*, Lange Medical Publications, 1977.

597 M. Kadic, *Veterinaria* (Sarajavo) 24 (2) 219–34, 1975.

598 *Int Conf Strontium Metab (Pap)* 2ND; Vol Conf-720818, 1973.

599 *The Merck Index*, Merck Co., Inc., 1983.

600 *Pediatrics*, 84, (3): 472–74, 1989.

601 A. Osol, and J.E. Hoover, *et al*, (eds.), *Remington's Pharamceutical Sciences*, Mack Publishing Co., Easton, Pennsylvania, 1975.

602 *American Hospital Formulary Service. Volumes I and II*, American Society of Hospital Pharmacists, to 1984.

603 *WHO Food Additives Series: Toxicological evaluation of some food colours, enzymes, flavour enhancers, thickening agents and certain food additives*, World Health Organization, Geneva, 1975.

604 *Drinking Water Criteria Document for Fluoride*, p.VI–II (1985) US EPA Contract No. 68–03–3279.

605 A. Osol, (ed.), *Remington's Pharmaceutical Sciences*, Mack Publishing Co., Easton, Pennsylvania, 1980.

606 *FDA Consumer*, Jan–Feb 1992, v26, n1, p34–5.

607 The *Financial Times*, 7 Dec, 1996, pWFT2(1).

608 A.G. Gilman, L.S. Goodman, and A. Gilman (eds.), *Goodman and Gilman's The Pharmacological Basis of Therapeutics*, Macmillan Publishing Co., Inc., New York, 1985.

609 *Ibid.*

610 M.J. Ellenhorn, and D.G. Barceloux, *Medical Toxicology – Diagnosis and Treatment of Human Poisoning*, Elsevier Science Publishing Co., Inc., New York, 1988.

611 *Annals of Internal Medicine*, 15 Sept, 1995 v123, n6, p401 (8).

612 *Journal of the American Dental Association*, August 1991, v122, n9, p86(6).

613 *The Back Letter*, April 1990, v4, n6, p3(1).

614 *Journal of the American Dental Association*, Dec 1995 v126, n12, p1617(8).

615 *Journal of Toxicology:* Clinical Toxicology, March 1996, v34, n2, p183(7).

616 *Nature*, 10–16 July, 1986, 322(6075): 125–9.

617 *Journal of the American Dental Association*, Sept 1991, v122, n10, p63(4).

618 *NCI Cancer Weekly*, 12 Feb, 1990 p9(1).

619 *Monographs on the Evaluation of the Carcinogenic Risk of Chemicals to Man*, World Health Organization, Geneva, International Agency for Research on Cancer, 1972–present, p. S7 63, 1987.

620 *Monographs on the Evaluation of the Carcinogenic Risk of Chemicals to Man*, World Health Organization, Geneva, International Agency for Research on Cancer, 1972–present, p. 54 178, 1992.

621 *Kirk-Othmer Encyclopedia of Chemical Toxicology*, vols 1–26, John Wiley and Sons,1978–84.

622 See note 620, above.

623 *Med J Aust*, 2, Nov 28 614–17, 1981.

624 T.E. Furia, (ed.). *CRC Handbook of Food Additives*, The Chemical Rubber Co., 1972.

625 R.E. Gosselin, R.P. Smith, H.C. Hodge, *Clinical Toxicology of Commercial Products*, Williams and Wilkins, Baltimore, 1984.

626 *WHO Food Additives Series: 35 Toxicological evaluation of certain food additives*, World Health Organization, Geneva, 1996.

627 R.E. Gosselin, R.P. Smith, H.C. Hodge, *Clinical Toxicology of Commercial Products*, Williams and Wilkins, Baltimore, 1984.

628 N.H. Booth, L.E. McDonald (eds.), *Veterinary Pharmacology and Therapeutics*, Iowa State University Press, 1982.

629 *The Merck Index*, Merck Co., Inc., 1983.

630 R.H. Dreisback, *Handbook of Poisoning*, Appleton and Lange, Norwalk, CT: 1987.

631 R.E. Gosselin, R.P. Smith, H.C. Hodge, *Clinical Toxicology of Commercial Products*, Williams and Wilkins, Baltimore, 1984.

632 *Ibid.*

633 R.H. Dreisbach, *Handbook of Poisoning*, Appleton and Lange, Norwalk, CT, 1987.

634 *Environment Canada;* Tech Info for Problem Spills: Sodium Sulphate p.41, 1985.

635 J.A. Maga, A.T. Tu (eds.), *Food Additive Toxicology*, Marcel Dekker Inc, 1995.

636 P.M. Davidson and A.L. Branen, *Antimicrobials in food*, Marcel Dekker, New York, 1993.

637 *J. Toxic. Environ. Health*, 21:141–162.

638 *Monographs on the Evaluation of the Carcinogenic Risk of Chemicals to Man*, World Health Organization, Geneva, International Agency for Research on Cancer, 1972–present, p. 54 178, 1992.

639 M.L. Clarke, D.G. Harvey and D.J. Humphreys, *Veterinary Toxicology*, Bailliere Tindall, London, 1981.

640 Teratogenic effect of potato glycoalkaloids. Wang X.G., *Chung Hua Fu Chan Ko Tsa Chih*, (China) Feb 1993, 28 (2).

641 F. Patty, (ed.), *Industrial Hygiene and Toxicology: Volume II: Toxicology*, Interscience Publishers, New York, 1963.

642 *WHO Food Additives Series: 17 Toxicological evaluation of certain food additives*, World Health Organization, Geneva, 1982.

643 N.I. Sax, *Dangerous Properties of Industrial Materials*, Van Nostrand Rheinhold, 1979.

644 *The Merck Index*, Merck & Co., Inc., 1976.

645 *American Hospital Formulary Service, Volumes I and II*, American Society of Hospital Pharmacists, to 1984.

646 *Foreign Compound Metabolism in Mammals. Volume 4: A Review of the Literature Published during 1974 and 1975*, The Chemical Society, London, 1977.

647 *Documentation of the Threshold Limit Values and Biological Exposure Indices*, American Conference of Governmental Industrial Hygienists, 1986.

648 *Pocket Guide to Chemical Hazards*, DHHS (NIOSH) Publ. No. 85–114. US Dept. of Health and Human Services, NIOSH/Supt. of Documents, GPO, February 1987.

649 *Chem Biol Interact*, 46 (2): 189–200, 1983.

650 *WHO; Environ. Health Criteria: Tin and Organotin Compounds – Executive Summary*, p.5 1980.

651 *WHO Food Additives Series: 17 Toxicological evaluation of certain food additives*, World Health Organization, Geneva, 1982.

652 A.G. Gilman, L.S. Goodman, and A. Gilman (eds.), *Goodman and Gilman's The Pharmacological Basis of Therapeutics*, Macmillan Publishing Co., Inc., New York, 1980.

653 *Monographs on the Evaluation of the Carcinogenic Risk of Chemicals to Man*,

World Health Organization, Geneva, International Agency for Research on Cancer, 1972–present, p. V60 248–9, 1994.

654 *Criteria Document: Stryene*, p. 18 1983, DHEW Pub. NIOSH 83–119.

655 *Food Surveillance Information Sheets Number 38*, October 1994, Ministry of Agriculture, Fisheries and Food.

656 *WHO Food Additives Series: 19 Toxicological evaluation of certain food additives and contaminants*, World Health Organization, Geneva, 1984.

657 *Monographs on the Evaluation of the Carcinogenic Risk of Chemicals to Man*, World Health Organization, Geneva, International Agency for Research on Cancer, 1972–present, p. 60 297, 1994.

658 F. Patty, (ed.), *Industrial Hygiene and Toxicology: Volume II: Toxicology*, Interscience Publishers, New York, 1963.

659 *Environ Health Criteria Number 32: Toxicological Evaluation of Certain Food Additives and Contaminants*, WHO, 1993.

660 *WHO Food Additives Series: 35 Toxicological evaluation of certain food additives*, World Health Organization, Geneva, 1996.

661 *Monographs on the Evaluation of the Carcinogenic Risk of Chemicals to Man*, World Health Organization, Geneva, International Agency for Research on Cancer, 1972–present, p. 47 187, 1989.

662 *WHO Food Additives Series: 20 Toxicological evaluation of certain food additives and contaminants*, World Health Organization, Geneva, 1987.

663 *American Hospital Formulary Service – Drug Information 88*, American Society of Hospital Pharmacists, 1988 (plus Supplements).

664 *Encyclopedia of Occupational Health and Safety*, vols I, II, International Labour Office, Geneva, 1983.

665 National Eczema Society.

666 J.A. Maga, A.T. Tu (eds.), *Food Additive Toxicology*, Marcel Dekker Inc, 1995.

667 *Federal Register*, 9833 (3/!5/90).

668 *Monitoring and Assessment Research Centre; Report #7*, 1978.

669 *Ibid.*

670 Howard E. Hesketh, *Understanding & Controlling Air Pollution*, Ann Arbor Science Publishers, 1974.

671 *WHO Food Additives Series: 21 Toxicological evaluation of certain food additives and contaminants*, World Health Organization, Geneva, 1987.

672 *Encyclopedia of Occupational Health and Safety*, vols I, II, International Labour Office, Geneva, 1983.

673 *Monographs on the Evaluation of the Carcinogenic Risk of Chemicals to Man*, World Health Organization, Geneva, International Agency for Research on Cancer, 1972–present, p. 54 178, 1992.

674 *Environment Canada*, Tech Info for Problem Spills: Sulphuric acid & Oleum (Draft) p82 (1984).

675 *Documentation of the Threshold Limit Values and Biological Exposure Indices*, American Conference of Governmental Industrial Hygienists, 1986.

676 *Monographs on the Evaluation of the Carcinogenic Risk of Chemicals to Man*, World Health Organization, Geneva, International Agency for Research on Cancer, 1972–present, p. 54 106, 1992.

677 *WHO Food Additives Series: 17 Toxicological evaluation of certain food additives*, World Health Organization, Geneva, 1982.

678 *CA* 7 (5): 417, 1977.

679 *Monographs on the Evaluation of the Carcinogenic Risk of Chemicals to Man*,

World Health Organization, Geneva, International Agency for Research on Cancer, 1972–present, p. S7 72, 1987.

680 *Pediatr Emerg Care*, 5 (1):43–8, 1989.

681 *Toxicology Letters*, 52 (2): 121–7, 1990.

682 *Am J Roentgenol*, 146 (2): 295–301, 1986.

683 *Obstet Gynecol*, 80 (1): 19–26, 1992.

684 *Monographs on the Evaluation of the Carcinogenic Risk of Chemicals to Man*, World Health Organization, Geneva, International Agency for Research on Cancer, 1972–present, p. V42 207, 1987.

685 *Monographs on the Evaluation of the Carcinogenic Risk of Chemicals to Man*, World Health Organization, Geneva, International Agency for Research on Cancer, 1972–present, p.S7 72, 1987.

686 E. Benk, Tara Grain Meal, *Riechst, Aromen, Kosmet*, 27(10) 275 (1977).

687 *Food Advisory Committee Report on the Review of The Emulsifiers and Stabilizers Regulations*, HMSO, 1992.

688 J.A. Maga, A.T. Tu (eds.), *Food Additive Toxicology*, Marcel Dekker Inc, 1995.

689 *CLIN ALLERGY*, 7 (5): 417, 1977.

690 *WHO Food Additives Series: 20 Toxicological evaluation of certain food additives and contaminants*, World Health Organization, Geneva, 1987.

691 *WHO Food Additives Series: 30 Toxicological evaluation of certain food additives*, World Health Organization, Geneva, 1993.

692 G.K. McEvoy, (ed.), *American Hospital Formulary Service – Drug Information 93*, American Society of Hospital Pharmacists, Inc., 1993 (plus Supplements, 1993).

693 R.E. Gosselin, R.P. Smith, H.C. Hodge, *Clinical Toxicology of Commercial Products*, Williams and Wilkins, Baltimore, 1984.

694 L. Friberg, G.F. Nordberg, E. Kessler, and V.B. Vouk, (eds), *Handbook of the Toxicology of Metals, Vols I, II*, Elsevier Science Publishers B.V., Amsterdam, 1986, p. V2.

695 *Scand J Dent Res*, Dec 1980, 88 (6).

696 *Monographs on the Evaluation of the Carcinogenic Risk of Chemicals to Man*, World Health Organization, Geneva, International Agency for Research on Cancer, 1972–present, p. 47 322, 1989.

697 *Bioassay of Titanium Dioxide for Possible Carcinogenicity (1978) Technical Rpt Series No. 97*, DHEW Pub No. (NIH) 78–1347, US Department of Health Education and Welfare, National Cancer Institute, Bethesda, MD 20014.

698 *WHO Food Additives Series: 20 Toxicological evaluation of certain food additives and contaminants*, World Health Organization, Geneva, 1987.

699 R.E. Gosselin, H.C. Hodge, R.P. Smith, and M.N. Gleason, *Clinical Toxicology of Commercial Products*, Williams and Wilkins, Baltimore, 1976.

700 *Labo-Pharma-Probl Tech*, 27(286) 306 (1979).

701 *Therapie*, 35(3) 423 (1980).

702 R.E. Gosselin, R.P. Smith, H.C. Hodge, *Clinical Toxicology of Commercial Products*, Williams and Wilkins, Baltimore, 1984.

703 R.H. Dreisbach, *Handbook of Poisoning*, Appleton and Lange, Norwalk, CT: 1987.

704 *The Merck Index*, Merck Co., Inc., 1983.

705 F. Patty, (ed.), *Industrial Hygiene and Toxicology: Volume II: Toxicology*, Interscience Publishers, New York, 1963.

706 General Electric Co; *Material Safety Data Sheet #375*, 1981.

707 R.E. Gosselin, H.C. Hodge, R.P. Smith, and M.N. Gleason, *Clinical Toxicology of Commercial Products*, Williams and Wilkins, Baltimore, 1976.

708 *WHO Food Additives Series: 21 Toxicological evaluation of certain food additives and contaminants*, World Health Organization, Geneva, 1987.

709 R.E. Gosselin, R.P. Smith, H.C. Hodge, *Clinical Toxicology of Commercial Products*, Williams and Wilkins, Baltimore, 1984.

710 L. Friberg, G.F. Nordberg, E. Kessler, and V.B. Vouk, (eds.), *Handbook of the Toxicology of Metals, Vols I, II*, Elsevier Science Publishers B.V., 1986.

711 E. Browning, *Toxicity of Industrial Metals*, Appleton-Century-Crofts, New York, 1969.

712 F. Patty, (ed.), *Industrial Hygiene and Toxicology: Volume II: Toxicology*, Interscience Publishers, New York, 1963.

713 American Medical Association, Council on Drugs, *AMA Drug Evaluations Annual 1994*, American Medical Association, 1994.

714 *TOXICOL ANNU*, 3: 1, 1979.

715 EC Directive 95/2/EC.

716 EC Directive 94/36/EC.

Index